A Level

Further Pure

FP3

Mark Rowland

OXFORD
UNIVERSITY PRESS

OXFORD
UNIVERSITY PRESS

Great Clarendon Street, Oxford OX2 6DP

Oxford University Press is a department of the University of Oxford.
It furthers the University's objective of excellence in research, scholarship,
and education by publishing worldwide in

Oxford New York

Auckland Cape Town Dar es Salaam Hong Kong Karachi
Kuala Lumpur Madrid Melbourne Mexico City Nairobi
New Delhi Shanghai Taipei Toronto

With offices in

Argentina Austria Brazil Chile Czech Republic France Greece
Guatemala Hungary Italy Japan South Korea Poland Portugal
Singapore Switzerland Thailand Turkey Ukraine Vietnam

First published 2010

British Library Cataloguing in Publication Data

Data available

ISBN 9780199127405

10 9 8 7 6 5

Printed in Great Britain by Ashford Colour Press Ltd., Gosport

Paper used in the production of this book is a natural, recyclable product made
from wood grown in sustainable forests. The manufacturing process conforms
to the environmental regulations of the country of origin.

Acknowledgements

The photograph on the cover is reproduced courtesy of Alan Baxter/Digital Vision

The Publisher would like to thank the following for permission to reproduce photographs:

P24 Robert Brown/iStockphoto;**P42** Joggie Botma/iStockphoto; **p78** Jose Manuel Ferrao/iStockphoto;
p114 Andrey Prokhorov/iStockphoto; **p150** Lorelyn Medina/Shutterstock; **p190** Vladitto/Shutterstock

The publishers would like to thank Ian Bettison, Charlie Bond,
David Bones and Daphne Perridge for their expert help in
completing this book.

Series managing editor Anna Cox.

About this book

This book is designed to help you achieve your best possible grade in Edexcel GCE Further Mathematics Further Pure 3 unit.

Each chapter starts with a list of objectives and a 'Before you start' section to check that you are fully prepared. Chapters are structured into manageable sections, and there are certain features to look out for within each section:

Key points are highlighted in a blue panel.

Key words are highlighted in **bold blue** type.

Worked examples demonstrate the key skills and techniques you need to develop. These are shown in boxes and include prompts to guide you through the solutions.

EXAMPLE 3

Solve the equation $\cosh x = 2$, giving answers as natural logarithms.

Use the result $\operatorname{arcosh} x = \ln\left(x + \sqrt{x^2 - 1}\right)$.

$\cosh x = 2$ so one possible value of x is

$$\operatorname{arcosh} 2 = \ln\left(2 + \sqrt{2^2 - 1}\right) = \ln\left(2 + \sqrt{3}\right)$$

Use the symmetry of the graph of $y = \cosh x$ in the y-axis to solve the equation:

The solution to the equation $\cosh x = 2$ is $x = \pm\ln\left(2 + \sqrt{3}\right)$

Derivations and additional information are shown in a panel.

Helpful hints are included as blue margin notes and sometimes as blue type within the main text.

Misconceptions are shown in the right margin to help you avoid making common mistakes.

Investigational hints prompt you to explore a concept further.

Each section includes an exercise with progressive questions, starting with basic practice and developing in difficulty. Some exercises also include 'stretch and challenge' questions marked with a stretch symbol.

At the end of each chapter there is a 'Review' section which includes exam style questions as well as past exam paper questions. There are also two 'Revision' sections per unit which contain questions spanning a range of topics to give you plenty of realistic exam practice.

The final page of each chapter gives a summary of the key points, fully cross-referenced to aid revision. Also, a 'Links' feature provides an engaging insight into how the mathematics you are studying is relevant to real life.

At the end of the book you will find full solutions and an index.

You can find a chapter 0 which covers background knowledge for this unit on the Oxford University Press web site for this series. This chapter is referenced throughout the book at the start of chapters by this icon: W

Contents FP3

1 Hyperbolic functions

This chapter will show you how to
- use e^x to define hyperbolic functions
- solve hyperbolic equations
- prove identities involving hyperbolic expressions
- define inverse hyperbolic functions in terms of natural logarithms
- sketch the graphs of hyperbolic and inverse hyperbolic functions.

See Section 0.1 W.

See C3 for revision.

Before you start

You should know how to:

1 Solve an exponential equation.
e.g. Solve $4e^{2x} = 36$

Make the exponential term the subject:
$4e^{2x} = 36$ so $e^{2x} = 9$

Take natural logs of both sides:
$2x = \ln 9$

$x = \frac{1}{2}\ln 9$, or $x = \ln 3$

2 Sketch the graph of $y = f^{-1}(x)$ for a given function f(x).
e.g. The graph of $y = f(x)$ is shown.

To sketch the graph of $y = f^{-1}(x)$, reflect the given graph and asymptote in the line $y = x$:

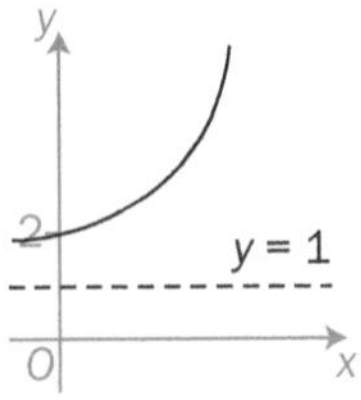

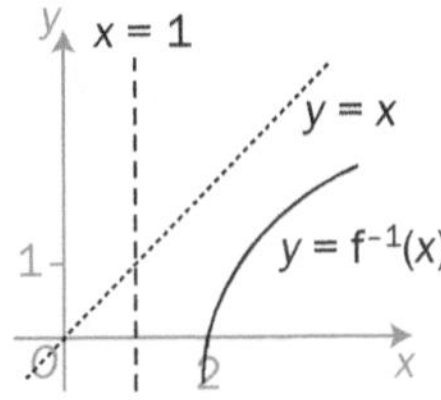

3 Prove a trigonometric identity.
e.g. Prove that $\sin 2\theta \sec\theta \equiv 2\sin\theta$

Use the identity $\sin 2\theta \equiv 2\sin\theta\cos\theta$:

LHS $= \sin 2\theta \sec\theta$

$= (2\sin\theta\cos\theta) \times \frac{1}{\cos\theta}$

$= 2\sin\theta$

= RHS, as required

Check in:

1 Solve these equations. Give answers as natural logarithms.

a $e^{3x} - 1 = 7$

b $2e^{-x} = 8$

c $e^{2x} - 4e^x = 0$

d $e^{2x} - 8e^x + 15 = 0$

e $e^x - 9e^{-x} = 8$

2 For each graph $y = f(x)$ sketch, on a separate diagram, the graph of $y = f^{-1}(x)$

a

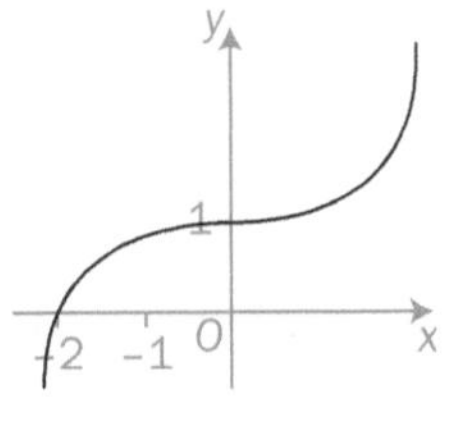

b

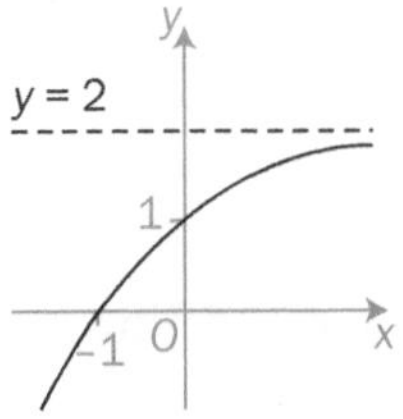

3 Prove these identities.

a $\frac{\cos 2\theta}{\cos^2\theta} \equiv 1 - \tan^2\theta$, for $\cos\theta \neq 0$

b $\cos^4\theta - \sin^4\theta \equiv \cos 2\theta$

c $\frac{1}{\sec\theta - 1} + \frac{1}{\sec\theta + 1} \equiv 2\cot\theta\,\mathrm{cosec}\,\theta$ $\quad |\cos\theta| \neq 1$

1.1 Basic hyperbolic functions and their graphs

You can define the hyperbolic functions $\cosh x$ and $\sinh x$, by analogy with the trigonometric functions, in terms of the exponential function e^x.

For all real values of x, $\cosh x = \frac{1}{2}(e^x + e^{-x})$, $\sinh x = \frac{1}{2}(e^x - e^{-x})$

$\cos x = \frac{1}{2}(e^{ix} + e^{-ix})$

$\sin x = \frac{1}{2i}(e^{ix} - e^{-ix})$

EXAMPLE 1

Evaluate

a cosh 2 to 1 decimal place

b sinh (ln 2)

a Use the definition $\cosh x = \frac{1}{2}(e^x + e^{-x})$:

$$\cosh 2 = \frac{1}{2}(e^2 + e^{-2})$$
$$= 3.762\ldots$$
$$= 3.8 \text{ to 1 d.p.}$$

b Use the definition $\sinh x = \frac{1}{2}(e^x - e^{-x})$:

$$\sinh(\ln 2) = \frac{1}{2}(e^{\ln 2} - e^{-\ln 2})$$
$$= \frac{1}{2}\left(2 - \frac{1}{2}\right)$$
$$= \frac{3}{4}$$

$\cosh x$ is the hyperbolic cosine of x. $\sinh x$ is pronounced 'shine$x$' or 'sinsh$x$'.

Most scientific calculators have inbuilt hyperbolic functions – look for the HYP key.

$e^{-\ln 2} = \frac{1}{e^{\ln 2}} = \frac{1}{2}$

You can define the hyperbolic tangent function, $\tanh x$ in terms of $\sinh x$ and $\cosh x$.

$\tanh x$ is pronounced 'than$x$' or 'tansh x'.

$$\sinh x = \frac{1}{2}(e^x - e^{-x}) = \frac{1}{2}\left(\frac{e^{2x} - 1}{e^x}\right)$$

$$\cosh x = \frac{1}{2}(e^x + e^{-x}) = \frac{1}{2}\left(\frac{e^{2x} + 1}{e^x}\right)$$

$$\tanh x \equiv \frac{\sinh x}{\cosh x} \equiv \frac{e^{2x} - 1}{e^{2x} + 1}$$

This definition resembles the result $\tan x \equiv \frac{\sin x}{\cos x}$, $\cos x \neq 0$ in trigonometry.

EXAMPLE 2

Evaluate $\tanh(\ln\sqrt{3})$

Use the exponential defintion of $\tanh x$:

$$\tanh(\ln\sqrt{3}) = \frac{e^{2\ln\sqrt{3}} - 1}{e^{2\ln\sqrt{3}} + 1}$$

$$= \frac{3-1}{3+1}$$

$$= \frac{1}{2}$$

$e^{2\ln\sqrt{3}} = (e^{\ln\sqrt{3}})^2 = (\sqrt{3})^2$
$= 3$

You can sketch the graph of hyperbolic functions by using properties of the exponential function e^x.

$$\cosh(-x_0) = \frac{1}{2}(e^{-x_0} + e^{-(-x_0)})$$

$$= \frac{1}{2}(e^{-x_0} + e^{x_0}) = \cosh(x_0)$$

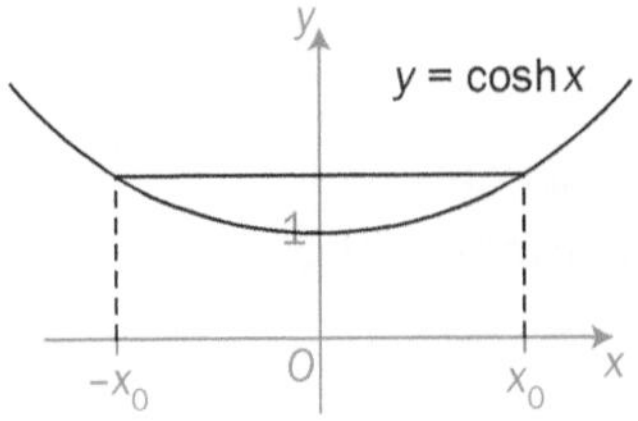

so the graph of $y = \cosh x$ is symmetrical about the y-axis.

$$\cosh(0) = \frac{1}{2}(e^0 + e^{-0}) = \frac{1}{2}(1+1)$$

$$= 1$$

so the y-intercept of the graph is 1.

As $x \to \infty$, $e^x \to \infty$ and $e^{-x} \to 0$

that is, $\cosh x \to \infty$ as $x \to \infty$

$x \to \infty$ means x increases without limit.

$\cosh(-x) \equiv \cosh x$

If $f(-x) = f(x)$ then f is an even function of x.

The graph $y = \cosh x$ passes through $(0, 1)$ and is symmetrical about the y-axis.
$\cosh x \geqslant 1$ for all $x \in \mathbb{R}$
These diagrams show the graphs of $y = \sinh x$ and $y = \tanh x$:

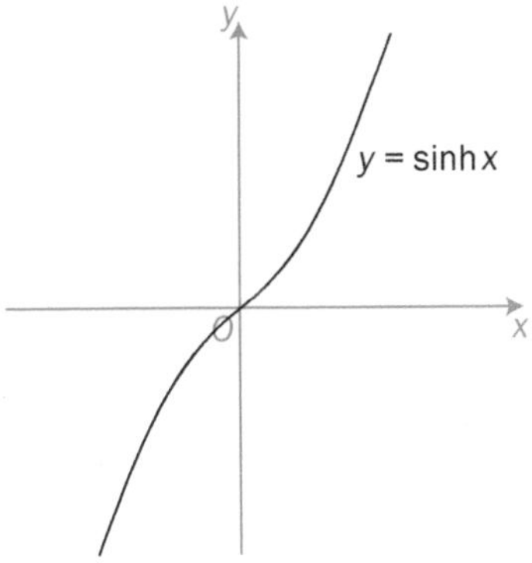

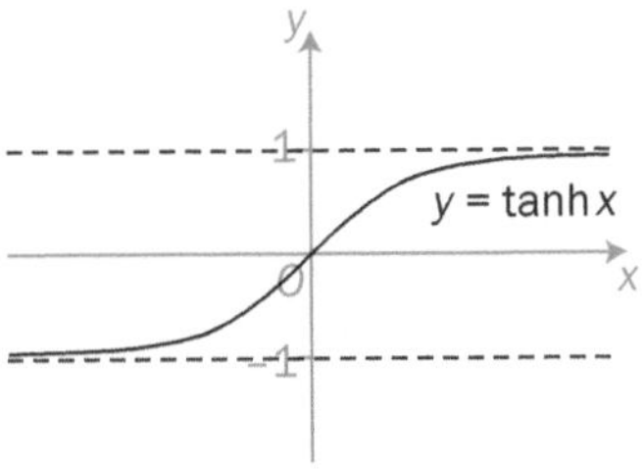

The lines $y = 1$ and $y = -1$ are asymptotes to the graph $y = \tanh x$.

FP3

$\sinh(-x) \equiv -\sinh x$

If $f(-x) = -f(x)$ then f is an odd function of x.

The graph $y = \sinh x$ passes through (0,0) and has rotational symmetry, order 2, about the origin.

$\tanh(-x) \equiv -\tanh x$

The graph $y = \tanh x$ passes through (0,0) and has rotational symmetry, order 2, about the origin.
$|\tanh x| < 1$ for all $x \in \mathbb{R}$

$|\tanh x| < 1$ means $-1 < \tanh x < 1$

Exercise 1.1

1 Evaluate these expressions. Give each answer to 2 decimal places.

a $\cosh 3$

b $\sinh(-1)$

c $\tanh\left(\frac{1}{3}\right)$

d $\cosh(2)\sinh(3)$

2 Find the exact value of these expressions. Where appropriate, give answers in simplified surd form.

a $\sinh(\ln 3)$

b $\tanh(\ln 2)$

c $2\cosh\left(\ln\sqrt{2}\right)$

d $\sinh\left(\ln\left(\sqrt{2}+1\right)\right)$

e $4\cosh\left(\ln\left(\sqrt{3}+1\right)\right)$

f $\tanh\left(\frac{1}{2}\ln\left(\sqrt{3}-1\right)\right)$

3 Evaluate these expressions. Leave simplified surds in your answers where appropriate.

a $\cosh(2x)$ when $x = \ln\left(1+\sqrt{2}\right)$

b $\sinh(y - \ln 2)$ when $y = \ln\left(4 - 2\sqrt{3}\right)$

c $\tanh\left(\frac{1}{2}z\right)$ when $z = \ln\left(1+\sqrt{3}\right)$

4 Use the exponential definitions of hyperbolic functions to prove these identities.

a $\cosh x + \sinh x \equiv e^x$

b $\dfrac{1+\tanh x}{1-\tanh x} \equiv e^{2x}$

c $\sinh(\ln x) \equiv \dfrac{(x+1)(x-1)}{2x}$, for $x > 0$

5 On separate diagrams sketch the graphs of these equations. Mark any axis-crossing points with their exact coordinates and label any asymptotes with their equations.

a $y = 1 - \cosh x$

b $y = \sinh(x - \ln 2)$

c $y = \frac{1}{2}\tanh x + 1$

6 a Sketch, on the same diagram, the graph with equation $y = \sinh x$ and the graph with equation $y = 1 + \tanh x$

b Hence state the number of real roots of the equation

$$\sinh x - \tanh x - 1 = 0$$

c Use a similar technique to determine the number of real roots of these equations.

i $\cosh x - \tanh x = 0$

ii $\cosh x + \tanh x - 2 = 0$

7 The diagram shows the curve with equation $y = b\cosh(x + a)$ where a and b are constants. Point $P(\ln 3, 2)$ on this curve is a minimum point.

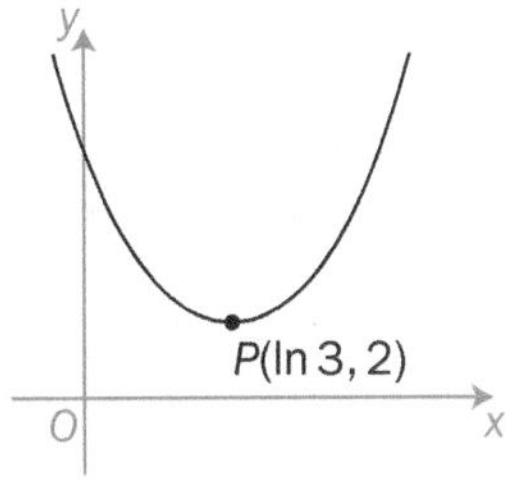

a State the exact value of a and the value of b.

b Find the y-coordinate of the point on this curve with x-coordinate $\ln 4$.

FP3

1.2 Reciprocal hyperbolic functions and their graphs

You can define the reciprocal hyperbolic functions $\operatorname{sech} x$, $\operatorname{cosech} x$ and $\coth x$ in terms of the basic hyperbolic functions and also in terms of e^x.

For all real values of x, $\operatorname{sech} x \equiv \dfrac{1}{\cosh x} \equiv \dfrac{2}{e^x + e^{-x}}$

For all $x \in \mathbb{R}$, $x \neq 0$, $\operatorname{cosech} x \equiv \dfrac{1}{\sinh x} \equiv \dfrac{2}{e^x - e^{-x}}$

$$\coth x \equiv \frac{1}{\tanh x} \equiv \frac{e^{2x} + 1}{e^{2x} - 1}$$
$$\equiv \frac{\cosh x}{\sinh x}$$

EXAMPLE 1

a Given that $e^a = 4$ find the value of $\operatorname{sech} a$.

b Prove that $\coth x \operatorname{sech} x = \operatorname{cosech} x$ for all $x \neq 0$.

a Use the definition $\operatorname{sech} x \equiv \dfrac{2}{e^x + e^{-x}}$:

$$\operatorname{sech} a = \frac{2}{4 + \frac{1}{4}}$$
$$= \frac{8}{16 + 1} = \frac{8}{17}$$

Multiply the numerator and denominator by 4 to clear the fraction.

In this question it is not necessary to find a in order to evaluate $\operatorname{sech} a$.

b Use the definitions $\coth x \equiv \dfrac{\cosh x}{\sinh x}$, $\operatorname{sech} x \equiv \dfrac{1}{\cosh x}$ and $\operatorname{cosech} x \equiv \dfrac{1}{\sinh x}$:

If $x \neq 0$ then $\coth x \operatorname{sech} x \equiv \dfrac{\cosh x}{\sinh x} \times \dfrac{1}{\cosh x}$

$$\equiv \frac{1}{\sinh x}$$

Cancel the $\cosh x$ terms.

You can use the properties of a basic hyperbolic function to sketch the corresponding reciprocal graph.

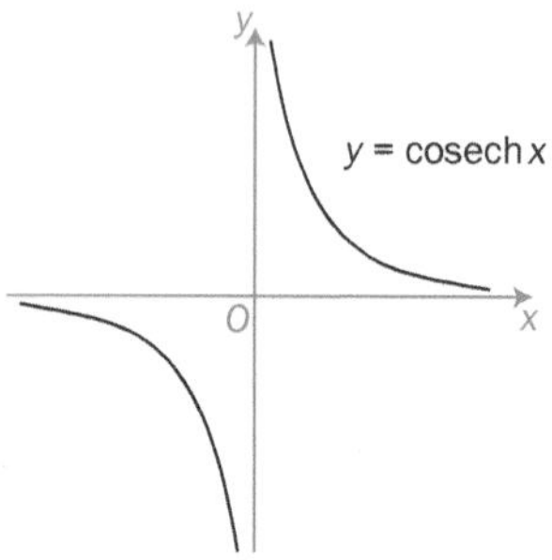

The diagram shows the graph with equation $y = \operatorname{cosech} x$. $\sinh 0 = 0$, so $\operatorname{cosech} 0$ is undefined, that is the line $x = 0$ is an asymptote to the curve.

As $x \to \infty$, $\sinh x \to \infty$ and so $\dfrac{1}{\sinh x} \to 0$

Refer to Section 1.1.

that is $\operatorname{cosech} x \to 0$ as $x \to \infty$

$$\operatorname{cosech}(-x) \equiv \frac{1}{\sinh(-x)} \equiv -\frac{1}{\sinh x} \equiv -\operatorname{cosech} x$$

so the graph $y = \operatorname{cosech} x$ has rotational symmetry, order 2, about the origin. That is, $y = \operatorname{cosech} x$ is an odd function of x. The line $y = 0$ is also an asymptote to the curve.

The graphs of the equations $y = \operatorname{sech} x$ and $y = \coth x$ are:

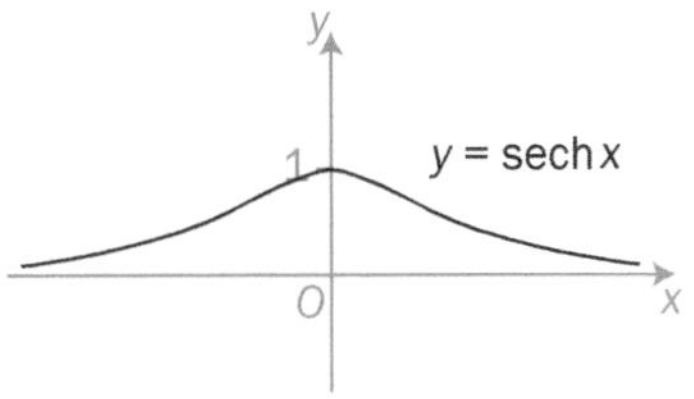

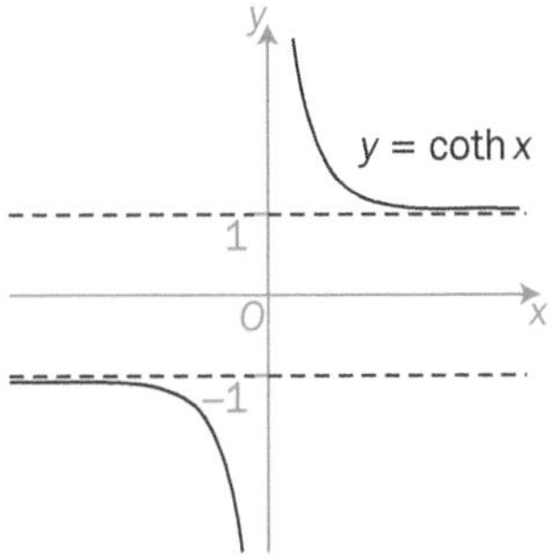

Exercise 1.2

1 Evaluate these expressions. Give each answer to 2 decimal places.

a $\operatorname{cosech} 2.5$ **b** $\operatorname{sech}\left(-\frac{1}{2}\right)$ **c** $\coth(\pi)$

2 Find the values of these expressions. Where appropriate, answers should be given in simplified surd form.

a $\coth(\ln 5)$ **b** $\operatorname{sech}\left(\ln\sqrt{5}\right)$ **c** $2\operatorname{cosech}\left(\frac{1}{2}\ln 3\right)$

FP3

3 Use appropriate definitions to prove these identities.

Assume $x \neq 0$ where appropriate.

a $\operatorname{sech} x \equiv \dfrac{2e^x}{e^{2x}+1}$ **b** $\operatorname{sech} x \sinh x \coth x \equiv 1$

c $\operatorname{cosech} x + \operatorname{sech} x \equiv e^x \operatorname{cosech} x \operatorname{sech} x$ **d** $\dfrac{\operatorname{cosech} x}{\coth x - 1} \equiv e^x$

4 Given that $e^a = \frac{5}{2}$ find the value of

a $\operatorname{sech} a$ **b** $\operatorname{cosech} a$ **c** $\coth a$

See Example 1.

Give each answer as a fraction in its lowest terms.

5 Given that $e^{2b} = 9$ find the value of

a $\coth b$ **b** $\operatorname{sech}(2b)$ **c** $\operatorname{cosech} b$

Give each answer as a fraction in its lowest terms.

6 **a** Given that $5\operatorname{sech} a - 3\operatorname{cosech} a = 0$, for a a constant, find the value of $\tanh a$.

b Show that $e^{2a} = 4$ and hence find the exact value of a.

7 Sketch, on separate diagrams, the graphs with these equations. Label any asymptotes with their equations and any axis-crossing points with their exact coordinates.

a $y = 2\operatorname{sech} x + 1$ **b** $y = 3\operatorname{cosech}(x + \ln 2)$ **c** $y = -\coth(x - 1)$

1.3 Solving equations involving hyperbolic functions

You can solve an equation involving hyperbolic functions by using their exponential definitions.

EXAMPLE 1

Find the values of x for which

$5\cosh x + \sinh x = 7$

giving each answer as a natural logarithm.

Replace the hyperbolic functions in the equation with their exponential definitions:

$$5\cosh x + \sinh x = 7$$

$\cosh x \equiv \frac{1}{2}(e^x + e^{-x})$, $\sinh x \equiv \frac{1}{2}(e^x - e^{-x})$

so $$\frac{5}{2}(e^x + e^{-x}) + \frac{1}{2}(e^x - e^{-x}) = 7$$

$$3e^x + 2e^{-x} = 7$$

Collect like terms: $\frac{5}{2}e^x + \frac{1}{2}e^x = 3e^x$, $\frac{5}{2}e^{-x} - \frac{1}{2}e^{-x} = 2e^{-x}$

Multiply all terms in this equation by e^x to produce a quadratic equation:

$$3(e^x)^2 + 2 = 7e^x$$

$2e^{-x} \times e^x = 2e^0 = 2$

$$3(e^x)^2 - 7e^x + 2 = 0$$

The quadratic equation is in the variable e^x

so $$(3e^x - 1)(e^x - 2) = 0$$

$$e^x = \frac{1}{3} \text{ or } e^x = 2$$

Hence the values of x are $x = \ln\left(\frac{1}{3}\right)$ or $x = \ln 2$

The answer $x = \ln\left(\frac{1}{3}\right)$ could also be written as $x = -\ln 3$

To solve an equation of the form $a\cosh x + b\sinh x = c$ where $a, b, c \in \mathbb{R}$, replace each hyperbolic function with its exponential form and solve, if possible, a quadratic in e^x.

Exercise 1.3

1 Solve these equations, giving each answer as a natural logarithm.

a $5\cosh x - \sinh x = 7$ **b** $4\cosh x + \sinh x = 8$ **c** $3\cosh x - 7\sinh x = 9$

2 Solve these equations, giving each answer correct to 2 decimal places.

a $4\cosh x + 3\sinh x = 3$ **b** $6\sinh x = 7\cosh x - 4$

3 Find the value of x for which

$$5\cosh x + 4\sinh x = 3$$

Give your answer as a natural logarithm.

4 Find the exact values of x which satisfy the equation

$$\frac{1}{2}\cosh x - \frac{1}{3}\sinh x = \frac{1}{2}$$

5 Find the non-zero value of x which satisfies the equation

$$\sqrt{3}\cosh x + \sqrt{2}\sinh x = \sqrt{3}$$

Give your answer in the form $\ln\left(a + b\sqrt{6}\right)$ for integers a and b.

6 It is given that the equation

$$7\cosh x + k\sinh x = 5$$

where k is a constant, is satisfied by the value $x = \ln 2$.

a Find the value of k.

b Hence find the other value of x which satisfies this equation. Give your answer as a natural logarithm.

7 **a** Find the exact value of x for which

$$5\cosh x + 9\sinh x = 13$$

$\cosh(-a) = \cosh a$
$\sinh(-a) = -\sinh a$

b Hence, or otherwise, find the solution of the equation

$$5\cosh\left(\frac{1}{2}x\right) - 9\sinh\left(\frac{1}{2}x\right) = 13$$

giving your answer in the form $\ln q$ for q a rational number in its lowest terms.

8 Solve these equations, giving answers as natural logarithms

a $7 + 4\tanh x = 17\operatorname{sech} x$ **b** $4\coth x - 7 = 16\operatorname{cosech} x$

9 Consider the equation

$$a\cosh x + b\sinh x = a$$

for non-zero constants a and b such that $a + b \neq 0$.

Prove that this equation has a non-zero real root exactly when

$b^2 < a^2$

In this case, write down this non-zero root in terms of a and b.

FP3

1.4 Further identities involving hyperbolic functions

You can prove standard identities involving hyperbolic functions by using their exponential definitions.

EXAMPLE 1

Prove that $2\sinh x\cosh x \equiv \sinh(2x)$

Replace $\sinh x$ and $\cosh x$ with their exponential definitions:

$$\text{LHS} \equiv 2\sinh x\cosh x$$
$$\equiv 2\left(\frac{1}{2}\left(e^x - e^{-x}\right)\right)\left(\frac{1}{2}\left(e^x + e^{-x}\right)\right)$$
$$\equiv \frac{1}{2}\left(\left(e^x\right)^2 - \left(e^{-x}\right)^2\right)$$
$$\equiv \frac{1}{2}\left(e^{2x} - e^{-2x}\right)$$
$$\equiv \sinh(2x) \equiv \text{RHS}$$

Hence $2\sinh x\cosh x \equiv \sinh(2x)$, as required.

By definition, $\sinh x = \frac{1}{2}(e^x - e^{-x})$ and so $\sinh(2x) = \frac{1}{2}(e^{2x} - e^{-2x})$

This result is usually written as $\sinh 2x \equiv 2\sinh x\cosh x$

Some standard identities involving hyperbolic functions are:

$\cosh^2 x - \sinh^2 x \equiv 1$ | $\cosh 2x \equiv \cosh^2 x + \sinh^2 x$

$1 - \tanh^2 x \equiv \text{sech}^2 x$ | $\cosh 2x \equiv 2\cosh^2 x - 1$

$\coth^2 x - 1 \equiv \text{cosech}^2 x,\ (x \neq 0)$ | $\cosh 2x \equiv 1 + 2\sinh^2 x$

$\sinh 2x \equiv 2\sinh x\cosh x$ | $\tanh 2x \equiv \dfrac{2\tanh x}{1 + \tanh^2 x}$

Learn these identities – only some of them appear in the formula book.

You can evaluate hyperbolic expressions by using an identity.

EXAMPLE 2

Given that $\sinh x = \sqrt{3}$ find the value of

a $\cosh x$ **b** $\tanh x$

a Replace $\sinh x$ with $\sqrt{3}$ in the identity $\cosh^2 x - \sinh^2 x \equiv 1$:

$$\cosh^2 x - (\sqrt{3})^2 = 1$$
$$\cosh^2 x = 1 + 3$$
$$\cosh x = 2$$

$\cosh^2 x = 4$ so $\cosh x = \pm 2$, but $\cosh x > 0$ for all x, so $\cosh x = 2$

Refer to Section 1.1.

b Use the definition $\tanh x \equiv \dfrac{\sinh x}{\cosh x}$:

$$\tanh x = \frac{\sinh x}{\cosh x} = \frac{\sqrt{3}}{2}$$

Osborn's rule provides a link between the identities involving hyperbolic functions and the trigonometric functions.

See C3 for revision of trigonometric functions.

Osborn's rule:

- Start with a standard trigonometric identity.
- Replace each trigonometric function in the given identity with the corresponding hyperbolic function (where $\sin x$ corresponds to $\sinh x$ etc.).
- Change the sign whenever a replaced function involves a product of two sine functions.

For example, to apply Osborn's rule to the trigonometric identity

$$\cos 2x \equiv 1 - 2\sin^2 x$$

replace $\cos 2x$ with $\cosh 2x$ and

and $\sin^2 x$ with $-\sinh^2 x$

Osborn's rule then gives

$$\cosh 2x \equiv 1 + 2\sinh^2 x$$

which is one of the standard hyperbolic identities.

$\sin^2 x$ is the product of $\sin x$ with itself, so change the sign.

Establish the identities
$\cos x = \cosh(ix)$
$\sin x = -i\sinh(ix)$
and use them to investigate Osborn's rule.

Likewise, applying Osborn's rule to

$$\tan 2x = \frac{2\tan x}{1-\tan^2 x}$$

replace $\tan 2x$ by $\tanh 2x$ and $\tan^2 x = \dfrac{\sin^2 x}{\cos^2 x}$ by $-\tanh^2 x$

to give $\tanh 2x = \dfrac{2\tanh x}{1+\tanh^2 x}$

FP3

Exercise 1.4

Take care when applying Osborn's rule - see question 12 in this exercise.

1 Use definitions in terms of e^x to prove these identities.

a $\cosh 2x \equiv \cosh^2 x + \sinh^2 x$

b $\sinh 3x \equiv \sinh x\left(3 + 4\sinh^2 x\right)$

c $1 - \tanh^2 x \equiv \operatorname{sech}^2 x$

$\operatorname{sech}^2 x$ means $(\operatorname{sech} x)^2$

2 a Use definitions in terms of e^x to prove

$$\sinh(x+y) \equiv \sinh x \cosh y + \cosh x \sinh y$$

b Deduce that

$$\sinh 2A \equiv 2\sinh A \cosh A \quad \text{for all } A \in \mathbb{R}$$

3 Given that $\sinh x = 2$ use an appropriate identity to find the exact value of

a $\cosh x$ b $\sinh 2x$ c $\cosh 2x$

4 Given that $\cosh x = \frac{3}{2}$ use an appropriate identity to find the possible values of

a $\sinh x$ **b** $\tanh x$ **c** $\tanh 2x$

Give each answer in the form $a\sqrt{5}$ where a is a rational number in its lowest terms.

5 **a** Write down the result of applying Osborn's rule to these trigonometric identities.

i $\cos(x+y) \equiv \cos x \cos y - \sin x \sin y$

ii $\cos 3x \equiv 4\cos^3 x - 3\cos x$

iii $\tan 2x \equiv \dfrac{2\tan x}{1-\tan^2 x}$

iv $\cot^2 x + 1 \equiv \operatorname{cosec}^2 x$

b Prove each identity found in part **a** by using definitions in terms of e^x.

6 It is given that $\tanh a = \frac{1}{2}\sqrt{3}$

a Using a suitable identity, show that $\cosh a = 2$

b Find the value of cosech $2a$. Give your answer in simplified surd form.

FP3

7 **a** Using only the identities given in the FP3 section of the formula booklet, prove that

$$\cosh 2x \equiv 1 + 2\sinh^2 x$$

b Hence show that

$$\frac{2}{(\cosh y) - 1} \equiv \operatorname{cosech}^2 \frac{1}{2}y \quad \text{for } y \neq 0$$

8 **a** By replacing $\cosh x$ and $\sinh x$ with their definitions in terms of e^x, prove that

$$(\cosh x + \sinh x)(\cosh x - \sinh x) \equiv 1$$

b Find the exact value of x which satisfies the simultaneous equations.

$$\cosh x - \sinh^2 x = \frac{11}{16}$$

$$\cosh^2 x + \sinh x = \frac{37}{16}$$

Add the equations together.

9 If $\sinh x = \tan\theta$, where θ is an acute angle,

a show that $\cosh x = \sec\theta$,

b express $\tanh 2x$ in terms of $\sin\theta$.

10 Use any standard results to prove these identities.

a $\dfrac{2}{1+\cosh 2x} \equiv \operatorname{sech}^2 x$

b $\coth x + \tanh x \equiv 2\coth 2x$

c $\sinh 2x \equiv \dfrac{2\tanh x}{1-\tanh^2 x}$

11 a Prove that

$e^{nx}\operatorname{sech} nx \equiv 1 + \tanh nx$, for any integer n

b Hence sketch the graph with equation

$$y = \frac{e^{3x}}{\cosh 3x}$$

Mark any axis-crossing points with their coordinates and label the equations of any asymptotes to this curve.

12 a Prove that

$$(\cos x + \sin x)^2 \equiv 1 + \sin 2x$$

b Show that applying Osborn's rule to this identity does *not* produce a valid identity involving hyperbolic functions. Justify your answer.

Osborn's rule may not work when applied to trigonometric functions which are nested inside a bracket.

13 a Find the possible values of $a \in \mathbb{R}$ for which

$$\left(\sqrt{2} + a\right)^4 = 17 + 12a\sqrt{2}$$

b Prove that

$$4\cosh^4 x + 4\sinh^4 x \equiv 3 + \cosh 4x$$

Express each of $\cosh^2 x$ and $\sinh^2 x$ in terms of $\cosh 2x$.

c Hence solve the equation

$$\cosh^4 x + \sinh^4 x = 5$$

Give each answer as a natural logarithm.

The inverse function of $\sinh x$ is $\text{arsinh}\, x$.
$\text{arsinh}\, x$ is the value y such that $\sinh y = x$

arsinh x is pronounced 'are shine x'.

For example, $\sinh(\ln 2) = \frac{3}{4}$, so $\text{arsinh}\left(\frac{3}{4}\right) = \ln 2$

$\sinh(\ln 2) = \frac{3}{4}$ Refer to Section 1.1, Example 1.

The inverse functions $\text{arcosh}\, x$ and $\text{artanh}\, x$ are similarly defined.

You can sketch the graph of an inverse hyperbolic function by using a reflection in the line $y = x$.

This diagram shows the graph with equation $y = \sinh x$ and its reflection (shown in bold) in the line $y = x$.
The graph in bold has equation $y = \text{arsinh}\, x$

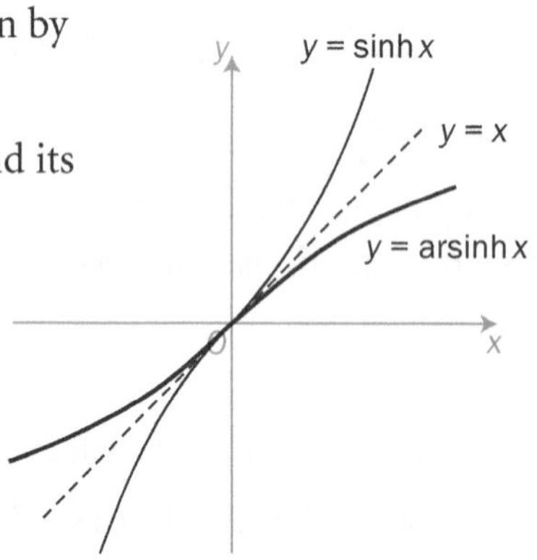

EXAMPLE 1

a Draw the graph of $y = \tanh x$
b Sketch the graph with equation $y = \text{artanh}\, x$.
Clearly label the asymptotes to each graph.

a

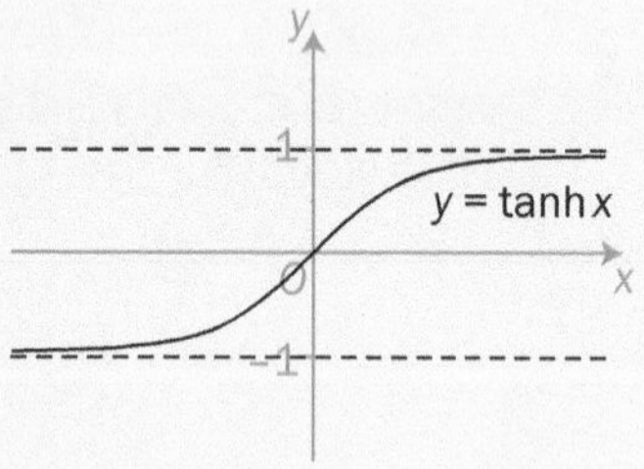

b Draw the line $y = x$ on a copy of the graph in part **a**.
Reflect this graph in the line.

Reflect the asymptotes in the line $y = x$

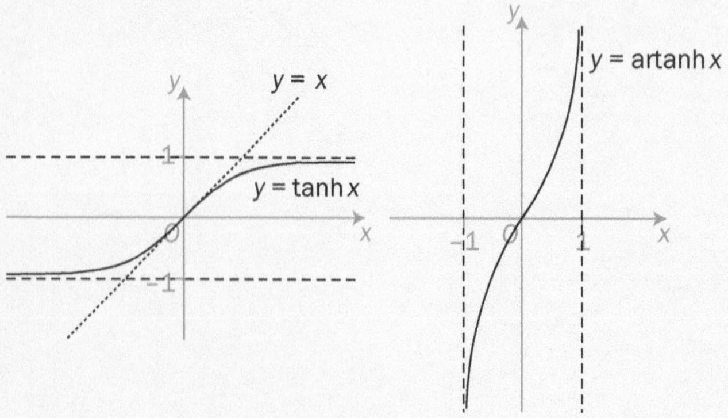

You can sketch the graph with equation $y = \text{arcosh}\, x$ where $x \in \mathbb{R}, x \geqslant 1$

Only one-to-one functions have inverses. Refer to C3.

In the diagram, the graph with equation $y = \cosh x$ for $x \in \mathbb{R}, x \geqslant 0$ displays a one-to-one function, with range $y \in \mathbb{R}, y \geqslant 1$.

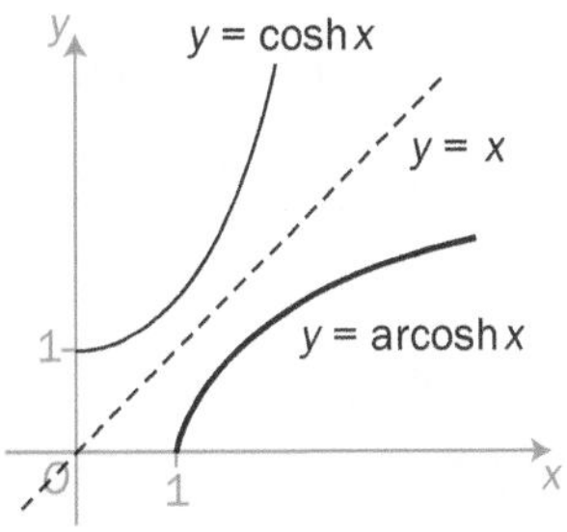

Reflecting this graph in the line $y = x$ gives the graph with equation $y = \text{arcosh}\, x$ (shown in bold), which has domain $x \in \mathbb{R}, x \geqslant 1$ and range $y \in \mathbb{R}, y \geqslant 0$

It is conventional to restrict $\cosh x$ over $x \geqslant 0$ rather than $x \leqslant 0$ when defining its inverse.

$\text{arsinh}\, x$ has domain $x \in \mathbb{R}$ and range $y \in \mathbb{R}$
$\text{arcosh}\, x$ has domain $x \in \mathbb{R}, x \geqslant 1$ and range $y \in \mathbb{R}, y \geqslant 0$
$\text{artanh}\, x$ has domain $x \in \mathbb{R}, -1 < x < 1$ and range $y \in \mathbb{R}$

The function $\text{arcosh}\, x$ is only defined for $x \geqslant 1$

You can express the functions $\text{arsinh}\, x$, $\text{arcosh}\, x$ and $\text{artanh}\, x$ using natural logarithms.

EXAMPLE 2

Show that $\text{arsinh}\, x = \ln\left(x + \sqrt{x^2 + 1}\right)$

Define $y = \text{arsinh}\, x$ and use the definition of this inverse function:

$y = \text{arsinh}\, x$ so $\sinh y = x$

Use the result $\cosh^2 y - \sinh^2 y = 1$ to find $\cosh y$ in terms of x:

Refer to Section 1.4

$$\cosh^2 y = \sinh^2 y + 1$$
$$= x^2 + 1$$

So $\cosh y = \sqrt{x^2 + 1}$

$\cosh y > 0$ so ignore the negative square root $-\sqrt{x^2 + 1}$

Use the result $\sinh y + \cosh y = e^y$ to find y in terms of x:

$\sinh y + \cosh y = \frac{1}{2}(e^y - e^{-y}) + \frac{1}{2}(e^y + e^{-y}) = e^y$

So $x + \sqrt{x^2 + 1} = e^y$

Hence $y = \ln\left(x + \sqrt{x^2 + 1}\right)$

that is $\text{arsinh}\, x = \ln\left(x + \sqrt{x^2 + 1}\right)$

$\text{arsinh}\, x = \ln\left(x + \sqrt{x^2 + 1}\right)$ for $x \in \mathbb{R}$

$\text{arcosh}\, x = \ln\left(x + \sqrt{x^2 - 1}\right)$ for $x \in \mathbb{R}, x \geqslant 1$

$\text{artanh}\, x = \frac{1}{2}\ln\left(\frac{1 + x}{1 - x}\right)$ for $x \in \mathbb{R}, -1 < x < 1$

These results are in the FP3 section of the formula book. However, you may be asked to prove them in the exam.

FP3

You can use logarithmic forms to solve equations involving hyperbolic functions.

EXAMPLE 3

Solve the equation $\cosh x = 2$, giving answers as natural logarithms.

Use the result $\operatorname{arcosh} x = \ln\left(x + \sqrt{x^2 - 1}\right)$:

$\cosh x = 2$ so one possible value of x is

$$\operatorname{arcosh} 2 = \ln\left(2 + \sqrt{2^2 - 1}\right) = \ln\left(2 + \sqrt{3}\right)$$

Use the symmetry of the graph of $y = \cosh x$ in the y-axis to solve the equation:

The solution to the equation $\cosh x = 2$ is $x = \pm\ln\left(2 + \sqrt{3}\right)$

The answers can also be written as $x = \ln\left(2 \pm \sqrt{3}\right)$

The equation $\cosh x = a$, where $a \geqslant 1$, has solution $x = \pm\ln\left(a + \sqrt{a^2 - 1}\right)$

This solution can also be written as $x = \ln\left(a \pm \sqrt{a^2 - 1}\right)$

FP3

Exercise 1.5

1 Use appropriate logarithmic forms to evaluate these expressions. Give answers as natural logarithms in as simple a form as possible.

a $\operatorname{arsinh} 3$ **b** $\operatorname{arcosh}\sqrt{2}$ **c** $2\operatorname{artanh}\frac{1}{3}$

d $\operatorname{arsinh}\left(\frac{4}{3}\right)$ **e** $\operatorname{arcosh}\left(\frac{\sqrt{5}}{2}\right)$ **f** $\operatorname{artanh}\frac{1}{\sqrt{2}}$

2 Sketch, on separate diagrams, the complete graphs with these equations. Use the largest possible domain for each graph. Mark any axis-crossing points with their exact values and any asymptotes with their equations.

a $y = 1 + \operatorname{arcosh}(x - 2)$ **b** $y = -\operatorname{artanh} 2x$ **c** $y = 2\operatorname{arsinh}\left(x + \sqrt{3}\right)$

3 Solve these equations. Give answers in form $\ln\left(a + b\sqrt{c}\right)$, for $a, b, c \in \mathbb{Z}$ and c is prime.

a $\sinh x = 4$ **b** $\cosh x = 3$ **c** $\sinh\frac{1}{2}x = 2$

d $\sqrt{3}\tanh\frac{1}{2}x = 1$ **e** $2\tanh x + \sqrt{3} = 0$ **f** $\cosh 2x = 3$

For part f express $3 + 2\sqrt{2}$ in the form $\left(a + \sqrt{b}\right)^2$ where $a, b \in \mathbb{Z}$.

4 **a** Given that $y = \operatorname{artanh} x$, where $x \in \mathbb{R}, -1 < x < 1$, show that $x = \dfrac{e^{2y} - 1}{e^{2y} + 1}$

b Deduce that $\operatorname{artanh} x = \frac{1}{2}\ln\left(\frac{1+x}{1-x}\right)$

$\mathrm{f}(x) = 2\operatorname{artanh}\left(\frac{x-1}{x}\right) x \in \mathbb{R}, x > \frac{1}{2}$

c Show that $\mathrm{f}(x) = \ln(ax + b)$, stating the value of the constants a and b.

5 Given that $\cosh x = a$, where $a \in \mathbb{R}$, $a \geqslant 1$

a show that $e^{2x} - 2ae^x + 1 = 0$

b Deduce that the equation $\cosh x = a$ has solutions given by

$$x = \ln\left(a \pm \sqrt{a^2 - 1}\right)$$

6 Solve these equations. Give answers in terms of natural logarithms.

a $\sinh^2 x = 2$

b $8\cosh^3 x = 27$

c $\sqrt{5\tanh x} = 2$

d $\text{sech}^2 \frac{1}{2}x = \frac{1}{2}$

7 a Use the definition of $\sinh y$ in terms of exponentials to show that

if $x = \sinh y$ then $e^{2y} - 2xe^y - 1 = 0$

b Hence, or otherwise, show that $\text{arsinh}\, x = \ln\left(x + \sqrt{x^2 + 1}\right)$

8 Use logarithmic forms to prove that

a $\text{arsinh}\, x + \text{arsinh}\,(-x) = 0, x \in \mathbb{R}$

b $\text{artanh}\, x + \text{artanh}\,(-x) = 0, -1 < x < 1.$

9 Given that $\tanh a = -\frac{1}{7}$

a find the exact value of a, giving your answer in the form $\ln k$.

b hence, or otherwise, show that $\sinh a = -\frac{1}{12}\sqrt{3}$

10 Given that $\sinh b = \sqrt{8}$

a find the exact value of b

b hence, or otherwise, find the value of $\tanh b$, giving your answer in the form $k\sqrt{2}$, where k is a rational number in its lowest terms.

11 a Simplify the expression $\text{arsinh}\left(\frac{1}{x}\right) + \ln x$, where $x > 0$, giving your answer as the natural logarithm of a function.

b Hence solve, in terms of e, the equation $\text{arsinh}\left(\frac{1}{x}\right) + \ln x = 1$

12 Show that

a $\text{arsinh}\left(\sqrt{x^2 - 1}\right) \equiv \text{arcosh}\, x$ for $x \geqslant 1$

b $\text{artanh}(1 - 2x) \equiv \frac{1}{2}\ln\left(\frac{1-x}{x}\right)$ for $0 < x < 1$

13 Use any appropriate identities to show that

$\text{artanh}\,(\text{sech}\, x) \equiv \ln\,(\coth x + \text{cosech}\, x)$ for all $x > 0$

FP3

1.6 Further equation solving

You can use an identity to solve an equation involving hyperbolic expressions.

EXAMPLE 1

Solve the equation $\sinh^2 x - 3\cosh x + 3 = 0$
giving answers as natural logarithms where appropriate.

Use the identity $\cosh^2 x - \sinh^2 x \equiv 1$ to rewrite the given equation in terms of $\cosh x$:

$\sinh^2 x - 3\cosh x + 3 = 0$ so $(\cosh^2 x - 1) - 3\cosh x + 3 = 0$

so $\cosh^2 x - 3\cosh x + 2 = 0$

hence $(\cosh x - 1)(\cosh x - 2) = 0$

$\sinh^2 x = \cosh^2 x - 1$
Refer to Section 1.4

So either $\cosh x = 1$ or $\cosh x = 2$

If $\cosh x = 1$ then $x = 0$

If $\cosh x = 2$ then $x = \ln\left(2 \pm \sqrt{2^2 - 1}\right)$

$= \ln\left(2 \pm \sqrt{3}\right)$

Hence the solution to the equation $\sinh^2 x - 3\cosh x + 3 = 0$ is

$x = 0,\ x = \ln\left(2 \pm \sqrt{3}\right)$

You can see from the graph of $y = \cosh x$ that the equation $\cosh x = 1$ is satisfied only by $x = 0$

If $\cosh x = a$ then
$x = \ln\left(a \pm \sqrt{a^2 - 1}\right)$
Refer to Section 1.5.

EXAMPLE 2

Find the values of x for which

$2\sinh^2 x = \sinh x \cosh x$

giving answers as natural logarithms where appropriate.

Gather terms to one side:

$2\sinh^2 x = \sinh x \cosh x$ so $2\sinh^2 x - \sinh x \cosh x = 0$

that is, $\sinh x\,(2\sinh x - \cosh x) = 0$

Avoid dividing through by $\sinh x$ which might be zero.

Hence, either $\sinh x = 0$ or $2\sinh x - \cosh x = 0$

If $\sinh x = 0$ then $x = 0$

$\sinh x = 0$ only when $x = 0$. Refer to the graph of $y = \sinh x$

If $2\sinh x - \cosh x = 0$

$$2\sinh x = \cosh x$$

$$\frac{2\sinh x}{\cosh x} = 1$$

$$2\tanh x = 1$$

$$\tanh x = \frac{1}{2}$$

You can divide by $\cosh x$ because $\cosh x \neq 0$ for all x.
see Section 1.1.

EXAMPLE 2 (CONT.)

Use the result $\text{artanh}\, x = \frac{1}{2}\ln\left(\frac{1+x}{1-x}\right)$:

$$\tanh x = \frac{1}{2} \quad \text{so} \quad x = \text{artan}\frac{1}{2}$$
$$= \frac{1}{2}\ln\left(\frac{1+\frac{1}{2}}{1-\frac{1}{2}}\right)$$
$$= \frac{1}{2}\ln\left(\frac{2+1}{2-1}\right)$$
$$= \frac{1}{2}\ln 3$$

Multiply all terms in the bracket by 2 to clear the fractions.

Hence the equation $2\sinh^2 x = \sinh x \cosh x$ has solutions $x = 0$, $x = \frac{1}{2}\ln 3$

Exercise 1.6

Unless told otherwise, give your solutions in exact form using natural logarithms.

1 Solve these equations.

a $\cosh^2 x - \sinh x - 7 = 0$

b $2\cosh^2 x + 5\sinh x + 1 = 0$

c $2\sinh^2 x - 5\cosh x + 5 = 0$

d $3\sinh^2 x + 3 = 7\cosh x$

2 Solve these equations.

a $4\sinh^2 x = 3\sinh x \cosh x$

b $3\sinh x \cosh x + 2\sinh^2 x = -2$

c $2\sinh^2 x + \sinh x \cosh x = 2\sinh x + \cosh x$

3 Solve the equation $\cosh x - 3\sinh x = 0$

a by using the definition $\tanh x \equiv \frac{\sinh x}{\cosh x}$

b by using the exponential definitions of $\cosh x$ and $\sinh x$.

4 Use suitable identities to solve these equations

a $2\sinh x \cosh x = 3$

b $\cosh^2 \frac{3}{2}x + \sinh^2 \frac{3}{2}x = \sqrt{2}$

c $\sinh 2x \cosh 2x = \sqrt{2}$

5 a Show that the equation $3\sinh^2 x = \sinh 2x$ can be expressed as $\sinh x(3\sinh x - 2\cosh x) = 0$

b Hence find the values of x for which $3\sinh^2 x = \sinh 2x$

FP3

6 Use any appropriate identities to solve these equations.

a $\cosh 2x - 7\cosh x + 6 = 0$ b $1 + \cosh 2x = 5\sinh x$

c $6\sinh^2 x + 3 = 8\sinh x\cosh x$ d $\sinh 2x + \cosh x = (\sinh x + 1)^2$

7 Use the identity $1 - \tanh^2 x = \text{sech}^2 x$ to solve these equations.

a $2\text{sech}^2 x + \tanh x - 2 = 0$ b $2\tanh^2 x + \text{sech}\, x = 2$

c $4\tanh^2 x = 5(1 - \text{sech}\, x)$ d $2\tanh^4 x + 3\text{sech}^2 x - 2 = 0$

8 a Simplify $\frac{1}{1-\tanh x} + \frac{1}{1+\tanh x}$

b Hence, or otherwise, solve the equation $\frac{1}{1-\tanh x} + \frac{1}{1+\tanh x} = 4$

9 a Use the result $\sinh(A + B) \equiv \sinh A \cosh B + \cosh A \sinh B$ to find an identity for $\sinh 3x$ in terms of $\sinh x$.

b Hence, or otherwise, find the value of x for which

$$8\sinh^3 x + 6\sinh x + \cosh 3x = 0$$

Give your answer in the form $\frac{1}{a}\ln 3$, where a is an integer to be stated.

10 a Show that the equation $2\tanh 2x = \coth x$, where $x > 0$, can be rearranged into the equation $3\tanh^2 x = 1$

b Hence, or otherwise, find the solution to the equation $2\tanh 2x = \coth x$.

Give your answer in the form $\ln\left(\frac{\sqrt{2}+\sqrt{a}}{2}\right)$, for a an integer to be stated.

11 a Use a suitable identity to show that the equation

$$3 + 3\tanh^2 x = 8\tanh x$$

can be expressed in the form

$\tanh 2x = k$, stating the value of the constant k.

b Hence, or otherwise, find the solution to the equation

$$3 + 3\tanh^2 x = 8\tanh x$$

12 **a** On the same diagram, sketch the graph with equation $y = \cosh x$ and the graph with equation $y = 1 + \operatorname{sech} 2x$

b Hence state the number of solutions to the equation $1 + \operatorname{sech} 2x = \cosh x$

P and Q are the points where the curves $y = \cosh x$ and $y = 1 + \operatorname{sech} 2x$ intersect.

c Prove that the line PQ is horizontal and find its length. Give your answer to 2 decimal places.

13 Solve the equation $\cosh 4x = 16 \sinh x + 1$.

14 **a** Express $\cosh^4 x - \sinh^4 x$ as a single hyperbolic function.

b Hence, or otherwise, solve the equation

$\cosh^4 x - \sinh^4 x = \tanh x + \coth x$, where $x \neq 0$

15 Solve these equations.

a $\sinh^3 x + 7 = 3 \cosh^2 x$

b $\sinh^2 x + 4 \tanh^2 x = 3$

c $2 - \operatorname{sech}^2 x = \coth 2x, x \neq 0$

FP3

1 Solve the equation

$$7\cosh x - 3\sinh x = 11$$

Give your answer as a natural logarithm.

2 It is given that the equation $5\tanh x - a\operatorname{sech} x = a$, where a is a constant, is satisfied by the value $x = \ln\left(\frac{7}{3}\right)$

a Find the value of a.

b Show that no other real value of x satisfies this equation.

3 a Use the definitions of cosh and sinh in terms of exponentials to prove that

$$\tanh(x+y) \equiv \frac{\tanh x + \tanh y}{1 + \tanh x \tanh y}$$

b Given that $\tanh x = \frac{a-1}{a+1}$ where $a > 0$ is a constant, show that

$$\tanh(x + \ln 2) = \frac{4a-1}{4a+1}$$

4 a Using the exponential definition of cosh$x$ prove that

$$\cosh 2x \equiv 2\cosh^2 x - 1$$

b Deduce that

$$\cosh 4x \equiv 8\cosh^4 x - 8\cosh^2 x + 1$$

c Hence, or otherwise, solve the equation

$$\cosh^4 x - \cosh^2 x = \frac{9}{64}$$

Give each answer in the form $q\ln 2$ for q a rational number in its lowest terms.

5 Solve the equation

$$\sinh 2x + \cosh x = \coth x, \text{ where } x \neq 0.$$

Give answers as natural logarithms.

6 Given that $\operatorname{arsinh} x = \ln\left(x + \sqrt{x^2+1}\right)$

a show that, for $x > 0$ $\operatorname{arcosech} x = \ln\left(\frac{1+\sqrt{1+x^2}}{x}\right)$

The graph with equation $y = \operatorname{arcosech} x$ intersects the graph with equation $y = \ln x$ at point P.

arcosech$x$ is the inverse function of cosech$x$.

b Find the exact coordinates of P.

7 a On the same diagram, sketch the graphs with equations

i $y = 3e^{-x}$

ii $y = 2\tanh\frac{1}{2}x$

Label axis crossing points with their coordinates and the asymptotes with their equations.

b Find the exact coordinates of the point where these graphs intersect.

8 Solve the equation $6\tanh^2 x + 5\operatorname{sech} x - 7 = 0$

Give your answers as natural logarithms.

9 Prove these identities. You may use any standard results in your proofs.

a $\dfrac{1}{\coth x - 1} + \dfrac{1}{\coth x + 1} \equiv \sinh 2x$

b $\dfrac{1}{1 - \tanh x} - \dfrac{\tanh x}{1 + \tanh x} \equiv \cosh 2x$

10 Solve the equation

$$2\coth x - 3\operatorname{cosech} x = 2$$

Give your answer in the form $\ln q$ for q a rational number in its lowest terms.

11 Given that

$$\cosh 2x + \sinh ax - 7 = 0$$

where $a \in \mathbb{R}$, solve this equation when

a $a = 1$ b $a = 2$

Give answers as natural logarithms.

12 a Prove that

$$(\operatorname{sech} x - \cosh x)^2 \equiv \sinh^2 x - \tanh^2 x$$

b Hence, or otherwise, solve the equation

$$\sinh^2 x + 3\tanh^2 x = 4$$

Give your answers as natural logarithms.

FP3

1 Exit

Summary

Refer to

- You can use the exponential function e^x to define hyperbolic functions:
  - $\cosh x = \frac{1}{2}(e^x + e^{-x})$, $\sinh x = \frac{1}{2}(e^x - e^{-x})$, $\tanh x = \frac{\sinh x}{\cosh x} = \frac{e^{2x} - 1}{e^{2x} + 1}$
  - $\cosh(-x) \equiv \cosh x$, $\sinh(-x) \equiv -\sinh x$
    $\tanh(-x) \equiv -\tanh x$, $|\tanh x| < 1$ for all $x \in \mathbb{R}$ 1.1
  - $\text{sech}\, x \equiv \frac{1}{\cosh x} \equiv \frac{2}{e^x + e^{-x}}$
  - $\text{cosech}\, x \equiv \frac{1}{\sinh x} \equiv \frac{2}{e^x - e^{-x}}$ $(x \neq 0)$
  - $\coth x \equiv \frac{1}{\tanh x} \equiv \frac{\cosh x}{\sinh x} \equiv \frac{e^{2x} + 1}{e^{2x} - 1}$ $(x \neq 0)$ 1.2
- You can use the exponential definitions of hyperbolic functions to establish these identities:
  - $\cosh^2 x - \sinh^2 x \equiv 1$
  - $\sinh 2x \equiv 2\sinh x \cosh x$
  - $\cosh 2x \equiv \cosh^2 x + \sinh^2 x \equiv 2\cosh^2 x - 1 \equiv 1 + 2\sinh^2 x$
  - $\tanh 2x \equiv \frac{2\tanh x}{1 + \tanh^2 x}$
  - $1 - \tanh^2 x \equiv \text{sech}^2 x$
  - $\coth^2 x - 1 \equiv \text{cosech}^2 x$, $(x \neq 0)$ 1.4
- You can use identities to show inverse hyperbolic functions have logarithmic equivalents.
  - $\text{arsinh}\, x = \ln\left(x + \sqrt{x^2 + 1}\right)$ has domain $x \in \mathbb{R}$ and range $y \in \mathbb{R}$
  - $\text{arcosh}\, x = \ln\left(x + \sqrt{x^2 - 1}\right)$ has domain $x \in \mathbb{R}, x \geqslant 1$ and range $y \in \mathbb{R}, y \geqslant 0$
  - $\text{artanh}\, x = \frac{1}{2}\ln\left(\frac{1 + x}{1 - x}\right)$ has domain $x \in \mathbb{R}, -1 < x < 1$ and range $y \in \mathbb{R}$ 1.5

Links

Hyperbolic functions can be used to describe curves which arise naturally. The shape taken by a freely hanging, heavy chain suspended by its end points is described by the hyperbolic cosine function, $y = \cosh x$.

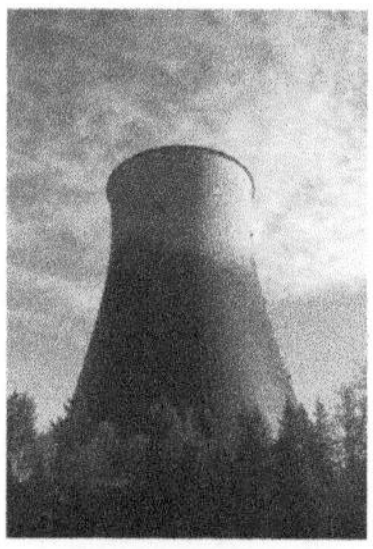

Robert Hooke showed that this shape, known as a *catenary*, is ideal for a uniform arch that supports only its own weight, and there are many examples of this in architecture. If the chain bears a uniform load, as in a suspension bridge, then the resulting shape is a parabola. Other curves which find use in architecture include hyperboloids which can be found in cooling towers and support columns.

2 Differentiation

This chapter will show you how to

- differentiate hyperbolic functions
- find an equation for the tangent or the normal to a hyperbolic curve
- find the coordinates of the stationary points on a hyperbolic curve
- differentiate inverse hyperbolic functions and inverse trigonometric functions.

See Section 0.2 W.
See C3 for revision.

Before you start

You should know how to:

1 Use the product, quotient and chain rules to differentiate a function.

e.g. Find $\frac{dy}{dx}$ when $y = \cos x \sin 2x$

Use the product and chain rules:

$y = (\cos x)(\sin 2x)$ so

$$\frac{dy}{dx} = (\cos x)(\sin 2x)' + (\sin 2x)(\cos x)'$$
$$= (\cos x)(2\cos 2x) + (\sin 2x)(-\sin x)$$
$$= 2\cos x \cos 2x - \sin x \sin 2x$$

2 Use differentiation to solve problems.
e.g. Find an equation for the tangent T to the curve with equation $y = e^{2x^2}$ at the point $P(1, e^2)$.

Use the chain rule to find $\frac{dy}{dx}$:

$y = e^{2x^2}$ so $\frac{dy}{dx} = 4xe^{2x^2}$

Calculate the gradient of T:

$x = 1$ so $\frac{dy}{dx} = 4e^2$

An equation for T is $y - e^2 = 4e^2(x - 1)$
that is, $y = e^2(4x - 3)$

3 Use the result $\frac{dy}{dx} = \frac{1}{\left(\frac{dx}{dy}\right)}$

e.g. If $x = y^2 + 1$, find $\frac{dy}{dx}$ in terms of x.

Find $\frac{dy}{dx}$: $x = y^2 + 1$ so $\frac{dx}{dy} = 2y$

So $\frac{dy}{dx} = \frac{1}{2y}$, that is $\frac{dy}{dx} = \frac{\pm 1}{2\sqrt{x-1}}$

Check in:

1 Find $\frac{dy}{dx}$ for these functions.

a $y = \ln(x^2 + 1)$

b $y = x^2 e^{-3x}$

c $y = \frac{\sin x}{\cos x + 1}$

d $y = \cos^2 x\, e^{\tan x}$

2 **a** Find an equation for the tangent to the curve with equation
$y = x\ln(4x - 1)$ at $P\left(\frac{1}{2}, 0\right)$.

b Find the gradient of the normal to the curve with equation $y = \frac{x^2}{\sin x}$ at the point where $x = \frac{1}{2}\pi$.

c Find the exact coordinates of the stationary points of the curve with equation $y = 4\ln(\cos x) + \tan^2 x$ for $0 \leqslant x < \frac{1}{2}\pi$.

3 Find $\frac{dy}{dx}$ in terms of x for these expressions.

a $x = y^3 - 1$

b $x = e^{y^2}$, $y > 0$

c $x = y^2 - 2y + 2$, $y > 1$

2.1 Differentiation of hyperbolic functions

You can use the exponential definitions $\cosh x = \frac{1}{2}(e^x + e^{-x})$ and $\sinh x = \frac{1}{2}(e^x - e^{-x})$ to differentiate hyperbolic functions.

Refer to Section 1.1

EXAMPLE 1

a If $y = \cosh x$ show that $\frac{dy}{dx} = \sinh x$

b Show that $\frac{d}{dx}[\sinh x] = \cosh x$

$\frac{d}{dx}[\sinh x]$ means the derivative of $\sinh x$ wrt x.

a Use the definition $\cosh x = \frac{1}{2}(e^x + e^{-x})$:

$$y = \frac{1}{2}(e^x + e^{-x}) \quad \text{so} \quad \frac{dy}{dx} = \frac{1}{2}(e^x + (-1)e^{-x})$$
$$= \frac{1}{2}(e^x - e^{-x})$$
$$= \sinh x$$

that is, $\frac{dy}{dx} = \sinh x$, as required.

$\frac{d}{dx}(e^{ax}) = ae^{ax}$, $a \in \mathbb{R}$ Refer to C3.

b Use the definition $\sinh x = \frac{1}{2}(e^x - e^{-x})$:

$$\frac{d}{dx}[\sinh x] = \frac{d}{dx}\left[\frac{1}{2}(e^x - e^{-x})\right]$$
$$= \frac{1}{2}(e^x - (-1)e^{-x})$$
$$= \frac{1}{2}(e^x + e^{-x})$$

that is, $\frac{d}{dx}[\sinh x] = \cosh x$, as required.

$$\frac{d}{dx}[\sinh x] = \cosh x \qquad \frac{d}{dx}[\cosh x] = \sinh x$$
$$\frac{d}{dx}[\tanh x] = \text{sech}^2 x$$

These results are in the FP3 section of the formula booklet.

Other useful results are:

$$\frac{d}{dx}[\text{sech}\, x] = -\tanh x\, \text{sech}\, x \qquad \frac{d}{dx}[\text{cosech}\, x] = -\coth x\, \text{cosech}\, x$$
$$\frac{d}{dx}[\coth x] = -\text{cosech}^2 x$$

These results are not given in the formula book. You may be asked to prove them.

You can combine standard results to find the derivatives of other functions.

EXAMPLE 2

a Show that $\dfrac{d}{dx}[\tanh x] = \text{sech}^2 x$

b If $y = \text{sech}\, x$ show that $\dfrac{dy}{dx} = -\tanh x \,\text{sech}\, x$

$\text{sech}^2 x$ means $\dfrac{1}{\cosh^2 x}$

Refer to Section 1.2

a Use the definition $\tanh x \equiv \dfrac{\sinh x}{\cosh x}$ and the quotient rule

$\dfrac{d}{dx}\left[\dfrac{u}{v}\right] = \dfrac{vu' - uv'}{v^2}$:

$\dfrac{d}{dx}[\tanh x] = \dfrac{d}{dx}\left[\dfrac{\sinh x}{\cosh x}\right]$

$= \dfrac{\cosh x(\sinh x)' - \sinh x(\cosh x)'}{\cosh^2 x}$

$= \dfrac{\cosh^2 x - \sinh^2 x}{\cosh^2 x}$

$= \dfrac{1}{\cosh^2 x}$

that is, $\dfrac{d}{dx}[\tanh x] = \text{sech}^2 x$

Refer to C3. u' means the derivative of u wrt x.

$\cosh^2 x - \sinh^2 x \equiv 1$
Refer to Section 1.4

$\text{sech}\, x = \dfrac{1}{\cosh x}$

so $\dfrac{1}{\cosh^2 x} = \text{sech}^2 x$

b Use the definition $\text{sech}\, x \equiv \dfrac{1}{\cosh x}$ and the chain rule:

$y = \text{sech}\, x$ so $y = (\cosh x)^{-1}$

Hence $\dfrac{dy}{dx} = (-1)(\cosh x)^{-2}(\cosh x)'$

$= -\dfrac{\sinh x}{\cosh^2 x}$

$= -\dfrac{\sinh x}{\cosh x} \times \dfrac{1}{\cosh x}$

$= -\tanh x \,\text{sech}\, x$

Hence $\dfrac{dy}{dx} = -\tanh x \,\text{sech}\, x$, as required.

You could also use the quotient rule.

$\dfrac{dy}{dx} = \dfrac{dy}{du} \times \dfrac{du}{dx}$ where $u = \cosh x$

Refer to C3.
$(\cosh x)' = \sinh x$

Exercise 2.1

Unless told otherwise you may use standard rules and results to find the required derivatives.

In part a, sinh 2*x* means sinh (2*x*) Refer to Section 1.4

1 Find the derivatives of these functions.

a $\sinh 2x$ b $\cosh(x^2)$ c $\tanh^2 x$

d $2\sinh(\sqrt{x})$ e $3\sqrt{\tanh x}$ f $\cosh^4 3x$

2 Find the derivatives of these functions. Factorise each answer as far as possible.

a $x^2 \sinh x$ b $x^3 \cosh 3x$ c $e^{2x} \tanh x$

d $\sinh 2x \cosh 4x$ e $\sinh^2 x \cosh x$ f $\sinh x \tanh x$

g $\dfrac{\cosh 2x}{\sqrt{1+x}}$ h $\sqrt{1+x^2}\,\sinh x$

3 Show that

a $\frac{d}{dx}[\ln(\cosh x)] = \tanh x$

b $\frac{d}{dx}[\ln(\tanh x)] = \coth x - \tanh x$

FP3

4 If $y = \sinh^2 x$

a express $\frac{dy}{dx}$ as a single hyperbolic function

b verify that $\frac{d^2y}{dx^2} - 4y = 2$

5 a Prove that

i $\frac{d}{dx}[\operatorname{cosech} x] = -\coth x \operatorname{cosech} x$

ii $\frac{d}{dx}[\coth x] = -\operatorname{cosech}^2 x$

b Deduce that if $y = \ln(\operatorname{cosech} x + \coth x)$, where $x > 0$, then

$$\frac{dy}{dx} = -\operatorname{cosech} x$$

6 If $y = x \tanh x$, express

a $\frac{dy}{dx}$ in terms of x and $\tanh x$

b $x\frac{dy}{dx} - x^2$ in terms of y.

7 $f(x) = \ln(1 + \tanh x), x \in \mathbb{R}$

a Show that $f'(x) = 1 - \tanh x$ and deduce that $f(x)$ is an increasing function.

b Find, in exact form, the coordinates of the point where the gradient of the curve

$y = f(x)$ is $\frac{8}{5}$

8 $y = \frac{\sinh x}{1 + \cosh x}$

a Find $\frac{dy}{dx}$, simplifying your answer as far as possible.

b Hence, or otherwise, evaluate $\int_0^{\ln 2} \frac{1}{1 + \cosh x} dx$

9 Using suitable identities, or otherwise, find these derivatives.
Give each answer in the form $a \sinh bx$, for integers a and b to be stated.

a $\frac{d}{dx}[\cosh^2 2x + \sinh^2 2x]$

b $\frac{d}{dx}[4\sinh^4 x + 4\sinh^2 x]$

c $\frac{d}{dx}\left[\frac{1 + \tanh^2 x}{1 - \tanh^2 x}\right]$

10 a Show that

$$\frac{d}{dx}[\text{sech}^n x] = -n\,\text{sech}^n x \tanh x$$

for all integers $n \geqslant 1$.

b Determine whether or not this result is true for all integers $n \leqslant -1$.

Write $n = -m$ where $m \geqslant 1$

11 The functions $C(x)$ and $S(x)$ have the following properties:

$$C'(x) = S(x),\ S'(x) = C(x),\ C(0) = 1 \text{ and } S(0) = 0$$

a If $U = C(x) + S(x)$, show that $\frac{dU}{dx} = U$
Solve this differential equation to express the function U in terms of x.

Refer to C4

b If $V = C(x) - S(x)$, write down and solve a suitable differential equation for V and hence express V in terms of x.

c Deduce that $C(x) = \cosh x$ and that $S(x) = \sinh x$

FP3

2.2 Applications of hyperbolic differentiation

You can find an equation for the tangent or normal to a curve whose equation involves hyperbolic functions.

EXAMPLE 1

Find an equation for the tangent T to the curve with equation

$$y = \tanh x$$

at the point where $x = \ln 2$. Give coefficients as integers where possible.

Use $y - y_1 = m(x - x_1)$ to find an equation for T:

$m =$ is the gradient of T
(x_1, y_1) lies on T.

When $x = \ln 2$, $y = \tanh(\ln 2)$

$$= \frac{e^{2\ln 2} - 1}{e^{2\ln 2} + 1}$$

$$= \frac{3}{5}$$

$\tanh x = \frac{e^{2x} - 1}{e^{2x} + 1}$ Refer to Section 1.1

$e^{2\ln 2} = e^{\ln(2^2)} = 4$

So T passes through the point $\left(\ln 2, \frac{3}{5}\right)$

The curve has equation $y = \tanh x$ so $\frac{dy}{dx} = \text{sech}^2 x$

Refer to Section 2.1

So when $x = \ln 2$, $\frac{dy}{dx} = \text{sech}^2(\ln 2)$

$$= 1 - \tanh^2(\ln 2)$$

$$= 1 - \left(\frac{3}{5}\right)^2$$

$$= \frac{16}{25}$$

$\text{sech}^2 x \equiv 1 - \tanh^2 x$ Refer to Section 1.4
You could also calculate $\text{sech}^2(\ln 2)$ directly:

$\text{sech}^2(\ln 2) = \left(\frac{2}{2 + \frac{1}{2}}\right)^2 = \left(\frac{4}{5}\right)^2 = \frac{16}{25}$

The gradient m of T is $\frac{16}{25}$

Hence an equation of T is $y - \frac{3}{5} = \frac{16}{25}(x - \ln 2)$

that is, $25y - 15 = 16(x - \ln 2)$

Multiply through by 25.
Give exact values in the answer unless told otherwise.

You can solve the equation $\frac{dy}{dx} = 0$ to find the coordinates of a stationary point on a curve.

EXAMPLE 2

The diagram shows the curve with equation $y = 4\cosh x - 3x$
Point P is a minimum point on this curve.

Find the exact coordinates of point P.

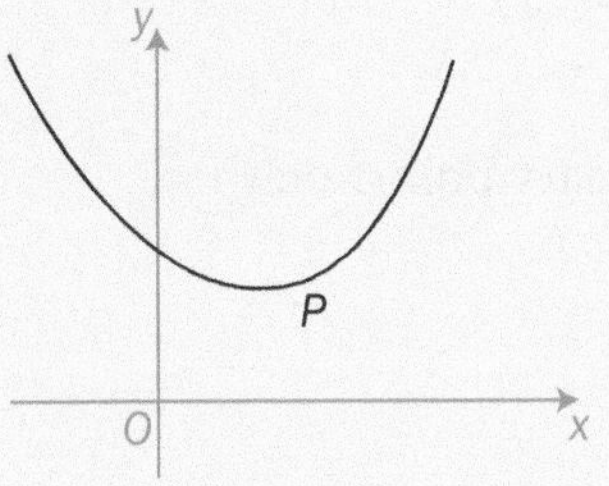

Solve the equation $\frac{dy}{dx} = 0$ to find the x-coordinate of P.

$y = 4\cosh x - 3x$ so $\frac{dy}{dx} = 4\sinh x - 3$

At point P, $\frac{dy}{dx} = 0$ so $\sinh x = \frac{3}{4}$

$x = \ln 2$

$x = \text{arsinh}\left(\frac{3}{4}\right) = \ln\left(\frac{3}{4} + \sqrt{\frac{9}{16} + 1}\right)$

$= \ln\left(\frac{3}{4} + \frac{5}{4}\right)$

$= \ln 2$ Refer to Section 1.5

The x-coordinate of P is $\ln 2$.

Substitute $x = \ln 2$ into $y = 4\cosh x - 3x$ to find the y-coordinate of P.

When $x = \ln 2$, $y = 4\cosh x - 3x$

$= 4 \times \frac{1}{2}\left(2 + \frac{1}{2}\right) - 3\ln 2$

$= 5 - 3\ln 2$

Point P has coordinates $(\ln 2, 5 - 3\ln 2)$

$\cosh(\ln 2) = \frac{1}{2}(e^{\ln 2} + e^{-\ln 2})$

$= \frac{1}{2}\left(2 + \frac{1}{2}\right)$

Refer to Section 1.1. Alternatively, use the identity $\cosh^2 x - \sinh^2 x \equiv 1$ to evaluate $\cosh(\ln 2)$

FP3

Exercise 2.2

1 Find an equation for the tangent to each curve at the given point.
Coefficients should be given as integers where possible.

a $y = \sinh x$ at $x = \ln 3$

b $y = \cosh 2x$ at $x = \ln 2$

c $y = \tanh(x^2 - 1)$ at $x = 1$

d $y = \sinh^2 x$ at $x = -\ln 2$

2 Find an equation for the normal to the curves with these equations at the given point.

a $y = \ln(2 + \sinh x)$ at $x = 0$

b $y = \cosh x - e^x$ at $x = \ln 3$

3 The curve C has equation $y = \sinh x \cosh x$
Find the exact coordinates of the two points on C where the gradient of C is $\frac{17}{8}$.

4 Find the x-coordinates of any stationary points on these curves. Give answers in exact form.

a $y = 4x - 3\cosh x$

b $y = 2\sinh x - 3\cosh x$

c $y = x - 5\tanh x$

d $y = 40x - 9\sinh^2 x$

5 The curve C has equation $y = \operatorname{sech} x$

a Given that $\frac{dy}{dx} = -\tanh x \operatorname{sech} x$, find an equation for the tangent T to C at the point where $x = \ln 2$. Give your answer in the form

$$25y + 12x = c$$

stating the exact value of the constant c.

b Find the exact coordinates of the other point P on C where the tangent to C at P is parallel to T.

6 The curve C has equation $y = 3\cosh x + 5\sinh x - 4x$

a Show that an equation for the normal to C at the point where $x = -\ln 4$ is

$$y + x = 3(\ln 4 - 1)$$

b Find the exact coordinates of the stationary point on C.

7 $f(x) = x + 2\operatorname{sech} x, x \in \mathbb{R}$

You may assume the result $\frac{d}{dx}[\operatorname{sech} x] = -\tanh x \operatorname{sech} x$ for this question.

a Prove that $f'(x) \geqslant 0$ for all x.

b Find the exact coordinates of the stationary point on the curve with equation $y = f(x)$. Determine the nature of this stationary point.

8 Find the exact coordinates of the stationary points on the curve with equation

$$y = 8\tanh x - \sinh x$$

9 $y = \dfrac{\tanh x + 1}{\tanh x - 1}$

a Show that y satisfies the differential equation

$$\frac{dy}{dx} = 2y$$

where $y = -1$ when $x = 0$

b Find the particular solution of this differential equation. Refer to C4

c Verify your answer to part **b** by using the exponential definition for $\tanh x$ in the equation $y = \dfrac{\tanh x + 1}{\tanh x - 1}$

10 The diagram shows the curve C with equation $y = 2\cosh x$. Tangents at the points P and Q on the curve have been drawn. Point P has x-coordinate 1 and point Q has x-coordinate -1.

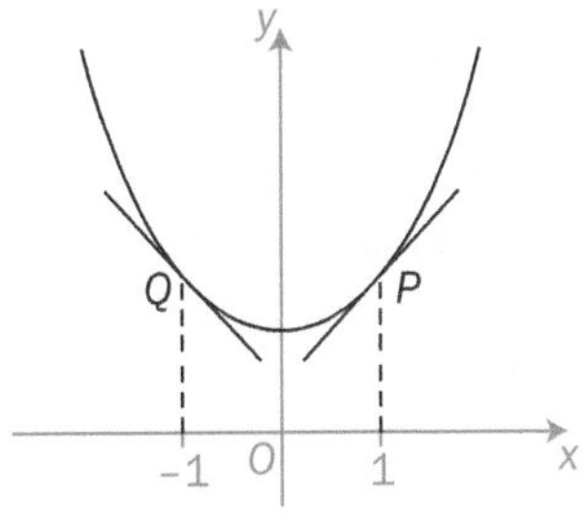

a Show that an equation for the tangent to C at point P is

$$ey = (e^2 - 1)x + 2$$

b Find a similar expression for the equation of the tangent to C at point Q.

c Find the coordinates of the point R where these two tangents meet and show that the area of triangle PQR is given by $2\sinh 1$.

11 A curve C has equation $y = 8\sinh^m x - \cosh^m x$, where $m > 2$ is an integer.

a Find an expression for $\dfrac{dy}{dx}$. Factorise your answer as far as possible.

Given that C has a stationary point at the point where $x = \frac{1}{2}\ln 3$

b show that $m = 5$

c determine whether this stationary point is a maximum or a minimum.

FP3

2.3 Differentiation of inverse hyperbolic functions

You can differentiate an inverse hyperbolic function by using the result $\frac{dy}{dx} = \frac{1}{\left(\frac{dx}{dy}\right)}$

Refer to C3

EXAMPLE 1

If $y = \text{arsinh}\, x$ show that $\frac{dy}{dx} = \frac{1}{\sqrt{1+x^2}}$

Use the properties of an inverse function:

If $y = \text{arsinh}\, x$ then $x = \sinh y$

Refer to Section 1.5

Differentiate $x = \sinh y$ with respect to y:

$x = \sinh y$ so $\frac{dx}{dy} = \cosh y$

Refer to Section 2.1

$$\frac{dy}{dx} = \frac{1}{\cosh y} = \frac{1}{\sqrt{1+\sinh^2 y}}$$

$\cosh^2 y - \sinh^2 y \equiv 1$

so $\cosh y \equiv +\sqrt{1+\sinh^2 y}$

Refer to Section 1.4

Hence $\frac{dy}{dx} = \frac{1}{\sqrt{1+x^2}}$, as required.

$x = \sinh y$ so $\sinh^2 y = x^2$

$$\frac{d}{dx}[\text{arsinh}\, x] = \frac{1}{\sqrt{1+x^2}} \qquad \frac{d}{dx}[\text{arcosh}\, x] = \frac{1}{\sqrt{x^2-1}},\ x > 1$$

$$\frac{d}{dx}[\text{artanh}\, x] = \frac{1}{1-x^2},\ |x| < 1$$

You can also establish these results using implicit differentiation. Refer to C4.

EXAMPLE 2

The curve C has equation

$y = 3\text{arsinh}\,(2x)$

Find an equation for the tangent to C at the point where $x = \sqrt{2}$

Use the chain rule to find $\frac{dy}{dx}$:

$$y = 3\text{arsinh}\,(2x) \quad \text{so} \quad \frac{dy}{dx} = \left(\frac{3}{\sqrt{1+(2x)^2}}\right) \times 2$$

$$= \frac{6}{\sqrt{1+4x^2}}$$

Evaluate the gradient of C when $x = \sqrt{2}$:

$$\text{When } x = \sqrt{2} \quad \frac{dy}{dx} = \frac{6}{\sqrt{1+4(\sqrt{2})^2}}$$

$$= \frac{6}{\sqrt{1+8}} = 2$$

Starting from

$\text{arsinh}\, x = \ln\left(x + \sqrt{x^2+1}\right)$

Find $\frac{d}{dx}\text{arsinh}\, x$.

Use the same method to find the derivatives of all the inverse hyperbolic functions.

EXAMPLE 2 (CONT.)

Find the value of y when $x = \sqrt{2}$:

$$\text{When } x = \sqrt{2},\ y = 3\,\text{arsinh}\left(2\sqrt{2}\right)$$
$$= 3\ln\left(2\sqrt{2} + 3\right)$$

$\text{arsinh}\,x \equiv \ln\left(x + \sqrt{x^2 + 1}\right)$

Hence an equation for the tangent to C at $x = \sqrt{2}$ is

$$y - 3\ln\left(2\sqrt{2} + 3\right) = 2\left(x - \sqrt{2}\right)$$

You need not rearrange this equation into the form $y = mx + c$

Exercise 2.3

1 Find $\frac{dy}{dx}$ for these equations. Simplify each answer where possible.

a $y = \text{arsinh}\,(3x)$

b $y = 4\text{arcosh}\,(2x)$

c $y = \text{artanh}\,(x^2)$

d $y = \text{arsinh}\left(\frac{1}{x}\right)$

e $y = \text{arcosh}\left(2\sqrt{x}\right)$

f $y = \text{artanh}\left(\frac{1}{1+x}\right)$

2 The curve C has equation

$$y = \text{arsinh}\left(\frac{1}{2}x\right)$$

a Show that $\frac{dy}{dx} = \frac{1}{\sqrt{4 + x^2}}$

b Find an equation for the tangent to C at the point where $x = 2\sqrt{3}$. Give coefficients in exact form.

3 a By writing $\text{arcosh}\,x$ in logarithmic form prove that

$$\frac{d}{dx}[\text{arcosh}\,x] = \frac{1}{\sqrt{x^2 - 1}},\ x > 1$$

b Use any appropriate method to show that

$$\frac{d}{dx}[\text{artanh}\,x] = \frac{1}{1 - x^2},\ |x| < 1$$

FP3

4 The diagram shows the curve C with equation

$$y = \operatorname{artanh}(1 - 2x), 0 < x < 1$$

Also shown is the point P on C where $x = \frac{1}{3}$, and the normal N to C at point P. The line N crosses the x-axis at point Q.

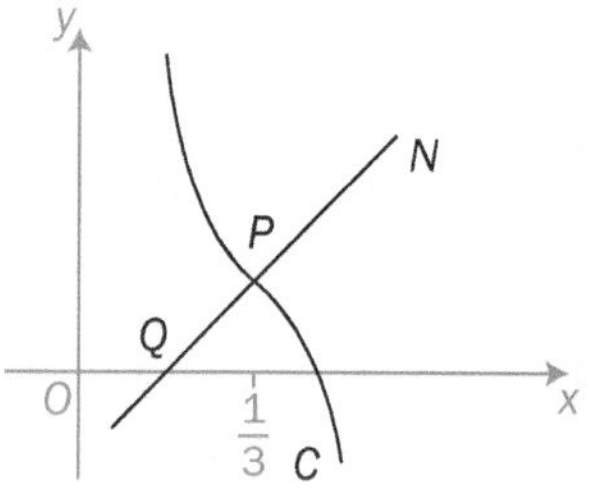

a Find the exact y-coordinate of point P.

b Show that $\frac{dy}{dx} = \frac{1}{2x(x-1)}$

c Hence find an equation for N.

d Show that the x-coordinate of point Q is $\left(\frac{1}{3} - \frac{9}{8}\ln 2\right)$ and hence find the distance PQ. Give your answer in the form $\frac{\sqrt{p}}{8}\ln 2$ where p is a prime number to be stated.

5 Find these derivatives.

a $\frac{d}{dx}\left[x^2 \operatorname{arsinh} x\right]$

b $\frac{d}{dx}\left[\left(x^2 - 1\right)^{\frac{1}{2}} \operatorname{arcosh} x\right]$

c $\frac{d}{dx}\left[\frac{\operatorname{artanh} x}{x^2 - 1}\right]$

d $\frac{d}{dx}\left[\sqrt{\operatorname{arsinh}(2x)}\right]$

6 Find the exact coordinates of any stationary points on the curves defined by these equations. In each case, determine the nature of each stationary point.

a $y = 3\operatorname{artanh} x - 4x, \quad -1 < x < 1$

b $y = 5\operatorname{arsinh}(2x) - 6x$

c $y = \operatorname{arcosh}(2x - 1) - \sqrt{5x}, \quad x \geqslant \frac{1}{2}$

7 **a** Find $\frac{d}{dx}[\sinh(\operatorname{arcosh} x)]$

b Hence, or otherwise, show that $\int_{\cosh 1}^{\cosh 2} \frac{2e^2 x}{\sqrt{x^2 - 1}} dx = (e - 1)(e^3 + 1)$

8 The curve C has equation

$$y = 3\operatorname{artanh}(kx) - 8x \quad -1 < kx < 1$$

where k is a positive constant.

C passes through the point $\left(\frac{3}{10}, \ln 8 - \frac{12}{5}\right)$

a Show that $k = 2$

b Find the exact coordinates of the stationary points of C and determine their nature.

9 A curve C has equation $y = \text{artanh}\,(\text{sech}\,x), x > 0$

a Show that

$$\frac{dy}{dx} = -\text{cosech}\,x$$

b Hence find an equation for the tangent to C at the point where $x = \ln 2$

This tangent crosses the x-axis at the point $(a, 0)$.

c Find the exact value of a. Give your answer in the form $\frac{1}{4}\ln q$ for q an integer to be stated.

10 By considering the derivative of $\text{arcosh}\left(\sqrt{x+1}\right)$ with respect to x, or otherwise, show that

$$\int_1^{(\sinh 2)^2} \frac{1}{\sqrt{x(x+1)}}\,dx = 4 - \ln\left(3 + \sqrt{8}\right)$$

11 a Solve exactly the equation

$$\sqrt{x^2 - 1} = 1 + \sqrt{2} - x$$

A curve C has equation $y = \tanh\,(\text{arcosh}\,x), x > 1$

b Show that $\frac{dy}{dx} = \frac{1}{x^2\sqrt{x^2 - 1}}$

c Find the equation of the tangent to C at the point where $y = \frac{1}{2}\sqrt{2}$

Give your answer in the form $ay + bx = c$ for integers a, b and c to be stated.

You may find the result $3 + 2\sqrt{2} = \left(1 + \sqrt{2}\right)^2$ useful.

FP3

2.4 Differentiation of inverse trigonometric functions

You can differentiate an inverse trigonometric function by using the result $\frac{dy}{dx} = \frac{1}{\left(\frac{dx}{dy}\right)}$

Refer to C3

EXAMPLE 1

If $y = \arccos x$ show that $\frac{dy}{dx} = -\frac{1}{\sqrt{1-x^2}}$

Use the properties of an inverse function:

If $y = \arccos x$ then $x = \cos y$

Differentiate $x = \cos y$ with respect to y:

$$x = \cos y \quad \text{so} \quad \frac{dx}{dy} = -\sin y$$

$$\frac{dy}{dx} = -\frac{1}{\sin y}$$

$$= -\frac{1}{\sqrt{1-\cos^2 y}}$$

$\cos^2 y + \sin^2 y \equiv 1$

so $\sin y = \sqrt{1-\cos^2 y}$

Hence $\frac{dy}{dx} = -\frac{1}{\sqrt{1-x^2}}$, as required.

$\cos y = x$ so $\cos^2 y = x^2$

$$\frac{d}{dx}[\arcsin x] = \frac{1}{\sqrt{1-x^2}} \qquad \frac{d}{dx}[\arccos x] = -\frac{1}{\sqrt{1-x^2}} \qquad \frac{d}{dx}[\arctan x] = \frac{1}{1+x^2}$$

Exercise 2.4

1 Find $\frac{dy}{dx}$ for these equations.

a $y = \arcsin(2x)$ **b** $y = \arccos(1-x)$ **c** $y = \arctan\left(\frac{1}{2}x\right)$

d $y = (\arccos x)^2$ **e** $y = \arctan(\ln x)$ **f** $y = \arcsin\left(\frac{1}{x}\right)$

2 A curve has equation $y = \arctan(2x)$

Show that an equation for the tangent to this curve at the point $x = \frac{1}{2}$ is given by

$$4y - 4x = \pi - 2$$

3 Use any appropriate method to show that

Follow the method of Example 1.

a $\frac{d}{dx}[\arcsin x] = \frac{1}{\sqrt{1-x^2}}$ b $\frac{d}{dx}[\arctan x] = \frac{1}{1+x^2}$

4 Find the exact coordinates of the stationary points on the curves defined by these equations.

a $y = \arcsin(x) - 2x$, $|x| < 1$ b $y = 6\arctan x - \sqrt{3}\ln(1+x^2)$

c $y = x^2 + \arccos x$, $0 \leqslant x \leqslant 1$

5 Find these derivatives. Simplify each answer as far as possible.

a $\frac{d}{dx}[(x^2-1)\arccos x]$ b $\frac{d}{dx}[2\sqrt{x}\arctan\sqrt{x}]$ c $\frac{d}{dx}\left[\frac{\arcsin(1-x^2)}{x}\right]$

6 $f(x) = \arcsin(\cos x)$

a Show that $f'(x) = -1$ for all x.

b Deduce that $\arcsin(\cos x) = \frac{1}{2}\pi - x$ for all x.

7 The curve C has equation $y = \arccos(\sqrt{1-x})$, $0 \leqslant x \leqslant 1$

a Find the equation of the normal to C at the point where $x = \frac{1}{2}$

Points A and B are where this normal intersects the x- and y-axes respectively.

b Show that the area of triangle AOB, for O the origin, is $\frac{1}{32}(2+\pi)^2$ square units.

8 a Find $\frac{d}{dx}(\arcsin(2\sqrt{x}))$

b Hence, or otherwise, find the exact value of $\int_{\frac{1}{16}}^{\frac{3}{16}} \frac{1}{\sqrt{x-4x^2}}\,dx$

9 By considering the derivative of $\arcsin(\tan x)$ with respect to x, or otherwise, find the exact value of $\int_0^{\arctan\left(\frac{1}{2}\right)} 2\sec x\sqrt{\sec 2x}\,dx$

10 $f(x) = \sin(\arccos x) - \sqrt{1-x^2}$, $|x| < 1$

a Show that $f'(x) = 0$ for all x.

b Deduce the identity $\sin(\arccos x) = \sqrt{1-x^2}$ for all $|x| < 1$

The curve C is defined by the equation $y = \arcsin x \arccos x$, $|x| < 1$

c Find the exact coordinates of the stationary point of C and determine the nature of this stationary point.

FP3

1 The curve C has equation $y = \frac{\sinh x + 1}{\cosh x}$

a Show that $\frac{dy}{dx} = \frac{1 - \sinh x}{\cosh^2 x}$

b Hence find the exact coordinates of the stationary point P of C.

c Determine the nature of this stationary point.

2 The curve C has equation $y = \tanh^3 x$, where $x \geqslant 0$.

a Find an expression for $\frac{dy}{dx}$ in terms of $\tanh x$ only.

The gradient of C at point P is $\frac{9}{16}$

b Find the possible values of the x-coordinates of P.
Give answers in the form $\ln\left(a + \sqrt{3}\right)$ where a is an integer.

3 a Show that $\frac{d}{dx}[\coth x] = 1 - \coth^2 x$

The curve C has equation $y = \ln(\coth x - 1), \quad x > 0$

b Find an expression for $\frac{dy}{dx}$ in terms of $\coth x$. Simplify your answer.

The curve C passes through the x-axis at point P.

c Find an equation for the tangent to C at point P.

4 The curve C has equation $y = \frac{x}{\tanh x}, \quad x > 0$

a Use exponential definitions to show that $\frac{d}{dx}[\tanh x] = \operatorname{sech}^2 x$

b Find the exact gradient of C at the point where $x = \ln\sqrt{2}$.
Give your answer in the form $a + b\ln 2$ for integers a and b to be stated.

5 The curve with equation $y = a\sinh x + b\cosh x - 2x$
where a and b are constants, has a stationary point at $P(0, -1)$.

a Find the value of a and the value of b.

b Find the exact coordinates of the other stationary point Q on this curve.

c Determine the nature of each of these stationary points.

6 $\mathrm{f}(x) = \operatorname{arsinh}(\sqrt{2}x^2)$

a Find an expression for $\mathrm{f}'(x)$

b Hence show that an equation for the normal to the curve with equation $y = \mathrm{f}(x)$ at the point where $x = \sqrt{2}$ is $\quad 4y + 3x = 4\ln(3 + 2\sqrt{2}) + 3\sqrt{2}$

7 Given that $\quad y = \operatorname{arcosh}(2e^x + 1)$

a show that $\dfrac{dy}{dx} = \left(\dfrac{e^x}{e^x + 1}\right)^{\frac{1}{2}}$

b hence, or otherwise, find the exact value of $\displaystyle\int_{-\ln 2}^{\ln 3} \frac{\sqrt{e^{x+1}}}{\sqrt{e^x + 1}}\,dx$

8 a Show that $\dfrac{d}{dx}[\operatorname{sech} x] = -\operatorname{sech} x \tanh x$

b Hence, or otherwise, show that if $y = \operatorname{arsech} x$, where $0 < x \leqslant 1$, then

$$\frac{dy}{dx} = \frac{-1}{x\sqrt{1 - x^2}}$$

c Find the x-coordinate of the stationary point of the curve with equation

$$y = 2\ln x + \operatorname{arsech} 2x,\ 0 < x \leqslant \frac{1}{2}$$

Give your answer in exact form.

9 The curve C has equation $y = 3\cosh x - 2\sinh x + 2x$

a Show that an equation for the tangent to C at the point where $x = \ln\sqrt{5}$ is $\quad y = 2x + \sqrt{5}$.

b Use algebra to determine whether or not this tangent intersects C again.

10 The curve C has equation $y = \arctan(kx)$, where k is a constant.

C passes through the point $P\left(\dfrac{\sqrt{3}}{2}, \dfrac{1}{3}\pi\right)$

a Find the value of k

b Show that an equation for the normal to C at point P is

$$3y + 6x = 3\sqrt{3} + \pi$$

11 a Prove that $e^x \operatorname{sech} x \equiv \dfrac{2e^{2x}}{e^{2x} + 1}$

b Find $\dfrac{d}{dx}[\arcsin(\tanh x)]$. Simplify your answer as far as possible.

c Hence, or otherwise, show that $\displaystyle\int_0^{\frac{1}{2}\ln 3} e^x \arcsin(\tanh x)\,dx = \frac{\sqrt{3}}{6}\pi - \ln 2$

2 Exit

Summary

Refer to

- You can use the rules of differentiation to establish the following results:
  - $\frac{d}{dx}[\sinh x] = \cosh x \quad \frac{d}{dx}[\cosh x] = \sinh x \quad \frac{d}{dx}[\tanh x] = \text{sech}^2 x$
  - $\frac{d}{dx}[\text{sech}\, x] = -\tanh x \,\text{sech}\, x \quad \frac{d}{dx}[\text{cosech}\, x] = -\coth x \,\text{cosech}\, x$
  - $\frac{d}{dx}[\coth x] = -\text{cosech}^2 x$ — 2.1
  - $\frac{d}{dx}[\text{arsinh}\, x] = \frac{1}{\sqrt{1+x^2}}$
  - $\frac{d}{dx}[\text{arcosh}\, x] = \frac{1}{\sqrt{x^2-1}}, x > 1$
  - $\frac{d}{dx}[\text{artanh}\, x] = \frac{1}{1-x^2}, |x| < 1$ — 2.3
  - $\frac{d}{dx}[\arcsin x] = \frac{1}{\sqrt{1-x^2}} \quad \frac{d}{dx}[\arccos x] = -\frac{1}{\sqrt{1-x^2}} \quad \frac{d}{dx}[\arctan x] = \frac{1}{1+x^2}$ — 2.4

Links

Many of the equations that describe real life situations are differential equations and often their solutions involve higher mathematical functions.

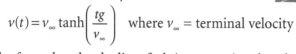

For example, a sky diver falling under gravity will experience an opposing air resistance which is proportional to their velocity squared. As a result their instantaneous velocity is given as a function of time by a tanh function.

$$v(t) = v_\infty \tanh\left(\frac{tg}{v_\infty}\right) \quad \text{where } v_\infty = \text{terminal velocity}$$

The force that the skydiver feels is proportional to their acceleration which is given by the derivative of this expression.

3 Integration

This chapter will show you how to

- integrate expressions involving hyperbolic functions, inverse hyperbolic functions or trigonometric functions
- evaluate integrals using an iterative formula
- calculate the exact length of a curve
- calculate the exact surface area of a solid of revolution.

See Section 0.3 W.
See C4 for revision.

Before you start

You should know how to:

1 Integrate using a substitution.

e.g. Use the substitution $u = 2x + 1$ to find

$$\int (2x+1)^3\,dx$$

Find dx in terms of du:

$u = 2x + 1$ so $\frac{du}{dx} = 2$, that is $dx = \frac{1}{2}du$

Express the integral in terms of u:

$$\int (2x+1)^3\,dx = \int u^3 \times \frac{1}{2}du = \frac{1}{8}u^4 + c$$

Substitute for u:

$$\int (2x+1)^3 dx = \frac{1}{8}(2x+1)^4 + c$$

2 Use integration by parts.

e.g. Evaluate $\int_0^{\frac{1}{2}\pi} x\sin x\,dx$

Use $\int uv'\,dx = uv - \int vu'\,dx$, $u = x$, $v' = \sin x$:

So $u' = 1$, $v = -\cos x$

$$\begin{aligned}\int x\sin x\,dx &= (x)(-\cos x) - \int(-\cos x)(1)\,dx\\ &= -x\cos x + \int \cos x\,dx\\ &= -x\cos x + \sin x + c\end{aligned}$$

So $\int_0^{\frac{1}{2}\pi} x\sin x\,dx = [-x\cos x]_0^{\frac{1}{2}\pi} + [\sin x]_0^{\frac{1}{2}\pi} = 1$

3 Integrate using a trigonometric identity.

e.g. Find $\int \tan x\,dx$

$$\tan x \equiv \frac{\sin x}{\cos x} \text{ so } \int \tan x\,dx = \int \frac{\sin x}{\cos x}dx = \int \frac{-(\cos x)'}{\cos x}dx$$

Use the substitution $u = \cos x$ (or 'inspection')

$$\int \tan x\,dx = -\ln|\cos x| + c = \ln|\sec x| + c$$

Check in:

1 Use the suggested substitution to find these integrals. Give answers in terms of x.

a $\int x(x^2+1)^4\,dx$, $u = x^2+1$

b $\int \frac{3x+2}{6x^2+8x+1}dx$, $u = 6x^2+8x+1$

c $\int x\sqrt{x+1}\,dx$, $u^2 = x+1$

d $\int x^3(x^2+1)^3\,dx$, $u = x^2+1$

2 Evaluate these integrals. Give answers in exact form.

a $\int_0^{\ln 2} xe^{-x}\,dx$

b $\int_{\frac{1}{2}}^{1} x^3\ln 2x\,dx$

c $\int_0^{\pi} 4x^2\cos 2x\,dx$

3 Use trigonometric identities to find these integrals.

a $\int \sin^3 x\,dx$

b $\int (\cos x - \sin x)^2\,dx$

c $\int \frac{2}{\cos x + 1}dx$

3.1 Integration by inspection

You can sometimes integrate an expression by recognising that the integrand involves a function and its derivative.

This method is known as integration by inspection. You need to make a sensible guess about the answer.

EXAMPLE 1

Find $\int x(x^2+1)^3 dx$

Make a sensible guess for the answer:

Try $(x^2+1)^4$

Powers increase by one when integrating.

Test the suitability of this guess by finding its derivative:

$$\frac{d}{dx}\left[(x^2+1)^4\right]=8x(x^2+1)^3$$

Refer to C3 for the Chain Rule.

So $\int 8x(x^2+1)^3\,dx=(x^2+1)^4+c$

Integration is the reverse process to differentiation.

Hence $\int x(x^2+1)^3\,dx=\frac{1}{8}(x^2+1)^4+c$

$\int x(x^2+1)^3\,dx=\frac{1}{8}\times\int 8x\,(x^2+1)^3\,dx$

Inspection works in this example because the integrand $x(x^2+1)^3$ is of the form $f'(x)\times(f(x))^3$ where $f(x)=x^2+1$

The expression $f'(x)\times(f(x))^3$ differs from the integrand only by the constant multiple 8.

Form of integrand	Guess
$f'(x)\times(f(x))^n,\ n\neq -1$	$(f(x))^{n+1}$
$\frac{f'(x)}{f(x)}$	$\ln\lvert f(x)\rvert$
$f'(x)e^{f(x)}$	$e^{f(x)}$
$f'(x)\cos(f(x))$	$\sin(f(x))$
$f'(x)\sin(f(x))$	$\cos(f(x))$

You cannot use inspection to find every integral. For example, $\int x^2(x^2+1)^3 dx$ cannot be expressed in terms of the function $f(x)=(x^2+1)$ and a *constant multiple* of its derivative because $f'(x)=2x$.

EXAMPLE 2

Use inspection to find $\int \frac{5x}{x^2+3}\,dx$

Inspect the form of the integrand to make a sensible guess:

$\frac{5x}{x^2+3}$ is of the form $\frac{f'(x)}{f(x)}$ where $f(x)=x^2+3$ so try $\ln(x^2+3)$

$x^2+3>0$ for all x so the modulus symbol is not needed.

Differentiate this function and adjust the answer accordingly:

$$\frac{d}{dx}\left[\ln(x^2+3)\right]=\frac{2x}{x^2+3}$$

So $\int\frac{2x}{x^2+3}\,dx=\ln(x^2+3)+c$

Hence $\int\frac{5x}{x^2+3}\,dx=\frac{5}{2}\ln(x^2+3)+c$

$\int\frac{5x}{x^2+3}=\frac{5}{2}\times\int\frac{2x}{x^2+3}\,dx$

Exercise 3.1

1 Use inspection to find these integrals. Check each answer by using differentiation.

a $\int x(3x^2 - 1)^2 \,dx$ b $\int x^3\sqrt{(x^4 + 5)}\,dx$

c $\int \frac{2x^2}{x^3 - 1}\,dx$ d $\int \frac{x - 1}{3x^2 - 6x + 1}\,dx$

e $\int 6xe^{2x^2}\,dx$ f $\int 3\sin x \cos^3 x \,dx$

2 Use inspection to evaluate these integrals. Give answers in exact form where appropriate.

a $\int_0^2 \frac{x}{\sqrt{2x^2 + 1}}\,dx$ b $\int_1^4 \frac{e^{\sqrt{x}}}{\sqrt{x}}\,dx$

c $\int_0^2 \frac{3x + 6}{(x + 1)(x + 3)}\,dx$

3 Use inspection to find these integrals.

a $\int \cot x \,dx$ b $\int \frac{1}{x \ln x}\,dx$

c $\int \frac{1}{\sin x \cos x}\,dx$

In Part **c**, divide top and bottom by $\cos^2 x$.

4 Find each of these integrals. Where possible, use inspection.

a $\int x\sqrt{x^2 - 1}\,dx$ b $\int x(x + 1)^2\,dx$

c $\int \frac{x + 2}{x^2}\,dx$ d $\int 5x \cos(x^2 + 1)\,dx$

e $\int \frac{2x - 1}{4x^2 - 1}\,dx$ f $\int \frac{x - 1}{(x - 3)(x + 1)}\,dx$

5 Use suitable trigonometric identities together with inspection to find these integrals.

a $\int \sin 2x \sin^2 x \,dx$ b $\int 3\sin x \cos 2x \,dx$

c $\int \frac{1 + \tan^2 x}{1 - \tan x}\,dx$

FP3

3.2 Integration of hyperbolic functions

You can integrate the hyperbolic functions $\sinh x$ and $\cosh x$

For example, $\frac{d}{dx}[\cosh x] = \sinh x$

Refer to Section 2.1.

so $\int \sinh x \, dx = \cosh x + c$

Similarly, $\int \cosh x \, dx = \sinh x + c$

You could also find these integrals by using the exponential definitions of each function.

EXAMPLE 1

Find **a** $\int x\cosh x \, dx$

b $\int \tanh 2x \, dx$

a Use integration by parts:

The integrand $= x\cosh x$ so let $u = x$, $v' = \cosh x$
Then $u' = 1$, $v = \sinh x$

$v' = \cosh x$
so $v = \int \cosh x \, dx = \sinh x$

$\int x\cosh x \, dx = x\sinh x - \int \sinh x \, dx$

$\int uv' \, dx = uv - \int vu' \, dx$

Refer to C4.

Hence $\int x\cosh x \, dx = x\sinh x - \cosh x + c$

b Use inspection:

The integrand $\tanh 2x$, or equivalently, $\frac{\sinh 2x}{\cosh 2x}$, is of the form $\frac{f'(x)}{f(x)}$, where $f(x) = \cosh 2x$

Refer to Section 3.1.

So try $\ln(\cosh 2x)$:

$\frac{d}{dx}[\ln(\cosh 2x)] = 2\left(\frac{\sinh 2x}{\cosh 2x}\right) = 2\tanh 2x$

Hence $\int \tanh 2x = \frac{1}{2}\ln(\cosh 2x) + c$

For a, a non-zero constant,

$\int \sinh ax \, dx = \frac{1}{a}\cosh ax + c$

$\int \cosh ax \, dx = \frac{1}{a}\sinh ax + c$

$\int \tanh ax \, dx = \frac{1}{a}\ln(\cosh ax) + c$

These integrals are in the FP3 section of the formula booklet for the case when $a = 1$.

EXAMPLE 2

The diagram shows the curve with equation $y = \sinh\left(\frac{1}{2}x\right)$ for $x \geqslant 0$. R is the region bounded by this curve, the x-axis and the line $x = \ln 4$.

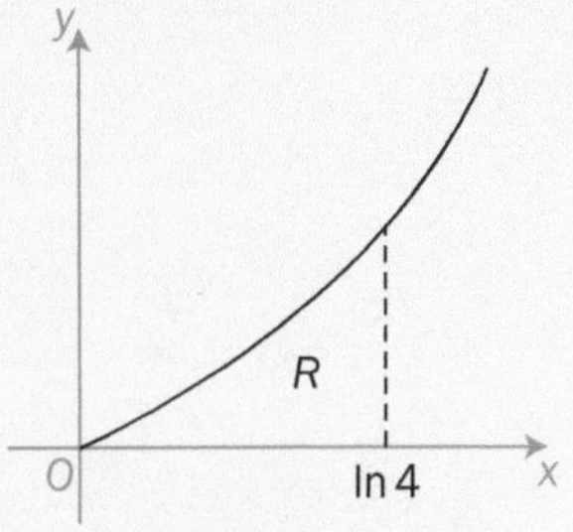

Find the area of R.

$$\text{Area of } R = \int_0^{\ln 4} \sinh\left(\frac{1}{2}x\right) dx$$

$$= \left[2\cosh\left(\frac{1}{2}x\right)\right]_0^{\ln 4}$$

$$= \left(2\cosh\left(\frac{1}{2}\ln 4\right)\right) - \left(2\cosh\left(\frac{1}{2} \times 0\right)\right)$$

$\frac{1}{2}\ln 4 = \ln\left(4^{\frac{1}{2}}\right)$, $\cosh 0 = 1$
$= \ln 2$

$$= 2\cosh(\ln 2) - 2$$

$$= 2\left(\frac{5}{4}\right) - 2$$

$\cosh(\ln 2) = \dfrac{2 + \frac{1}{2}}{2} = \dfrac{5}{4}$

Refer to Section 1.1.

$$= \frac{1}{2}$$

The area of R is $\frac{1}{2}$ square unit.

FP3

Exercise 3.2

1 Find these integrals.

a $\int \cosh 2x \, dx$ b $\int 2\sinh 3x \, dx$ c $\int 4\tanh \frac{1}{3}x \, dx$

2 Find the exact value of these integrals.

a $\int_0^{\ln 4} \sinh \frac{3}{2}x \, dx$ b $\int_0^{\ln 8} 2\tanh \frac{2x}{3} \, dx$ c $\int_0^1 3x\cosh(x^2) \, dx$

3 Use integration by parts to find these integrals.

a $\int x\sinh x \, dx$ b $\int x\cosh 3x \, dx$ c $\int x^2\cosh 2x \, dx$

4 **a** Use the identity $\cosh 2x \equiv 1 + 2\sinh^2 x$ to show that

$$\int \sinh^2 x \, dx = \frac{1}{4}\sinh 2x - \frac{1}{2}x + c$$

The diagram shows the curve with equation $y = 4\sinh^2 x$ for $x \geqslant 0$

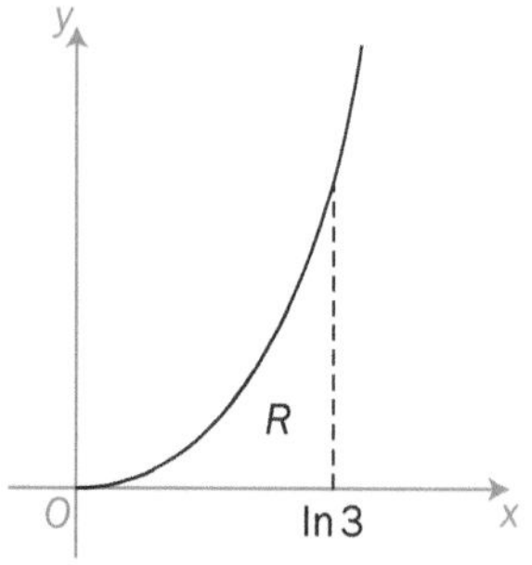

R is the region bounded by this curve, the x-axis and the line $x = \ln 3$

b Find the exact area of region R.

5 Integrate these expressions with respect to x.

a $\cosh x \sinh^3 x$ **b** $\sinh x\sqrt{\cosh x}$

c $\sinh 3x \operatorname{sech} 3x$ **d** $\tanh^3 x \operatorname{sech}^2 x$

e $\coth \frac{1}{2}x$ **f** $\sinh x \operatorname{sech}^2 x$

In part f, consider $(\operatorname{sech} x)'$

6 Use integration by parts to evaluate these integrals. Give answers in exact form.

a $\displaystyle\int_0^{\ln 4} 2x \sinh \frac{1}{2}x \, dx$ **b** $\displaystyle\int_0^{\ln 2} x \operatorname{sech}^2 x \, dx$

7 Find

a $\displaystyle\int e^x \cosh x \, dx$ **b** $\displaystyle\int 4e^x \sinh^2 x \, dx$

Refer to Section 1.1.

8 Use any appropriate identities to integrate these expressions with respect to x.

a $\cosh^2 2x + \sinh^2 2x$ **b** $\tanh^2 x$

c $\sinh 2x \cosh^2 x$ **d** $\cosh^3 x$

e $\dfrac{1}{\cosh 2x + 1}$ **f** $\dfrac{\sinh^2 x}{\cosh x - 1}$

FP3

9 $I = \int \frac{\tanh x}{\cosh x + 1}\,dx$

a Using the substitution $u = \cosh x + 1$, show that

$$I = \int \frac{1}{u(u-1)}\,du$$

b Hence find the value of

$$\int_{\ln 2}^{\ln 3} \frac{\tanh x}{\cosh x + 1}\,dx$$

Give your answer in the form $\ln q$ for q a rational number in its lowest terms to be stated.

10 Use appropriate identities to integrate these functions with respect to x.

a $\cosh^2 x$

b $8\sinh^2 x \cosh^2 x$

c $\text{sech}^4 x$

d $\tanh^4 x - \text{sech}^4 x$

11 The diagram shows the curve with equation $y = 5\tanh x$ for $x \geqslant 0$

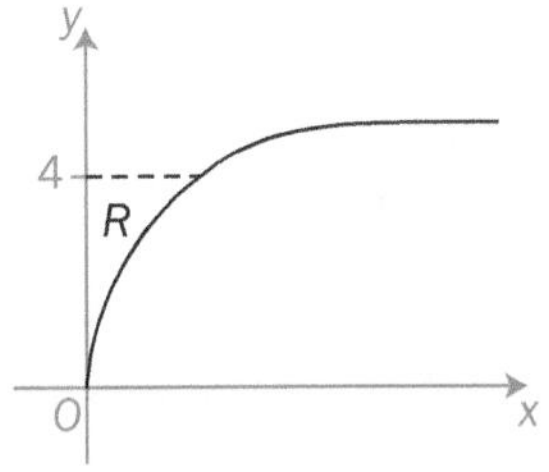

R is the region bounded by this curve, the y-axis and the line $y = 4$.

a Show that the area of R is

$9\ln 3 - 5\ln 5$ square units.

b Find the volume when region R is rotated once about the x-axis. Give your answer in the form $\pi(a - b\ln 3)$ for integers a and b to be stated.

FP3

3.3 Further integration using a substitution

In Section 2.3 you saw that $\frac{d}{dx}[\text{arsinh}\, x] = \frac{1}{\sqrt{1+x^2}}$

from which it follows that $\int \frac{1}{\sqrt{1+x^2}}\, dx = \text{arsinh}\, x + c$

You can also show this result directly by using a hyperbolic substitution.

EXAMPLE 1

Use the substitution $x = \sinh\theta$ to show that

$$\int \frac{1}{\sqrt{1+x^2}}\, dx = \text{arsinh}\, x + c$$

Express dx in terms of $d\theta$:

$$x = \sinh\theta \text{ so } \frac{dx}{d\theta} = \cosh\theta$$

$$dx = \cosh\theta\, d\theta$$

In the exam, you may need to find your own substitution.

Express the integrand in terms of θ and then integrate:

$$x = \sinh\theta \text{ so } \frac{1}{\sqrt{1+x^2}} = \frac{1}{\sqrt{1+\sinh^2\theta}}$$

$$= \frac{1}{\cosh\theta}$$

$\cosh^2\theta - \sinh^2\theta \equiv 1$
Refer to Section 1.4.

$$\text{Hence } \int \frac{1}{\sqrt{1+x^2}}\, dx = \int \frac{1}{\cosh\theta}(\cosh\theta\, d\theta)$$

$$= \int 1\, d\theta$$

$$= \theta + c$$

Express the answer in terms of x:

$$\int \frac{1}{\sqrt{1+x^2}}\, dx = \text{arsinh}\, x + c$$

$x = \sinh\theta$ so $\theta = \text{arsinh}\, x$
This final step may not be necessary if the integral involves limits.

For a a positive constant,

Standard integral	Appropriate substitution
$\int \frac{1}{\sqrt{a^2+x^2}}\, dx = \text{arsinh}\left(\frac{x}{a}\right) + c$	$x = a\sinh\theta$
$\int \frac{1}{\sqrt{x^2-a^2}}\, dx = \text{arcosh}\left(\frac{x}{a}\right) + c,\ (x > a)$	$x = a\cosh\theta$
$\int \frac{1}{a^2-x^2}\, dx = \frac{1}{a}\text{artanh}\left(\frac{x}{a}\right) + c,\ (\lvert x\rvert < a)$	$x = a\tanh\theta$

These results are in the FP3 section of the formula booklet.

$$\int \frac{1}{\sqrt{a^2-x^2}}\,dx = \arcsin\left(\frac{x}{a}\right)+c,\ (|x|<a) \qquad x = a\sin\theta$$

$$\int \frac{1}{a^2+x^2}\,dx = \frac{1}{a}\arctan\left(\frac{x}{a}\right)+c \qquad x = a\tan\theta$$

Using $x = a\cos\theta$ the first integral is also given by $c - \arccos\left(\frac{x}{a}\right)$

Unless the exam question specifically asks you to use a substitution, you can use these standard results to find more complicated integrals.

EXAMPLE 2

Find $\int \frac{1}{\sqrt{12-3x^2}}\,dx$

Identify the standard result which most closely resembles the given integral:

$\int \frac{1}{\sqrt{12-3x^2}}\,dx$ is of the form $\int \frac{1}{\sqrt{a^2-x^2}}\,dx$

Re-express the integral so that the standard result can be applied:

$$\int \frac{1}{\sqrt{12-3x^2}}\,dx = \int \frac{1}{\sqrt{3(4-x^2)}}\,dx$$

$$= \frac{1}{\sqrt{3}}\int \frac{1}{\sqrt{4-x^2}}\,dx$$

Apply the result $\int \frac{1}{\sqrt{a^2-x^2}}\,dx = \arcsin\left(\frac{x}{a}\right)+c$, where $a^2 = 4$, so $a = 2$

Hence $\int \frac{1}{\sqrt{12-3x^2}}\,dx = \frac{1}{\sqrt{3}}\arcsin\left(\frac{x}{2}\right)+c$

Exercise 3.3

1 Use standard results to find these integrals.

a $\int \frac{1}{4+x^2}\,dx$ b $\int \frac{1}{\sqrt{9+x^2}}\,dx$ c $\int \frac{5}{4-x^2}\,dx$

d $\int \frac{4}{\sqrt{2x^2-32}}\,dx$ e $\int \frac{1}{\sqrt{1-9x^2}}\,dx$ f $\int \frac{3}{9+4x^2}\,dx$

2 a Use the substitution $x = \sqrt{2}\sin\theta$ to show that

$$\int \frac{1}{\sqrt{2-x^2}}\,dx = \arcsin\left(\frac{x}{\sqrt{2}}\right)+c$$

You must show the method of substitution.

b Hence evaluate $\int_1^{\sqrt{\frac{3}{2}}} \frac{1}{\sqrt{2-x^2}}\,dx$, giving your answer in terms of π.

FP3

3 Evaluate these integrals. Give each answer in exact form.

a $\displaystyle\int_0^{2\sqrt{3}} \frac{3}{\sqrt{36+9x^2}}\,dx$ **b** $\displaystyle\int_1^3 \frac{1}{9+3x^2}\,dx$ **c** $\displaystyle\int_{\frac{1}{6}}^{\frac{1}{4}} \frac{2}{(1+2x)(1-2x)}\,dx$

4 a Use the substitution $x=\frac{2}{3}\cosh\theta$ to show that

$$\int \frac{1}{\sqrt{9x^2-4}}\,dx = \frac{1}{3}\operatorname{arcosh}\left(\frac{3x}{2}\right)+c$$

The diagram shows part of the curve with equation

$y=\dfrac{3}{\sqrt{9x^2-4}}$ for $x>\frac{2}{3}$.

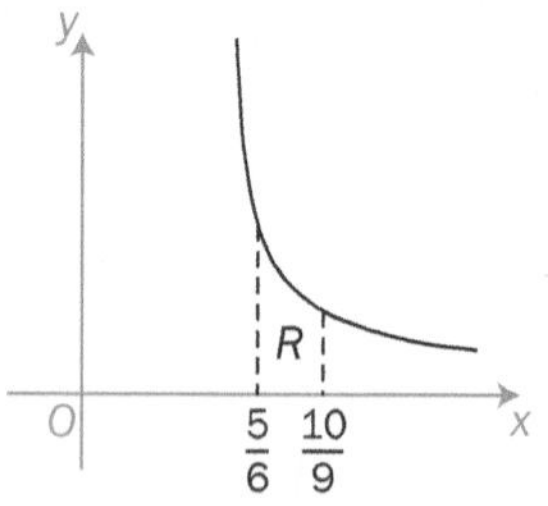

R is the region bounded by this curve, the x-axis, the line $x=\frac{5}{6}$ and the line $x=\frac{10}{9}$.

b Find the area of region R. Give your answer in the form $\ln p$, where p is a rational number in its lowest terms to be stated.

5 The diagram shows the curve with equation $y=\dfrac{1}{\sqrt{3+x^2}}$ for $x \geqslant 0$

R is the region bounded by this curve, the x- and y-axes and the line $x=k$, for $k>0$ a constant.

The area of region R is $\ln(1+\sqrt{2})$ square units.

a Show that $k=\sqrt{3}$

b Find the volume of the solid formed when R is rotated once about the x-axis. Leave π in your answer.

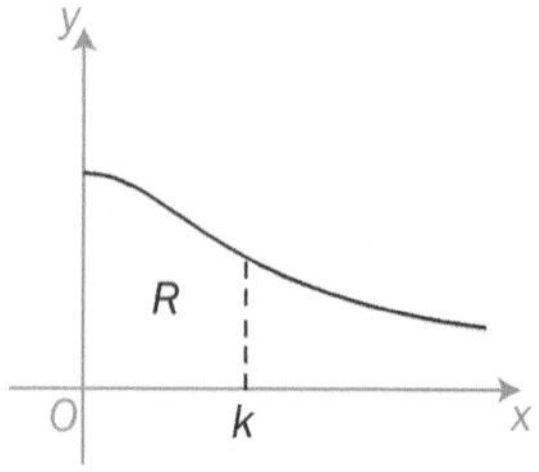

6 Use integration by parts to find these integrals.

a $\displaystyle\int (1-x^2)^{\frac{1}{2}}\frac{1}{x^2}\,dx$ **b** $\displaystyle\int \frac{\ln(4+x^2)}{x^2}\,dx$

c $\displaystyle\int \frac{\ln(3+x)}{(3-x)^2}\,dx$

7 a By writing the integrand $I=\displaystyle\int \frac{1+x}{1+x^2}\,dx$ as the sum of two functions, show that

$$I=\arctan x+\ln\left(\sqrt{1+x^2}\right)+c$$

b Use a similar technique to that in part **a** to find these integrals.

i $\displaystyle\int \frac{x-1}{\sqrt{x^2-9}}\,dx$ **ii** $\displaystyle\int \frac{2x-1}{1+4x^2}\,dx$

iii $\displaystyle\int \frac{1-3x}{\sqrt{16+9x^2}}\,dx$

FP3

8 Use the suggested substitution to find each of these integrals. Give each answer in terms of x.

a $\int \frac{x}{\sqrt{1+x^4}}\,dx,\ u = x^2$

b $\int \frac{e^x}{1-e^{2x}}\,dx,\ u = e^x$

c $\int \frac{1}{x\sqrt{1+x^2}}\,dx,\ u = \frac{1}{x}$

9 a Given that $x = \sinh\theta$, express $\sinh 2\theta$ in terms of x.

b Hence, using the substitution $x = \sinh\theta$, show that

$$\int \frac{2x^2}{\sqrt{1+x^2}}\,dx = x\sqrt{1+x^2} - \text{arsinh}\,x + c$$

Use the identities $\sinh 2\theta \equiv 2\sinh\theta\cosh\theta$ and $\cosh^2\theta - \sinh^2\theta \equiv 1$

10 Use the suggested substitution to find these integrals. Give each answer in terms of x.

Try question 9 before attempting these questions.

a $\int 2\sqrt{x^2-1}\,dx,\ x = \cosh\theta$

b $\int \sqrt{4-x^2}\,dx,\ x = 2\sin\theta$

c $\int (1+4x^2)^{-\frac{3}{2}}\,dx,\ x = \frac{1}{2}\sinh\theta$

FP3

11 a Use the substitution $u = \sinh x$ to show that

$$\int \text{sech}\,x\,dx = \arctan(\sinh x) + c$$

b Hence find the exact value of the positive constant k such that

$$\int_0^k \text{sech}\,x\,dx = \frac{1}{6}\pi$$

12 a Use the substitution $x = \sinh\theta$ to show that

$$\int \frac{1}{x^2\sqrt{1+x^2}}\,dx = -\frac{1}{x}\sqrt{1+x^2} + c,$$

b Hence find $\int \frac{\sqrt{1+x^2}}{x^2}\,dx$

3.4 Integrals involving quadratic functions

You can complete the square to help find an integral involving a quadratic expression.

EXAMPLE 1

Find $\int \frac{1}{x^2+2x+5}\,dx$

Express the denominator in completed square form:

$$x^2+2x+5 \equiv (x+1)^2-1+5$$
$$\equiv (x+1)^2+4$$

Use the completed square form and a standard result to find the integral:

$$\int \frac{1}{x^2+2x+5}\,dx = \int \frac{1}{(x+1)^2+4}\,dx$$
$$= \frac{1}{2}\arctan\left(\frac{x+1}{2}\right)+c$$

Since $\frac{d}{dx}[x+1]=1$, replacing x with the term $(x+1)$ in the standard result $\int \frac{1}{x^2+a^2}\,dx = \frac{1}{a}\arctan\left(\frac{x}{a}\right)+c$ gives the correct answer.

EXAMPLE 2

Find $\int \frac{2}{\sqrt{4x^2-8x+3}}\,dx$

Notice that the coefficient of x^2 in the quadratic is not 1.

Express the quadratic in the integrand in the form $a(x^2+\ldots)$ and complete the square:

$$4x^2-8x+3 \equiv 4\left(x^2-2x+\frac{3}{4}\right)$$
$$\equiv 4\left[(x-1)^2-\frac{1}{4}\right]$$

Taking out a factor of 4 avoids the need for using a substitution later on.

Find the integral using a standard result:

$$\int \frac{2}{\sqrt{4x^2-8x+3}}\,dx = \int \frac{2}{\sqrt{4\left[(x-1)^2-\frac{1}{4}\right]}}\,dx$$

Deal with the constant terms: $\frac{2}{\sqrt{4}}=1$

$$= \int \frac{1}{\sqrt{(x-1)^2-\frac{1}{4}}}\,dx$$

$$\int \frac{2}{\sqrt{4x^2-8x+3}}\,dx = \text{arcosh}[2(x-1)]+c$$

Use $\int \frac{1}{\sqrt{x^2-a^2}}\,dx = \text{arcosh}\left(\frac{x}{a}\right)+c$ where $a^2=\frac{1}{4}$, so $a=\frac{1}{2}$

Refer to Section 3.3.

To find an integral of the form $\int \frac{1}{Q(x)}\,dx$ or $\int \frac{1}{\sqrt{Q(x)}}\,dx$,
where $Q(x) = ax^2 + bx + c$, with $a \neq 0, 1$, express $Q(x)$ in the form $a\left(x^2 + \frac{b}{a}x + \frac{c}{a}\right)$ and then complete the square.
If $a < 0$, let the minus sign take effect *before* attempting the integral.

For example, $3 + 2x - x^2 \equiv -(x^2 - 2x - 3)$

$$\equiv -[(x-1)^2 - 4]$$

$$\equiv 4 - (x-1)^2$$

Do not attempt to integrate with the initial form.

You can now use this final form to find an integral.

Exercise 3.4

1 Find these integrals.

a $\int \frac{1}{x^2+4x+5}\,dx$ b $\int \frac{1}{\sqrt{x^2-12x+11}}\,dx$

c $\int \frac{1}{\sqrt{x^2-4x+13}}\,dx$ d $\int \frac{1}{\sqrt{x^2+x-2}}\,dx$

e $\int \frac{1}{x^2-6x+11}\,dx$ f $\int \frac{1}{\sqrt{x(x-4)}}\,dx$

2 Find $\int \frac{1}{\sqrt{15+2x-x^2}}\,dx$

3 Evaluate $\int_{-1}^{0} \frac{6}{5-4x-x^2}\,dx$

Give your answer in the form $\ln p$, for p a rational number in its lowest terms.

4 Integrate these functions with respect to x.

a $\frac{1}{\sqrt{4x^2-8x+5}}$ b $\frac{1}{\sqrt{3x^2-4x+1}}$

c $\frac{1}{2+x-x^2}$ d $\frac{1}{\sqrt{7+12x-4x^2}}$

Consider

$$\int_0^1 \frac{1}{1+x^2}\,dx$$

By using a Maclaurin series expansion of the integrand and integrating term-by-term show that

$$\frac{\pi}{4} = 1 - \frac{1}{3} + \frac{1}{5} - \frac{1}{7} + \dots + \frac{(-1)^n}{(2n+1)} \dots$$

FP3

5 A curve C has equation $y = \frac{1}{\sqrt{1+kx+kx^2}}$, where k is a constant.

Given that C passes through the point $\left(\frac{1}{3}, 3\right)$

a show that $k = -2$

b evaluate $\int_{-\frac{1}{2}}^{\frac{1}{4}} y \, dx$

Give your answer in the form $\frac{\pi}{6}\sqrt{a}$, for a an integer to be stated.

6 The diagram shows the curve with equation

$$y = \frac{1}{\sqrt{4x^2 - 4x + 5}}$$

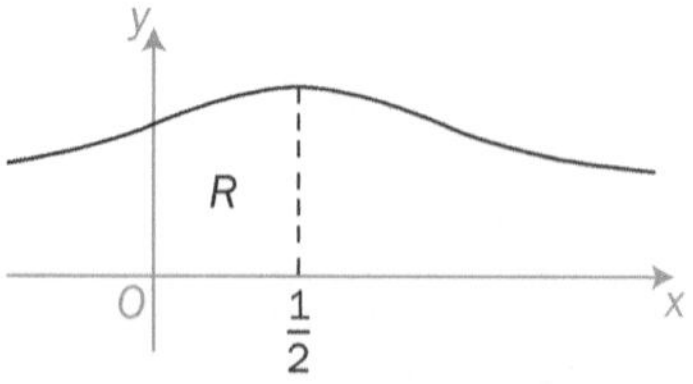

R is the region bounded by this curve, the x- and y-axes and the line $x = \frac{1}{2}$

a Show that the area of R is $\frac{1}{2}\ln\left(\frac{\sqrt{5}+1}{2}\right)$ square units.

b Calculate the volume of the solid formed when R is rotated through 2π about the x-axis.

Give your answer correct to two decimal places.

7 a Find $\int \frac{1}{x^2+2x+2} \, dx$

b Hence show that

$$\int \frac{2x+3}{x^2+2x+2} \, dx = \ln(x^2+2x+2) + \arctan(x+1) + c$$

Express the integrand as the sum of two functions.

8 Integrate these expressions with respect to x.

a $\frac{2x+1}{\sqrt{9+x^2}}$ b $\frac{2x-3}{\sqrt{x^2-4x-5}}$ c $\frac{x}{\sqrt{x^2-2x+5}}$

Use a similar method to question 7.

FP3

9 Show that

a $\int_{1}^{2} \frac{1}{x^2 - 2x + 4}\, dx = \frac{\pi\sqrt{3}}{18}$

b $\int_{-\frac{1}{2}}^{0} \frac{2\sqrt{3}}{1 - 2x - 2x^2}\, dx = \ln(2 + \sqrt{3})$

c $\int_{\frac{1}{2}}^{\frac{3}{4}} \frac{1}{\sqrt{3x - 3x^2}}\, dx = \frac{\sqrt{3}}{18}\pi$

d $\int_{-\frac{1}{2}}^{\frac{3}{2}} \frac{1}{\sqrt{4x^2 + 4x + 3}}\, dx = \ln(1 + \sqrt{2})$

10 The diagram shows part of the curve with equation

$$y = \frac{25}{\sqrt{9x^2 - 6x + 10}}$$

The line $y = 5$ intersects this curve at the points P and Q.
R is the region bounded by this curve and the line $y = 5$.

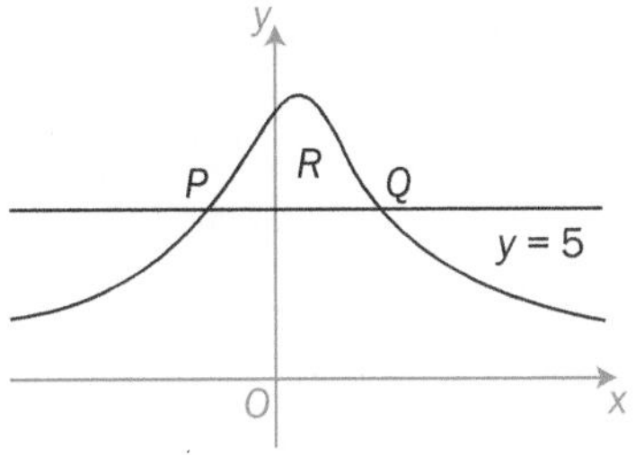

Show that the area of region R is given by

$$R = \frac{10}{3}(5\ln 3 - 4) \text{ square units.}$$

11 $I = \int \frac{1}{2x - x^2}\, dx$

a By expressing $2x - x^2$ in completed square form, show that

$$I = \text{artanh}(x - 1) + c$$

b Find an expression for I using partial fractions.

c Using suitable identities demonstrate the equivalence of the expressions for I found in parts **a** and **b**.

FP3

3.5 Integrating inverse hyperbolic or trigonometric functions

You can use integration by parts to find the integral of an inverse hyperbolic or inverse trigonometric function.

EXAMPLE 1

Find $\int \text{arsinh}\, x \, dx$

Express the integrand as a product:

$$\text{arsinh}\, x = \text{arsinh}\, x \times 1$$

So $\int \text{arsinh}\, x \, dx = \int (\text{arsinh}\, x) \times 1 \, dx$

$v' = \frac{dv}{dx}$

Label the terms in the integrand appropriately:

$$u = \text{arsinh}\, x,\ v' = 1$$

So $u' = \frac{1}{\sqrt{1+x^2}},\ v = x$

$\frac{d}{dx}(\text{arsinh}\, x) = \frac{1}{\sqrt{1+x^2}}$

Refer to Section 2.3.

$v = \int 1 \, dx = x$

Apply the 'parts' formula:

$$\int \text{arsinh}\, x \, dx = (\text{arsinh}\, x)\,(x) - \int \frac{x}{\sqrt{1+x^2}} dx$$

$$= x\,\text{arsinh}\, x - \sqrt{1+x^2} + c$$

Parts: $\int uv' \, dx = uv - \int vu' \, dx$

Refer to C4.

Hence $\int \text{arsinh}\, x \, dx = x\,\text{arsinh}\, x - \sqrt{1+x^2} + c$

$\int x(1+x^2)^{-\frac{1}{2}} dx = (1+x^2)^{\frac{1}{2}} + c$

Use inspection. Refer to Section 3.1.

EXAMPLE 2

Show that $\int_0^{\frac{1}{2}} \arctan(2x)\, dx = \frac{1}{8}(\pi - \ln 4)$

Use integration by parts:

$$\int_0^{\frac{1}{2}} \arctan(2x)\, dx = \int_0^{\frac{1}{2}} \arctan(2x) \times 1 \, dx$$

$$= [x\arctan(2x)]_0^{\frac{1}{2}} - \int_0^{\frac{1}{2}} \frac{2x}{1+4x^2} dx$$

$\frac{d}{dx}[\arctan(2x)] = \left(\frac{1}{1+(2x)^2}\right) \times 2$

$= \frac{2}{1+4x^2}$

Refer to Section 2.3.

$$= [x\arctan(2x)]_0^{\frac{1}{2}} - \left[\frac{1}{4}\ln(1+4x^2)\right]_0^{\frac{1}{2}}$$

$\int \frac{2x}{1+4x^2} dx = \frac{1}{4}\ln(1+4x^2) + c$

Use inspection. Refer to 3.1.

$$= \left[\frac{1}{2}\arctan(1) - (0)\right] - \frac{1}{4}[\ln(2) - (0)]$$

$\ln 1 = 0$

$$= \frac{1}{8}\pi - \frac{1}{4}\ln 2$$

$\arctan(1) = \frac{1}{4}\pi$

Refer to C3.

$$= \frac{1}{8}(\pi - 2\ln 2)$$

so $\int_0^{\frac{1}{2}} \arctan(2x)\, dx = \frac{1}{8}(\pi - \ln 4)$, as required.

$2\ln 2 = \ln(2^2)$

$= \ln 4$

Exercise 3.5

1 Find these integrals.

a $\int \text{arcosh}\, x \, dx$ b $\int \text{artanh}\, 3x \, dx$ c $\int \arcsin \frac{1}{2}x \, dx$

2 Evaluate these integrals. Give answers in exact form.

a $\int_0^2 \text{arsinh}\sqrt{2}x \, dx$ b $\int_0^1 \arccos \frac{1}{\sqrt{2}}x \, dx$ c $\int_0^{\frac{1}{\sqrt{2}}} 4x\, \text{artanh}\,(x^2) \, dx$

3 a Show that $\int \frac{x^2}{1+x^2} dx = x - \arctan x + c$

b Hence find $\int 2x \arctan x \, dx$

4 a Find $\int \frac{1}{\sqrt{x}} \arcsin(\sqrt{x}) dx$

b Hence show that

$$\int_{\frac{3}{4}}^{1} \frac{3}{\sqrt{x}} \arcsin(\sqrt{x}) \, dx = \pi(3-\sqrt{3}) - 3$$

5 Integrate these expressions with respect to x.

a $\text{arsinh}\left(\frac{1}{x}\right)$ b $2x\,\text{artanh}\, x$ c $\frac{1}{\sqrt{x}} \text{arcosh}\left(\frac{1}{2}x+1\right)$

6 The diagram shows the curve with equation $y = 4x\,\text{arsinh}\, x,\ x \geqslant 0$

R is the region bounded by this curve, the x- and y-axes and the line $x = \sqrt{3}$

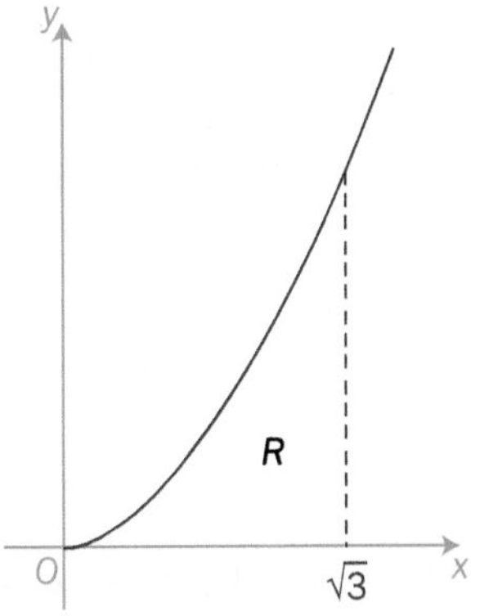

a Using the substitution $x = \sinh\theta$, or otherwise, show that

$$\int \frac{2x^2}{\sqrt{1+x^2}} dx = x\sqrt{1+x^2} - \text{arsinh}\, x + c$$

b Show that the exact area of R is

$$7\ln(\sqrt{3}+2) - 2\sqrt{3} \text{ square units.}$$

7 a Find the value of the constants A and B for which

$$\frac{9x^3}{9x^2+1} \equiv Ax + \frac{Bx}{9x^2+1}$$

b Show that

$$\int_0^{\frac{1}{\sqrt{3}}} 9x^2 \arctan 3x \, dx = \frac{1}{18}(2\sqrt{3}\pi + \ln 4 - 3)$$

8 **a** Using the substitution $u^2 = 1 + x^2$, or otherwise, show that

$$\int \frac{3x^3}{\sqrt{1+x^2}}\,dx = (1+x^2)^{\frac{1}{2}}(x^2-2)+c$$

where c is an arbitrary constant.

b Hence find the exact value of

$$\int_0^{\sqrt{3}} 9x^2 \operatorname{arsinh} x\,dx$$

9 Integrate these expressions with respect to x.

a $\sin x \operatorname{artanh}(\sin x)$ **b** $\cosh x \arcsin(\tanh x)$

c $e^x \operatorname{artanh}(e^x)$

10 Show that

$$\int \frac{\operatorname{arcosh} x}{\sqrt{x-1}}\,dx = 2\sqrt{x-1}\operatorname{arcosh} x - 4\sqrt{x+1}+c$$

11 **a** Using the definition of $\sinh x$ in terms of exponentials, show that

$$\sinh\left(\ln\left(2+\sqrt{3}\right)\right)=\sqrt{3}$$

b Evaluate $\displaystyle\int_0^{\ln(2+\sqrt{3})} \sinh x \arctan(\sinh x)\,dx$.

Give your answer in exact form.

12 **a** Use the substitution $x = \sin\theta$ to show that

$$\int \frac{2x^2}{\sqrt{1-x^2}}\,dx = \arcsin x - x\sqrt{1-x^2}+c$$

where c is an arbitrary constant.

b Hence, or otherwise, evaluate $\displaystyle\int_0^{\frac{\sqrt{3}}{2}} x \arcsin x\,dx$.

Give your answer in exact form.

FP3

13 The diagram shows part of the graph with equation $y = \cos 2x \operatorname{artanh}(\sin x)$. The graph passes through the x-axis at the point $P(k, 0)$, where $0 < k < \frac{1}{2}\pi$. R is the region bounded by this curve, the x- and y-axes and the line $x = k$.

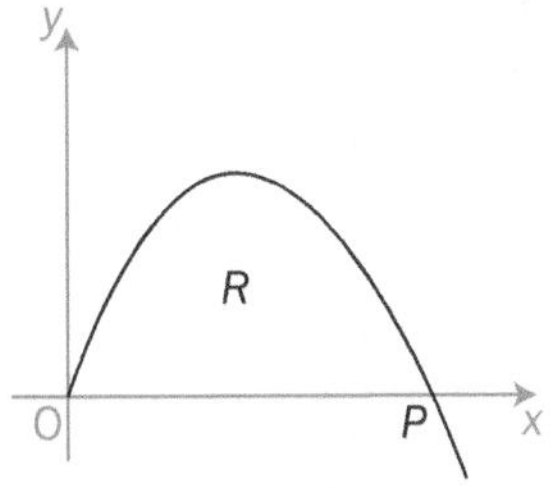

a Find the value of k. Give your answer in terms of π.

b Use integration by parts to show that

$$\int \cos 2x \operatorname{artanh}(\sin x)\, dx = \cos x(\sin x \operatorname{artanh}(\sin x) + 1) + c$$

where c is an arbitrary constant.

c Hence show that the area of region R is $\frac{1}{2}\left(\ln\left(\sqrt{2}+1\right)+\sqrt{2}-2\right)$ square units.

14 **a** Use integration by parts to find

$$\int \frac{x \operatorname{arsinh} x}{\sqrt{1+x^2}}\, dx$$

b Hence find $\int \operatorname{arsinh}^2 x\, dx$

The diagram shows the graph of the increasing function $f(x) = \operatorname{arsinh} x$ for $x \geqslant 0$. Point $P(a, b)$ lies on this curve.

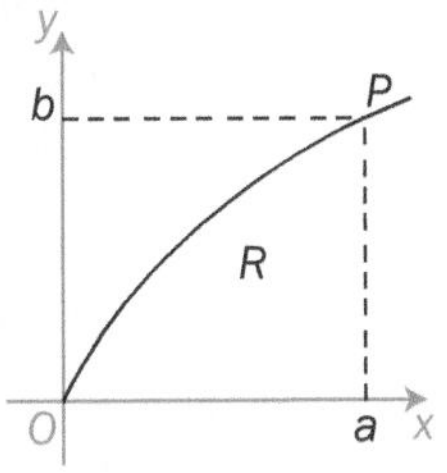

R is the region bounded by this curve, the x- and y-axes and the line $x = a$. When R is rotated 2π radians about the x-axis the solid formed has volume $\pi\left(b-\sqrt{2}\right)^2$ cubic units.

c Find the coordinates of point P. Give your answer for b in exact form.

You may find the identity $\left(\sqrt{2}+\sqrt{1+x^2}\right)\left(\sqrt{2}-\sqrt{1+x^2}\right) \equiv 1-x^2$ useful.

3.6 Reduction formulae

You can use a reduction formula to help find an integral which involves a function raised to a power. It is useful to denote integrals of this type by using a subscript n, where $n \geqslant 0$ is an integer.

For example, if $I_n = \int \cos^n x \, dx$, then,

$$I_2 = \int \cos^2 x \, dx,\ I_6 = \int \cos^6 x \, dx \text{ etc}$$

EXAMPLE 1

$I_n = \int x^n e^x \, dx$ where $n \geqslant 0$

a Show that $I_n = x^n e^x - I_{n-1}$ for $n \geqslant 1$

b Hence find $\int x^2 e^x \, dx$

---

a Use integration by parts, choosing suitable expressions for u and $\frac{dv}{dx}$:

$u = x^n,\ v' = e^x$ so $u' = nx^{n-1}$ and $v = e^x$

$u = x^n$ ensures the integrand vu' includes the term x^{n-1}.

Hence $I_n = \int x^n e^x \, dx$

$= x^n e^x - \int e^x (nx^{n-1}) \, dx$

$\int uv' \, dx = uv - \int vu' \, dx$ Refer to C4.

$= x^n e^x - n \int e^x x^{n-1} \, dx$

$= x^n e^x - nI_{n-1}$

By definition, $I_n = \int x^n e^x \, dx$ so $I_{n-1} = \int x^{n-1} e^x \, dx$

so $I_n = x^n e^x - nI_{n-1}$ for $n \geqslant 1$, as required.

The relationship $I_n = x^n e^x - I_{n-1}$ is called a *reduction formula*. The power of x in I_{n-1} is 1 less than that which appears in I_n.

b Identify the integral to be found in terms of I_n:

$$\int x^2 e^x \, dx = I_2$$

Find expressions for I_0, I_1 and I_2, using the reduction formula where appropriate:

$I_0 = \int e^x \, dx = e^x$

I_0 must be found directly, since the reduction formula in part **a** is only valid for $n \geqslant 1$.

Using the reduction formula, $I_1 = x^1 e^x - 1 \times I_0$

$= xe^x - e^x$

$= e^x(x - 1)$

Factorise where possible.

Similarly $I_2 = x^2 e^x - 2I_1$

$= x^2 e^x - 2e^x (x - 1)$

$= e^x (x^2 - 2x + 2)$

Hence $\int x^2 e^x \, dx = e^x(x^2 - 2x + 2) + c$

Investigate the reduction formula for

$$\Gamma(n) = \int_0^\infty dx\, x^{n-1} e^{-x}$$

You can use a reduction formula to evaluate an integral.

EXAMPLE 2

$$I_n = \int_0^{\frac{1}{2}\pi} \cos^n x\,dx,\ n \geqslant 0$$

a Show that $I_n = \frac{n-1}{n} I_{n-2},\ n \geqslant 2$

b Hence evaluate $\int_0^{\frac{1}{2}\pi} \cos^3 x\,dx$

---

a Let $C = \cos x$, $S = \sin x$

Then $I_n = \int_0^{\frac{1}{2}\pi} C^n\,dx = \int_0^{\frac{1}{2}\pi} C \times C^{n-1}\,dx$

Express the integrand as a product, one of whose terms involves a reduced power.

Apply the 'parts' formula with limits, using appropriate choices for u and $\frac{dv}{dx}$:

$u = C^{n-1}$ $\quad v' = C$

so $u' = -(n-1)\,C^{n-2}S$ and $v = S$

Chain Rule. Refer to C3.

Hence $I_n = [C^{n-1}S]_0^{\frac{1}{2}\pi} + (n-1)\int_0^{\frac{1}{2}\pi} S^2C^{n-2}\,dx$

Take care with the signs.

$$= 0 + (n-1)\int_0^{\frac{1}{2}\pi} S^2C^{n-2}\,dx$$

$\left[C^{n-1}S\right]_0^{\frac{1}{2}\pi}$ because $\cos\left(\frac{1}{2}\pi\right) = \sin 0 = 0$

$$= (n-1)\int_0^{\frac{1}{2}\pi} (1 - C^2)\,C^{n-2}\,dx$$

$S^2 = \sin^2 x \equiv 1 - \cos^2 x$
$\equiv 1 - C^2$

$$= (n-1)\int_0^{\frac{1}{2}\pi} C^{n-2} - C^n\,dx$$

so $\quad I_n = (n-1)[I_{n-2} - I_n]$

$I_n = C^n\,dx$ so

$I_{n-2} = C^{n-2}\,dx$

Rearrange this expression to make I_n the subject:

$I_n = (n-1)I_{n-2} - (n-1)I_n$

$nI_n = (n-1)\,I_{n-2}$

so $\quad I_n = \frac{n-1}{n} I_{n-2}$ as required.

b Apply the result of part a when $n = 3$:

Use the reduction formula when $n = 3$.

$$\int_0^{\frac{1}{2}\pi} \cos^3 x\,dx = I_3 = \frac{2}{3} I_1$$

$$= \frac{2}{3} \times 1$$

I_1 must be found directly.

$I_1 = \int_0^{\frac{1}{2}\pi} \cos x\,dx = [\sin x]_0^{\frac{1}{2}\pi}$

$= 1$

Hence $\int_0^{\frac{1}{2}\pi} \cos^3 x\,dx = \frac{2}{3}$

FP3

Exercise 3.6

1 $I_n = \int x^n e^{-x}\, dx,\ n \geqslant 0$

a Show that $I_n = nI_{n-1} - x^n e^{-x}$ for $n \geqslant 1$.

b Hence find an expression for $\int x^2 e^{-x}\, dx$

Factorise your answer as far as possible.

2 $I_n = \int x^n e^{4x}\, dx,\ n \geqslant 0$

a Show that $I_n = \frac{1}{4}x^n e^{4x} - \frac{1}{4}nI_{n-1},\ n \geqslant 1$

b Hence find an expression for $\int (2xe^{2x})^2\, dx$

3 $I_n = \int_0^1 (x^2 - 1)^n\, dx,\ n \geqslant 0$

a Simplify $(x^2 - 1)^n + (x^2 - 1)^{n-1}$

b Hence show that $I_n = \frac{-2n}{2n+1} I_{n-1},\ n \geqslant 1$

Use parts on $\int_0^1 (x^2 - 1)^n \times 1\, dx$

c Evaluate $\int_0^1 (x^2 - 1)^3\, dx$

4 $I_n = \int x^n \sinh x\, dx,\ n \geqslant 0$

a Show that $I_n = x^n \cosh x - n\int x^{n-1} \cosh x\, dx$

b Hence, by using integration by parts on $\int x^{n-1} \cosh x\, dx$, show that

Make $u = x^{n-1}$

$$I_n = x^{n-1}(x\cosh x - n\sinh x) + n(n-1)I_{n-2},\ n \geqslant 2$$

c Find an expression for $\int x^4 \sinh x\, dx$

giving your answer in the form $P(x)\cosh x - P'(x)\sinh x + c$, where $P(x)$ is a polynomial to be stated, and c is an arbitrary constant.

5 $I_n = \int 2x(\ln x - 1)^n\, dx,\ n \geqslant 0$

a Show that $I_n = x^2(\ln x - 1)^n - \frac{n}{2} I_{n-1},\ n \geqslant 1$

b Hence evaluate $\int_1^e 2x(\ln x - 1)^2\, dx$, giving your answer in terms of e.

You may assume that the reduction formula in part **a** can be used with limits.

6 $I_n = \int_0^{\pi} \sin^n x \, dx,\ n \geqslant 0$

See the method of Example 2.

a Show that $I_n = \frac{n-1}{n} I_{n-2},\ n \geqslant 2$

b Hence find the exact value of $\int_0^{\pi} \sin^4 x \, dx$

c Show that $\int_0^{\pi} \sin^7 x \, dx = \frac{32}{35}$

7 $I_n = \int \cosh^n x \, dx$

a Show that $I_n = \frac{1}{n}\left[\cosh^{n-1} x \sinh x + (n-1) I_{n-2}\right],\ n \geqslant 2$

b Hence evaluate $\int_0^{\text{arcosh } 2} 8\cosh^4 x \, dx$, giving your answer in exact form.

8 $I_n = \int_0^{\pi} 4x^n \sin 2x \, dx,\ n \geqslant 0$

a Show that $I_n = -2\pi^n - \frac{1}{4} n(n-1) I_{n-2},\ n \geqslant 2$

b Hence find the exact value of

i $\int_0^{\pi} 4x^3 \sin 2x \, dx$ **ii** $\int_0^{\pi} x^4 \sin x \cos x \, dx$

9 $I_n = \int x^n \sqrt{1-x^2} \, dx,\ n \geqslant 0$

a Show that $(n+2) I_n = (n-1) I_{n-2} - x^{n-1}(1-x^2)^{\frac{3}{2}}$ for $n \geqslant 2$

b Prove by induction that $\int_{-1}^{1} x^{2n-1} \sqrt{1-x^2} \, dx = 0$ for all integers $n \geqslant 1$.

Use parts with $u = x^{n-1}$

c Find the exact value of $\int_{-1}^{1} x^4 \sqrt{1-x^2} \, dx$

FP3

3.7 Arc length

If A and B are two fixed points on a curve then you can use integration to find the length of the curve, s, from A to B.

If the equation of the curve is given in cartesian form then the length s of the arc AB is

$$s = \int_a^b \sqrt{1 + \left(\frac{dy}{dx}\right)^2}\, dx$$

If the equation of the curve is given in terms of a parameter, say t, then

$$s = \int_{t_1}^{t_2} \sqrt{\left(\frac{dx}{dt}\right)^2 + \left(\frac{dy}{dt}\right)^2}\, dt$$

where t_1 and t_2 are the values of t corresponding to the points A and B, respectively.

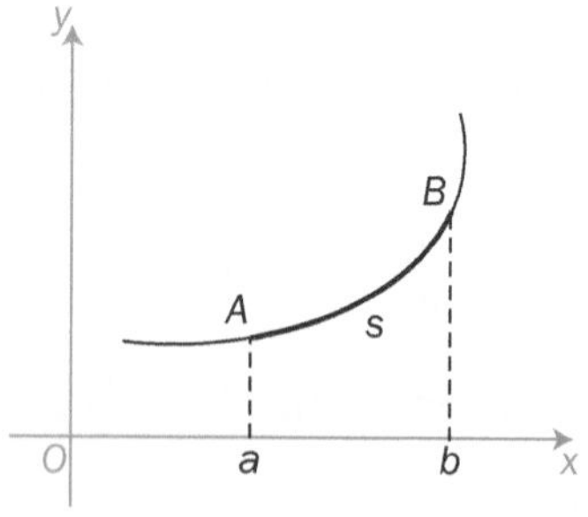

These formulae are in the FP3 section of the formula booklet.

EXAMPLE 1

The diagram shows the curve with equation $y = \cosh x$, which passes through the points A and B.

The x-coordinate of point A is 0 and the x-coordinate of point B is $\ln 3$.
Find the length of the arc AB.

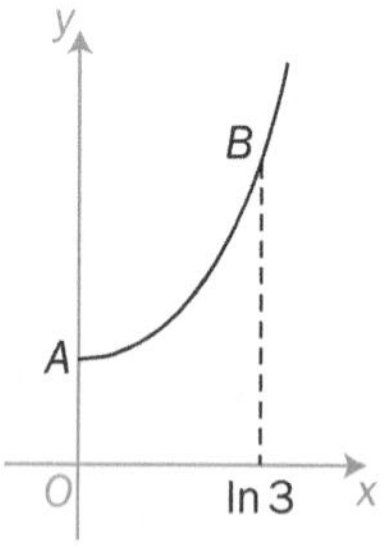

The curve equation is in cartesian form, so use the formula

$$s = \int_0^{\ln 3} \sqrt{1 + \left(\frac{dy}{dx}\right)^2}\, dx$$

Find $\frac{dy}{dx}$ and simplify the integrand:

$$y = \cosh x \text{ so } \frac{dy}{dx} = \sinh x$$

$$\sqrt{1 + \left(\frac{dy}{dx}\right)^2} = \sqrt{1 + \sinh^2 x} = \cosh x$$

$\cosh^2 x - \sinh^2 x \equiv 1$
Refer to Section 1.4.

Calculate the arc length:

$$s = \int_0^{\ln 3} \sqrt{1 + \left(\frac{dy}{dx}\right)^2}\, dx$$

$$= \int_0^{\ln 3} \cosh x\, dx = [\sinh x]_0^{\ln 3}$$

$$= \sinh(\ln 3) - \sinh 0$$

$$= \frac{1}{2}(e^{\ln 3} - e^{-\ln 3}) = \frac{1}{2}\left(3 - \frac{1}{3}\right)$$

$$= \frac{4}{3}$$

Hence the length of the arc AB is $\frac{4}{3}$ units.

EXAMPLE 2

A curve is defined by the parametric equations

$x=\frac{1}{2}t^2,\ y=\frac{1}{3}t^3,\ \sqrt{3}\leqslant t\leqslant\sqrt{8}$

Find the length of this curve.

Use the formula $s=\int_{\sqrt{3}}^{\sqrt{8}}\sqrt{\left(\frac{dx}{dt}\right)^2+\left(\frac{dy}{dt}\right)^2}\,dt$

Use the limits given by the extreme values of t in the definition of the curve.

Find $\frac{dx}{dt}, \frac{dy}{dt}$ and simplify the integrand:

$$x=\frac{1}{2}t^2 \text{ so } \frac{dx}{dt}=t \quad y=\frac{1}{3}t^3 \text{ so } \frac{dy}{dt}=t^2$$

$$\text{Hence } \sqrt{\left(\frac{dx}{dt}\right)^2+\left(\frac{dy}{dt}\right)^2}=\sqrt{t^2+t^4}$$

$$=t\sqrt{1+t^2}$$

$$\text{Hence the arc length } s=\int_{\sqrt{3}}^{\sqrt{8}}\sqrt{\left(\frac{dx}{dt}\right)^2+\left(\frac{dy}{dt}\right)^2}\,dt$$

$$=\int_{\sqrt{3}}^{\sqrt{8}} t(1+t^2)^{\frac{1}{2}}\,dt$$

$$=\left[\frac{1}{3}(1+t^2)^{\frac{3}{2}}\right]_{\sqrt{3}}^{\sqrt{8}}$$

Use inspection. Refer to 3.1

$$=\frac{1}{3}[27-8]$$

When $t=\sqrt{8}$, $(1+t^2)^{\frac{3}{2}}=9^{\frac{3}{2}}=27$

When $t=\sqrt{3}$, $(1+t^2)^{\frac{3}{2}}=4^{\frac{3}{2}}=8$

The length of the curve is $\frac{19}{3}$ units.

Exercise 3.7

1 Find the length of the curves with these equations between the given points.

a $y=2x^{\frac{3}{2}}$ from the point where $x=0$ to the point where $x=\frac{1}{3}$

b $y=2\cosh\frac{1}{2}x$ from the point where $x=0$ to the point where $x=\ln 4$

c $y=\frac{1}{3}(2x+5)^{\frac{3}{2}}$ from the point where $x=-1$ to the point where $x=5$

FP3

2 $\frac{1}{4}x^2+\frac{1}{2}+\frac{1}{4x^2}\equiv\left(ax+\frac{1}{bx}\right)^2$, where a and b are positive constants.

a Find the value of a and the value of b.

A curve has equation $y=\frac{1}{4}x^2-\frac{1}{2}\ln x,\ x>0$

b Show that the length of this curve from the point where $x=1$ to the point where $x=e^2$ is $\frac{1}{4}(e^4+3)$ units.

3 a Using the substitution $x=\sinh\theta$, or otherwise, find $\int\sqrt{1+x^2}\,dx$
You may leave your answer in terms of θ.

b Hence find the exact length of curve with equation $y=\frac{1}{2}x^2$ between the points where $x=0$ and $x=\frac{3}{4}$

4 The diagram shows the curve with equation

$$y=\frac{1}{12}x^3+\frac{1}{x},\ x>0$$

Point A is a stationary point of this curve. The x-coordinate of A is a.
Point B on this curve has x-coordinate 2.

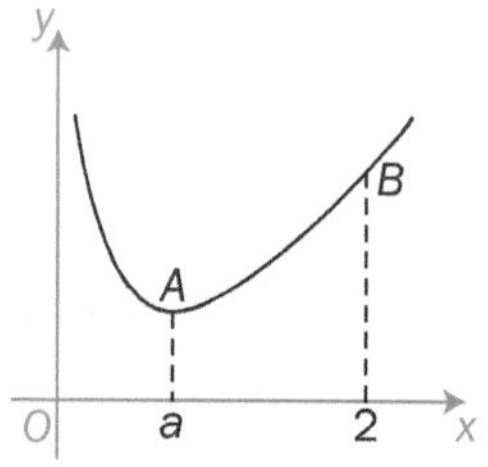

a Find the exact value of a.

b Express $1+\left(\frac{dy}{dx}\right)^2$ in the form $\left(px^2+\frac{q}{x^2}\right)^2$ for constants $p, q>0$ to be stated.

c Hence show that arc AB has length $\frac{1}{6}(1+2\sqrt{2})$ units.

5 The curve C has equation $y=\ln(\cos x),\ 0\leqslant x<\frac{1}{2}\pi$

a Show that $\sqrt{1+\left(\frac{dy}{dx}\right)^2}=\sec x$

Point P on C has x-coordinate k, where k is a positive constant.

b Given that the length of the arc OP, where O is the origin, is $\ln\sqrt{3}$ units, find the exact value of k.

6 Find the lengths of the curves defined by these parametric equations.

a $x=2t,\ y=2t^{\frac{3}{2}}$ between the points where $t=0$ and $t=\frac{4}{3}$

b $x=3t^2,\ y=t^3$ between the points where $t=0$ and $t=\sqrt{5}$

c $x=e^t,\ y=\frac{2}{3}e^{\frac{3}{2}t}$ between the points where $t=\ln 3$ and $t=\ln 8$

7 The diagram shows the curve C defined by the parametric equations
$x=\frac{1}{2}t^2-t,\ y=\frac{4}{3}t^{\frac{3}{2}},\ t\geqslant 0$

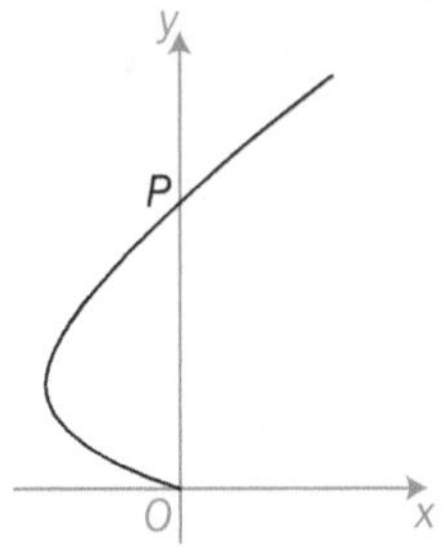

The curve crosses the y-axis at the origin O and at the point P.

a Find the value of t corresponding to point P.

b For these parametric equations, show that $\left(\frac{dx}{dt}\right)^2+\left(\frac{dy}{dt}\right)^2=(t+1)^2$

c Hence find the length of the arc OP.

8 **a** Using the substitution $u = 1 + t$, or otherwise, show that
$\int t\sqrt{1+t}\ dt=\frac{2}{5}u^{\frac{5}{2}}-\frac{2}{3}u^{\frac{3}{2}}+c$ where c is an arbitrary constant.

b Find the length of the arc of the curve defined by the parametric equations
$x=\frac{1}{2}t^2,\ y=\frac{2}{5}t^{\frac{5}{2}},\ t\geqslant 0$ between the points where $t=0$ and $t=3$

9 A curve has parametric equations $x = 3 + 2\cos t,\ y = 2t + 2\sin t,\ t \in \mathbb{R}$

a For these parametric equations, show that $\left(\frac{dx}{dt}\right)^2+\left(\frac{dy}{dt}\right)^2=16\cos^2\left(\frac{1}{2}t\right)$

b Find, in simplified surd form, the exact length of this curve between the points where $t=\frac{1}{3}\pi$ and $t=\frac{1}{2}\pi$.

10 $\frac{d}{d\theta}\ln\left(\tan\frac{\theta}{2}\right)=\frac{a}{\sin\theta}$, where a is a constant.

a Find the value of a.

b Show that the length of the curve $y = \ln x$ from the point where $x=\frac{3}{4}$ to the point where $x=\frac{4}{3}$ is $\frac{5}{12}+\ln\left(\frac{3}{2}\right)$ Units

You may find the substitution $x = \tan\theta$ helpful.

Area of surface of revolution

When an arc of a curve is rotated once about the x-axis, a solid shape is formed. You can use integration to find the surface area S of this shape.

If the equation of the curve is given in cartesian form then the surface area of this solid shape is given by

$$S = 2\pi \int_a^b y\sqrt{1+\left(\frac{dy}{dx}\right)^2}\,dx$$

If the curve is given in terms of a parameter, say t, then

$$S = 2\pi \int_{t_1}^{t_2} y\sqrt{\left(\frac{dx}{dt}\right)^2+\left(\frac{dy}{dt}\right)^2}\,dt$$

where t_1 and t_2 are the values of t corresponding to the points on the curve with x-coordinates a and b, respectively.

The limits a and b are the values of x which define the region being rotated.

These formulae are in the FP3 section of the formula booklet.

EXAMPLE 1

The diagram shows the curve with equation $y = \frac{1}{3}x^3$ for $0 \leqslant x \leqslant 1$.
Find, in exact form, the surface area of the solid generated when this curve is rotated 2π radians about the x-axis.

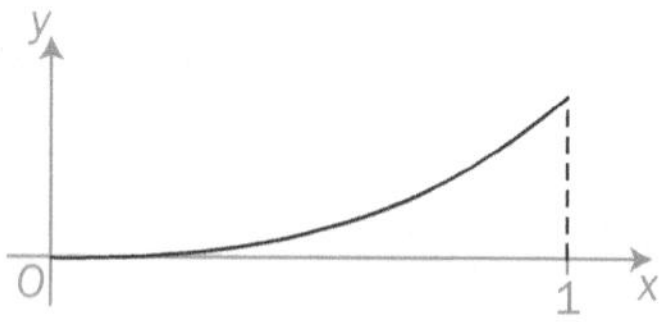

The equation of the curve is in cartesian form, so use the formula

$$S = 2\pi \int_0^1 y\sqrt{1+\left(\frac{dy}{dx}\right)^2}\,dx$$

Find $\frac{dy}{dx}$ and simplify the integrand:

$$y = \frac{1}{3}x^3 \quad \text{so} \quad \frac{dy}{dx} = x^2 \quad \text{and} \quad y\sqrt{1+\left(\frac{dy}{dx}\right)^2} = \frac{1}{3}x^3\sqrt{1+x^4}$$

Calculate the surface area:

$$S = 2\pi \int_0^1 y\sqrt{1+\left(\frac{dy}{dx}\right)^2}\,dx$$

$$= \frac{2}{3}\pi \int_0^1 x^3(1+x^4)^{\frac{1}{2}}\,dx$$

Gather constants outside the integral sign.

$$= \frac{1}{9}\pi\left[(1+x^4)^{\frac{3}{2}}\right]_0^1$$

Use inspection.
Refer to Section 3.1.

$$= \frac{1}{9}\pi\left[2^{\frac{3}{2}} - 1\right]$$

The required surface area is $\frac{1}{9}\pi(2\sqrt{2}-1)$ square units.

$2^{\frac{3}{2}} = 2^1 \times 2^{\frac{1}{2}} = 2\sqrt{2}$

EXAMPLE 2

A curve is defined by the parametric equations

$x=\frac{1}{2}t^2-\ln t,\ y=2t,\ t>0$

The arc of this curve between the points where $t=1$ and $t=4$ is rotated 2π radians about the x-axis.
Find the surface area of the solid formed.

The equation of the curve is in parametric form, so use the formula

$$S=2\pi\int_1^4 y\sqrt{\left(\frac{dx}{dt}\right)^2+\left(\frac{dy}{dt}\right)^2}\,dt$$

Find $\frac{dx}{dt}$, $\frac{dy}{dt}$ and simplify the integrand:

$$x=\frac{1}{2}t^2-\ln t \text{ so } \frac{dx}{dt}=t-\frac{1}{t},\quad y=2t \text{ so } \frac{dy}{dt}=2$$

$$\text{Hence } y\sqrt{\left(\frac{dx}{dt}\right)^2+\left(\frac{dy}{dt}\right)^2}=2t\sqrt{\left(t-\frac{1}{t}\right)^2+4}$$

$$=2t\left(t+\frac{1}{t}\right)$$

$\left(t-\frac{1}{t}\right)^2+4=t^2+2+\frac{1}{t^2}=\left(t+\frac{1}{t}\right)^2$

$\left(t-\frac{1}{t}\right)^2+4$ factorises into a perfect square, a common feature of many exam questions.

$$\text{So } S=2\pi\int_1^4 y\sqrt{\left(\frac{dx}{dt}\right)^2+\left(\frac{dy}{dt}\right)^2}\,dt$$

$$=2\pi\int_1^4 2t\left(t+\frac{1}{t}\right)dt$$

$$=4\pi\left[\frac{1}{3}t^3+t\right]_1^4$$

$\int_1^4 2t\left(t+\frac{1}{t}\right)dt=2\int_1^4 t^2+1\,dt$

$$=4\pi\left[\left(\frac{64}{3}+4\right)-\left(\frac{1}{3}+1\right)\right]$$

$\left(\frac{64}{3}+4\right)-\left(\frac{1}{3}+1\right)=21+4-1$
$=24$

$$=96\pi \text{ square units}$$

Exercise 3.8

Unless told otherwise, give answers in exact form.

1 A curve has equation $y=2\sqrt{x}$ for $x\geqslant 0$

a For this curve show that $1+\left(\frac{dy}{dx}\right)^2=\frac{x+1}{x}$

b Hence find the area of the surface formed when this curve is rotated 2π radians about the x-axis between the points where $x=0$ and $x=3$.

2 The diagram shows the curve with equation $y = \cosh x$.

The line with equation $y = \frac{5}{4}$ intersects this curve at points A and B, as shown.

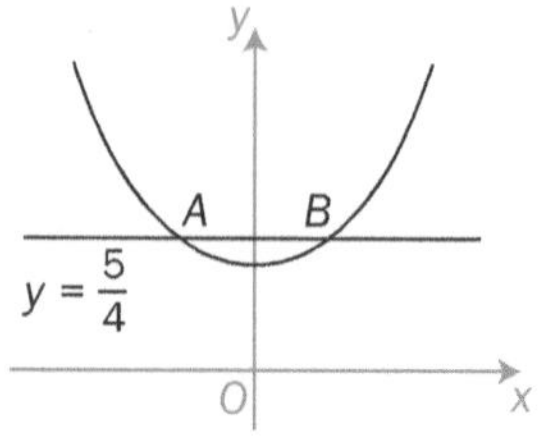

a Find the x-coordinates of point A and point B. Give each answer in exact form.

The arc AB is rotated once about the x-axis to form a solid.

b Show that the surface area of this solid is $\pi\left(\frac{15}{8} + \ln 4\right)$ square units.

3 For the curve with equation $y = \frac{1}{4}x^3 + \frac{1}{3x}, x > 0$

a show that $1 + \left(\frac{dy}{dx}\right)^2 = \left(\frac{3}{4}x^2 + \frac{1}{3x^2}\right)^2$

b Find the area of the surface of the solid generated when the arc of this curve between the points where $x = \sqrt{2}$ and $x = 2$ is rotated once about the x-axis.

4 The diagram shows the curve with equation

$$y = \frac{1}{3}x^{\frac{3}{2}} - x^{\frac{1}{2}},\ 0 \leqslant x \leqslant 6$$

The curve passes through the x-axis at point A.

Point B has x-coordinate 6.

a Find the x-coordinate of point A.

The arc AB of this curve is rotated once about the x-axis to form a solid.

b Show that the area of the surface of this solid is 9π square units.

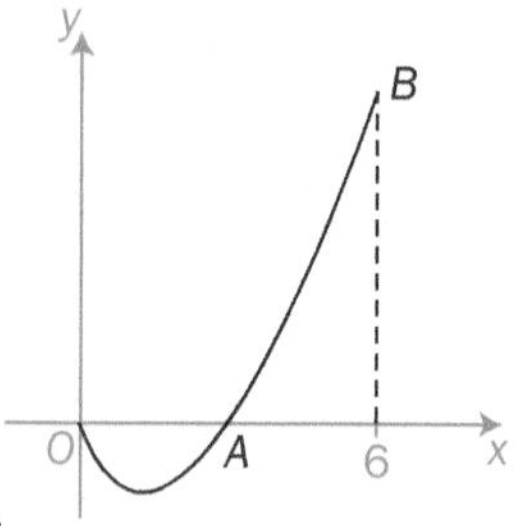

5 A curve is defined by the parametric equations $x = \frac{1}{2}t^2,\ y = 2t,\ t \geqslant 0$

Find the surface area of the solid formed when this curve is rotated once about the x-axis between the points where $t = 0$ and $t = \sqrt{5}$

6 A curve is defined by the parametric equations $x = 2t,\ y = \frac{1}{2}t^3,\ t \geqslant 0$

Find the surface area of the solid formed when this curve is rotated once about the x-axis between the points where $t = 0$ and $t = 1$

7 The diagram shows the curve defined by the parametric equations

$$x = t^2 + 4t,\ \ y = 3t + 6,\ \ t \geqslant -2$$

The curve crosses the x-axis at A and the y-axis at B.

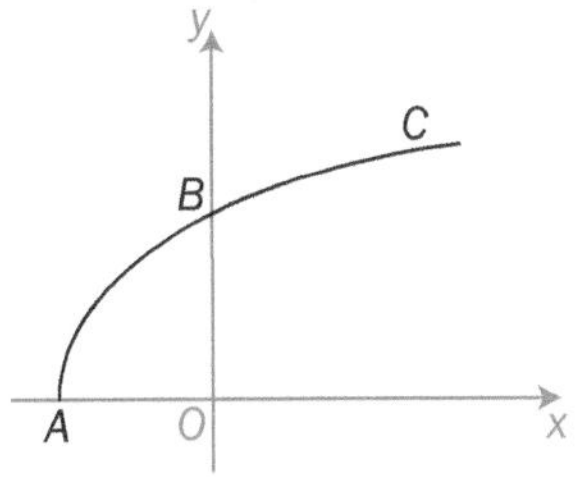

a Show that when the arc AB is rotated once about the x-axis, the surface area of the solid formed is 49π square units.

Point C on this curve is such that when the arc AC is rotated once about the x-axis, the surface area of the solid so formed is $\frac{27}{2}\pi\left(5\sqrt{5}-1\right)$ square units.

b Find the coordinates of point C.

8 The diagram shows the curve defined by the parametric equations

$$x = \ln t + \frac{1}{t},\ \ y = 4t^{-\frac{1}{2}},\ \ t \geqslant 1$$

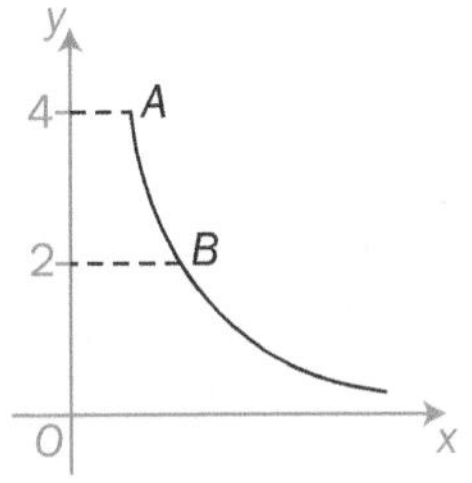

Points A and B on this curve have y-coordinates 4 and 2, respectively.

Find the surface area of the solid generated when the arc AB is rotated once about the x-axis.

9 The arc of the curve with equation $y = \tan x$ between the point where $x = 0$ and the point where $x = \frac{1}{6}\pi$ is rotated once about the x-axis to form a solid.

a Using the substitution $u^2 = 1 + \sec^4 x$, where $u > 0$, show that the surface area S of this solid is given by

$$S = \pi \int_a^b \left(1 + \frac{1}{u^2 - 1}\right) du$$

giving the values of a and b.

b Hence show that $S = \frac{1}{3}\pi\left(5 - 3\sqrt{2} - 3\ln 2\left(\sqrt{2}-1\right)\right)$ square units.

FP3

1 a Using the substitution $u = \cosh\theta$, or otherwise, find

$$\int \frac{\sinh^3\theta}{\cosh\theta + 1}\,d\theta$$

Give your answer in terms of $\cosh\theta$.

b Find the value of the positive constant k for which

$$\int_0^k \frac{\sinh^3\theta}{\cosh\theta + 1}\,d\theta = \frac{1}{32}$$

Give your answer as a natural logarithm.

2 $I_n = \int_{-1}^{0} x^n (1+x)^{\frac{1}{2}}\,dx, \quad n \geqslant 0$

a Show that

$$I_n = \frac{-2n}{2n+3} I_{n-1} \quad n \geqslant 1$$

b Hence evaluate $\int_{-1}^{0} x^2 (1+x)^{\frac{1}{2}}\,dx$

3 The diagram shows the curve with equation

$$y = \frac{1}{\sqrt{15 + 4x - 4x^2}}, \quad -\frac{3}{2} < x < \frac{5}{2}$$

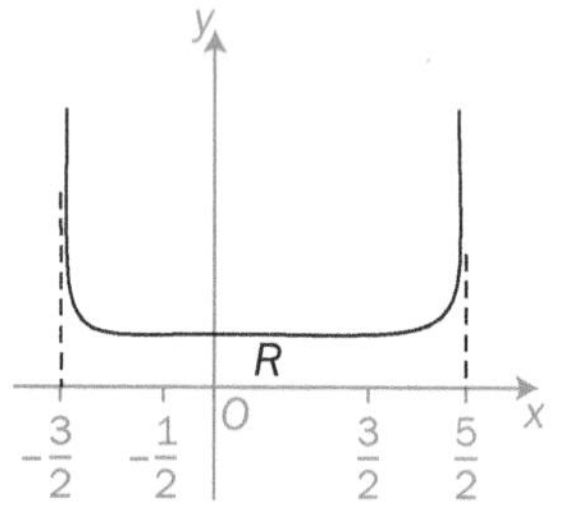

R is the region bounded by this curve, the x-axis and the lines $x = -\frac{1}{2}$ and $x = \frac{3}{2}$

a Show that the area of R is $\frac{1}{6}\pi$ square units.

b Find the volume of the solid formed when region R is rotated once about the x-axis. Give your answer in the form $\frac{\pi}{8}\ln a$, where a is an integer to be stated.

4 a Find $\int \sqrt{1+t^2}\ dt$

Give your answer in terms of t.

The curve C is defined by the parametric equations

$$x = 4t\sin t,\ y = 4t\cos t,\ 0^c \leqslant t \leqslant \frac{3^c}{4}$$

$\frac{3^c}{4} = \frac{3}{4}$ radians

b Show that the exact length of this curve is $\frac{15}{8} + \ln 4$ units.

5 The diagram shows the curve with equation $y = \sqrt{2x-1}$ for $x \geqslant \frac{1}{2}$

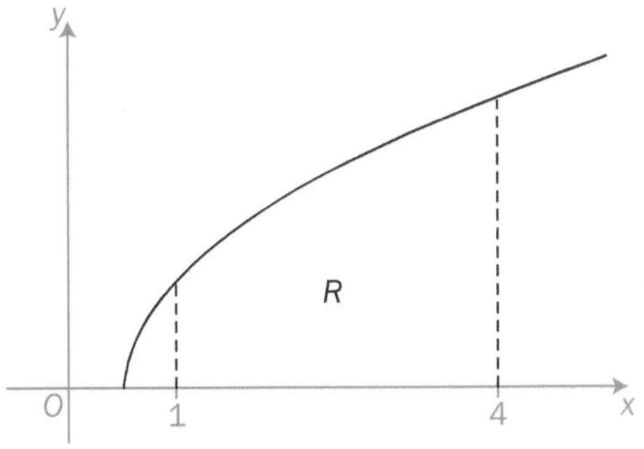

R is the region bounded by this curve, the x-axis and the lines $x = 1$ and $x = 4$

R is rotated once about the x-axis to form a solid S.

Find the exact surface area of S.

6 a Using the substitution $x = \sin\theta$, or otherwise, show that

$$\int \frac{1}{(1-x^2)^{\frac{3}{2}}}\,dx = \frac{x}{\sqrt{1-x^2}} + c$$

where c is an arbitrary constant.

b Evaluate

$$\int_{\frac{3}{5}}^{\frac{4}{5}} \frac{5+x}{(1-x^2)^{\frac{3}{2}}}\,dx$$

7 The diagram shows part of the curve with equation

$$y = \sin(ax)\operatorname{arsinh}(\tan x)$$

where a is a constant, $0 \leqslant a \leqslant 3$.

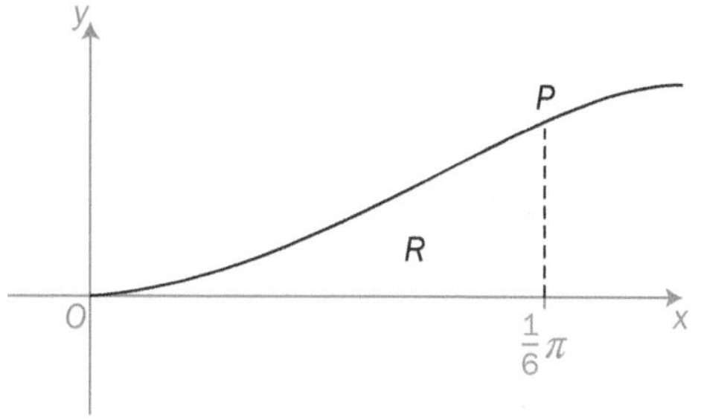

The curve passes through the point P with coordinates

$$P\left(\frac{1}{6}\pi, \frac{\sqrt{3}}{4}\ln 3\right)$$

R is the region bounded by this curve, the x-axis and the lines

$$x = 0,\ x = \frac{1}{6}\pi$$

a Find the value of a.

b Show that the area of region R is $\frac{1}{8}(4 - 3\ln 3)$ square units.

8 $I_n = \int_0^{\pi} x^n \cos x \, dx, \ n \geqslant 0$

a Show that

$$I_n = -n\left[\pi^{n-1} + (n-1)I_{n-2}\right], \ n \geqslant 2$$

b Evaluate $\int_0^{\pi} x^4 \cos x \, dx$

Give your answer in the form $a\pi(b - \pi^2)$ for integers a and b to be stated.

9 Evaluate

$$\int_3^{13} \frac{1}{\sqrt{x^2 + 2x - 3}} \, dx$$

Give your answer as a natural logarithm.

10 a Show that

$$\int \frac{1}{\sqrt{9x^2-18x+25}}\,dx = \frac{1}{3}\text{arsinh}\left(\frac{3}{4}(x-1)\right)+c$$

where c is an arbitrary constant.

b Hence find the exact value of

$$\int_1^2 \frac{9x-8}{\sqrt{9x^2-18x+25}}\,dx$$

11 $I_n = \int_0^1 \frac{x^n}{\sqrt{3+x^2}}\,dx$

a Show that $I_n = \frac{a-3(n-1)I_{n-2}}{n}$, $n \geqslant 2$, stating the value of the constant a.

b Hence show that $\int_0^1 \frac{x^4}{\sqrt{3+x^2}}\,dx = \frac{27\ln 3 - 28}{16}$

Given that $J_n = \int_0^1 x^n \,\text{arsinh}\left(\frac{x}{\sqrt{3}}\right) dx$

c show that $J_n = \frac{1}{n+1}\left(\frac{1}{2}\ln 3 - I_{n+1}\right)$, $n \geqslant 1$

d hence, or otherwise, find the exact value of $\int_0^1 x^3 \,\text{arsinh}\left(\frac{x}{\sqrt{3}}\right) dx$

12 a Using the substitution $x = \cosh\theta$, or otherwise, find

$$\int \frac{x^3}{\sqrt{x^2-1}}\,dx$$

The diagram shows the curve with equation

$y = 9x^2 \,\text{arcosh}\, x, \; x \geqslant 1$

R is the region bounded by this curve, the x-axis and the lines $x = 1$ and $x = \sqrt{10}$.

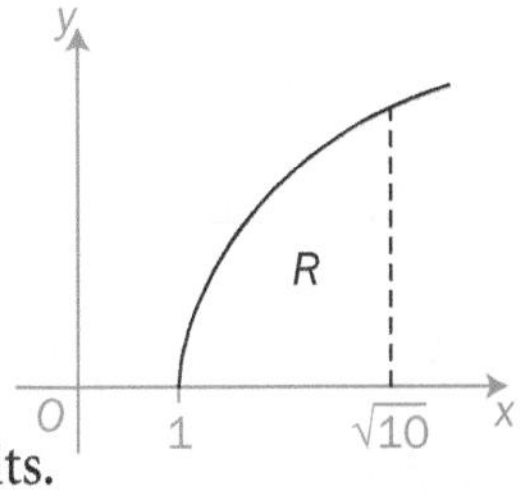

b Show that the area of R is $6\left(5\sqrt{10}\ln\left(3+\sqrt{10}\right)-6\right)$ square units.

FP3

3 Exit

Summary

Refer to

- For $a \neq 0$, $a \in \mathbb{R}$, you can use the rules of integration to establish these results:

  $\int \sinh ax \, dx = \frac{1}{a}\cosh ax + c$ $\quad \int \cosh ax \, dx = \frac{1}{a}\sinh ax + c$ $\quad \int \tanh ax \, dx = \frac{1}{a}\ln(\cosh ax) + c$ 3.2

- You can use a suitable substitution to establish these results:
  - $\int \frac{1}{\sqrt{a^2 + x^2}} \, dx = \text{arsinh}\left(\frac{x}{a}\right) + c$ $\qquad x = a\sinh\theta$
  - $\int \frac{1}{\sqrt{x^2 - a^2}} \, dx = \text{arcosh}\left(\frac{x}{a}\right) + c, \ (x > a)$ $\qquad x = a\cosh\theta$
  - $\int \frac{1}{a^2 - x^2} \, dx = \frac{1}{a}\text{artanh}\left(\frac{x}{a}\right) + c, \ (|x| < a)$ $\qquad x = a\tanh\theta$
  - $\int \frac{1}{\sqrt{a^2 - x^2}} \, dx = \arcsin\left(\frac{x}{a}\right) + c, \ (|x| < a)$ $\qquad x = a\sin\theta$
  - $\int \frac{1}{a^2 + x^2} \, dx = \frac{1}{a}\arctan\left(\frac{x}{a}\right) + c$ $\qquad x = a\tan\theta$ 3.3

- You can complete the square on $Q(x) = ax^2 + bx + c$ to find an integral of the form $\int \frac{1}{Q(x)} \, dx$ or $\int \frac{1}{\sqrt{Q(x)}} \, dx$ 3.4

- You can use integration by parts to find integrals, or you can use a reduction formula to find integrals which depend on $n \in \mathbb{N}$ 3.5 and 3.6

- You can use the formulae $\int_a^b \sqrt{1 + \left(\frac{dy}{dx}\right)^2} \, dx$ or $\int_{t_1}^{t_2} \sqrt{\left(\frac{dx}{dt}\right)^2 + \left(\frac{dy}{dt}\right)^2} \, dt$ to find the arc length s of a curve. 3.7

- You can use the formulae $2\pi \int_a^b y\sqrt{1 + \left(\frac{dy}{dx}\right)^2} \, dx$ or $2\pi \int_{t_1}^{t_2} y\sqrt{\left(\frac{dx}{dt}\right)^2 + \left(\frac{dy}{dt}\right)^2} \, dt$ to calculate the surface area S of a solid of revolution about the x-axis. 3.8

Links

Using integration, you can calculate exact areas, volumes and arc lengths associated with curves.

In designing an object, such as a glass vase, it may be important to control the surface area of the vase, for a given volume, in order to reduce production costs. By rotating a suitable curve around the x-axis and using integration, the exact surface area and volume of the vase can be calculated.

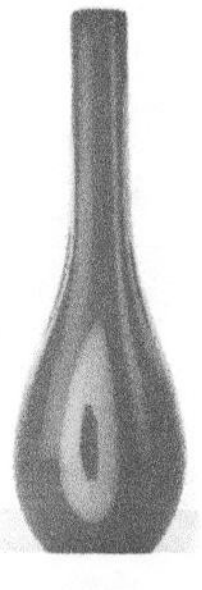

Revision 1

1 Solve the equation $\cosh x + 2\sinh x + 1 = 0$ Mock Q1

2 a Prove that $\dfrac{\cosh x + \operatorname{sech} x}{\cosh x - \operatorname{sech} x} = 2\operatorname{cosech}^2 x + 1$ for all $x \neq 0$

b Hence, or otherwise, solve the equation

$$\cosh x + \operatorname{sech} x = 3\operatorname{cosech} x(\cosh x - \operatorname{sech} x)$$

Give answers as natural logarithms.

3 The curve C shown in the figure, has parametric equations

$$x = t - \ln t,\quad y = 4\sqrt{t},\quad 1 \leqslant t \leqslant 4$$

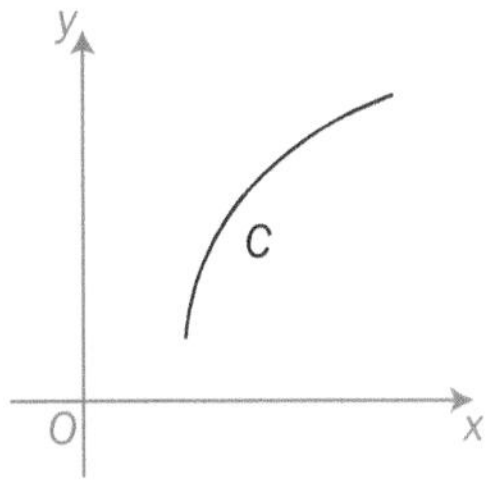

a Show that the length of C is $3 + \ln 4$

The curve is rotated through 2π radians about the x-axis.

b Find the exact area of the curved surface generated.

4 $I_n = \int (\ln x)^n \, dx, \quad n \geqslant 0$

a Show that $I_n = x(\ln x)^n - nI_{n-1}, \quad n \geqslant 1$

b Hence find the exact value of $\int_1^e (\ln x)^3 \, dx$

5 A curve has equation $y = \ln(\cosh 2x) - kx,\ x \geqslant 0$, for k a positive constant.

Point $P\left(\frac{1}{2}\ln 3, \ln 5 - \frac{8}{5}\ln 3\right)$ lies on this curve.

a Show that $k = \frac{6}{5}$

b Find the exact x-coordinate of the stationary point of this curve.

c Prove that this stationary point is a minimum.

6 Using the substitution $x = \sinh\theta$, or otherwise, show that

$$\int_{\operatorname{arsinh} 2}^{\operatorname{arsinh} 4} \frac{\sinh^3\theta}{\cosh\theta(\sinh^2\theta - 1)} \, d\theta = \frac{1}{4}\ln a$$

stating the value of the integer a.

7 The diagram shows the curve with equation

$$y = \text{arcosh}(x^2 + 1),\ x \geqslant 0$$

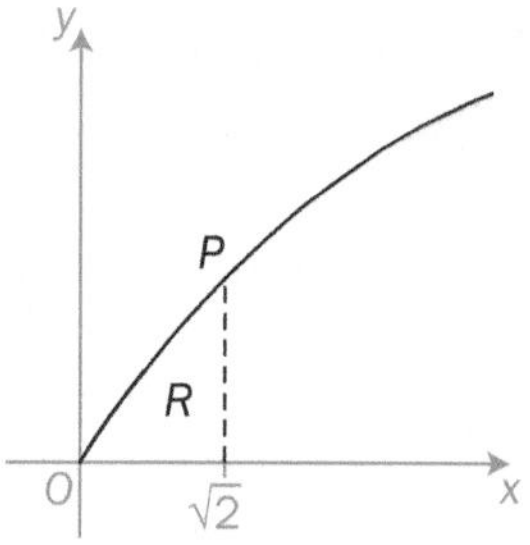

Point P on this curve has x-coordinate $\sqrt{2}$

a Show that $\frac{dy}{dx} = \frac{2}{\sqrt{x^2+2}}$

b Find an equation for the tangent to this curve at point P.

R is the region bounded by this curve, the x-axis and the line $x = \sqrt{2}$

c Show that the area of R is $\sqrt{2}\ln(3 + 2\sqrt{2}) + 2\sqrt{2} - 4$ square units.

8 Show that $\int_5^6 \frac{3+x}{\sqrt{x^2-9}}\,dx = 3\ln\left(\frac{2+\sqrt{3}}{3}\right) + 3\sqrt{3} - 4$

9 $I = \int (a^2 - x^2)^{\frac{1}{2}}\,dx$, where $-a < x < a$, for a a positive constant.

a Using the substitution $x = a\sin\theta$, show that

$$I = \frac{1}{2}\left(x(a^2 - x^2)^{\frac{1}{2}} + a^2 \arcsin\left(\frac{x}{a}\right)\right) + c, \text{ for } c \text{ an arbitrary constant.}$$

A curve has equation $y = \frac{1}{2}\left(x(1 - x^2)^{\frac{1}{2}} + \arcsin x\right)$ for $0 \leqslant x \leqslant 1$

b Find the exact length of this curve.

10 **a** Show that $\text{artanh}\left(\sin\frac{\pi}{4}\right) = \ln(1 + \sqrt{2})$

b Given that $y = \text{artanh}(\sin x)$, show that $\frac{dy}{dx} = \sec x$

c Find the exact value of $\int_0^{\frac{1}{4}\pi} \sin x\,\text{artanh}(\sin x)\,dx$

11 Find the exact value of $\int_{-\frac{1}{4}}^{\frac{1}{6}} \frac{8x+13}{\sqrt{4x^2+12x+5}}\,dx$

Give your answer in the form $a + \frac{1}{2}\ln b$ for rational numbers a and b, in their lowest terms, to be stated.

12 $I_n = \int_0^{\frac{1}{4}\pi} \tan^n x \, dx, \quad n \geqslant 0$

a By writing $\tan^n x$ as $\tan^2 x \tan^{n-2} x$ and using a trigonometric identity, show that

$$I_n = \frac{1}{(n-1)} - I_{n-2}, \text{ for } n \geqslant 2$$

b Hence show that $\int_0^{\frac{1}{4}\pi} \tan^5 x \, dx = \frac{1}{4}(\ln 4 - 1)$.

c Find the exact value of $\int_0^{\frac{1}{4}\pi} \tan^6 x \, dx$ and deduce that $\int_0^{\frac{1}{4}\pi} \sec^6 x \, dx = \frac{28}{15}$

13 A curve has equation $y = x + \sinh 2x - 7\cosh x$

a Find the exact coordinates of the stationary points of this curve.

b Determine the nature of each of these stationary points.

14 The diagram shows the curve with equation

$$y = \frac{1}{\sqrt{2x^2 - 6x + 5}}$$

R is the region bounded by this curve, the x-axis and the lines $x = 0$ and $x = 3$.

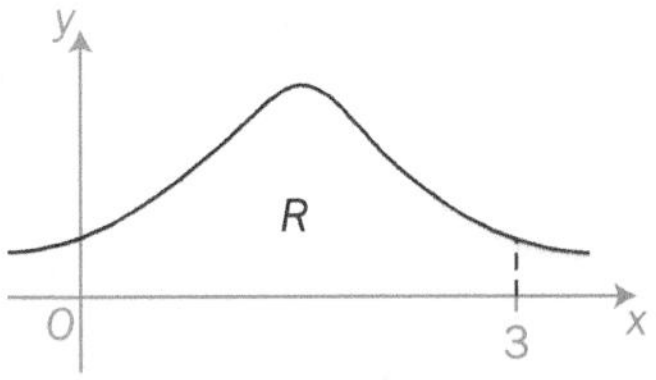

a Show that the area of R is $\sqrt{2}\ln\left(3 + \sqrt{10}\right)$ square units.

b Find the exact volume of the solid formed when R is rotated once about the x-axis.

15 Using the substitution $x = \cosh 2\theta$, or otherwise, find $\int \sqrt{\frac{x+1}{x-1}} \, dx$

Give your answer as a function of x.

16 Using the definitions of $\cosh x$ and $\sinh x$ in terms of exponentials

a prove that $\cosh^2 x - \sinh^2 x = 1$

b solve $\operatorname{cosech} x - 2\coth x = 2$
giving your answer in the form $k \ln a$, where k and a are integers.

17 a Show that $\frac{d}{dx}[\arctan(\sinh x)] = \operatorname{sech} x$ and find $\frac{d}{dx}[\operatorname{sech} x]$

The curve C has equation $y = \arctan(\sinh x) + 5\tanh x - 4x$

b Find the x-coordinate of the stationary point of C with $x \geqslant 0$.
Give your answer as a natural logarithm.

c Show that $\int_0^{\operatorname{arsinh} 1} \operatorname{sech}^2 x \arctan(\sinh x) \, dx = \frac{\pi + 4}{4\sqrt{2}} - 1$

FP3

18 Given that $I_n = \int_0^8 x^n (8-x)^{\frac{1}{3}}\,dx,\ n \geqslant 0$

a show that $I_n = \dfrac{24n}{3n+4} I_{n-1},\ n \geqslant 1$

b hence find the exact value of $\int_0^8 x(x+5)(8-x)^{\frac{1}{3}}\,dx,\ n \geqslant 0$

19 a Show that, for $0 < x \leqslant 1$, $\ln\left(\dfrac{1-\sqrt{1-x^2}}{x}\right) = -\ln\left(\dfrac{1+\sqrt{1-x^2}}{x}\right)$

b Using the definitions of cosh$x$ and sinh$x$ in terms of exponentials,

show that, for $0 < x \leqslant 1$,

$$\operatorname{arsech} x = \ln\left(\frac{1+\sqrt{1-x^2}}{x}\right)$$

c Solve the equation $3\tanh^2 x - 4\operatorname{sech} x + 1 = 0$ giving exact answers in terms of natural logarithms.

20 A curve C is defined by the parametric equations

$$x = 2\cosh^3 t,\ y = 2\sinh^3 t,\ t \geqslant 0$$

a Show that $\left(\dfrac{dx}{dt}\right)^2 + \left(\dfrac{dy}{dt}\right)^2$ can be expressed in the form $a\sinh^2 bt \cosh bt$, stating the values of the constants a and b

b Find the exact length of this curve between the points where $t = 0$ and $t = \ln 3$.

21 a Show that $\int 32\sinh^2 x \cosh^2 x\, dx = \sinh 4x - 4x + c$, where c is an arbitrary constant.

The arc of the curve with equation $y = \sinh^2 x$ between the points where $x = 0$ and $x = 1$ is rotated once about the x-axis, to form a solid.

b Find the surface area of this solid. Give your answer to 3 decimal places.

4 Further coordinate systems

This chapter will show you how to

- sketch an ellipse or a hyperbola
- use the focus-directrix property of an ellipse or hyperbola to solve problems
- determine if a line is a tangent to an ellipse or hyperbola
- find equations for the tangent or normal to an ellipse or hyperbola at a given point
- describe an ellipse or hyperbola using parametric equations
- solve loci problems involving an ellipse or hyperbola

See Section 0.2. W

See C2, C4 and FP1 for revision.

Before you start

You should know how to:

1 Determine if a line is a tangent to a curve.
e.g. Show that the line $y = x + 2$ is a tangent to the circle $x^2 + y^2 = 2$

Solve the two equations simultaneously:

$x^2 + (x + 2)^2 = 2$, that is, $x^2 + 2x + 1 = 0$

Hence $(x + 1)^2 = 0$ so $x = -1$ is a repeated root, so $y = x + 2$ is a tangent to the circle.

2 Use parametric differentiation.
e. g. Find the gradient of the curve given by $x = e^{2t}, y = 4e^t$ at the point P when $t = 0$.

Use $\frac{dy}{dx} = \frac{dy}{dt} \times \frac{dt}{dx}$:

$y = 4e^t$ so $\frac{dy}{dt} = 4e^t$, $x = e^{2t}$ so $\frac{dx}{dt} = 2e^{2t}$

$\frac{dy}{dx} = 4e^t \times \frac{1}{2e^{2t}} = 2e^{-t}$

At P, $t = 0$ so the gradient $\frac{dy}{dx} = 2e^{-0} = 2$

3 Solve problems involving a parabola.
The point (3, 6) lies on the parabola $y^2 = kx$, $k \in \mathbb{R}$. Find the coordinates of the focus of the parabola.

Use the point (3, 6) to find k:

At P, $y^2 = kx$ so $36 = 3k$ and $k = 12$

Hence the focus of C is at (3, 0).

Check in:

1 **a** Show that line l is a tangent to curve C and find the coordinates of the point where l touches C.

i $l: y = 1 - x$, $C: 2x^2 + 2y^2 = 1$

ii $l: y = 2x + 3$, $C: x^2 - y^2 = 3$

b The line $y = kx$, $k \in \mathbb{R}$, is a tangent to the curve $x^4 - y^2 + 1 = 0$

Find the possible values of k.

2 **a** Find an equation for the tangent to these curves at the given point.

i $x = 2t^2 - 1, y = 3t + 1$, where $t = \frac{1}{2}$

ii $x = 2\sin t, y = \cos t$, where $t = \frac{1}{4}\pi$

iii $x = \tan t, y = \sin 2t$, where $t = \frac{1}{6}\pi$

b Find an equation for the normal to the curve given by $x = \ln t, y = t\ln t, t > 0$ at the point where $x = 0$

3 The parabola C has equation $y^2 = 8x$

a Find the equation of the directrix of C.

b Find an expression for the tangent T to C at the point $P(2t^2, 4t)$.

c Find the coordinates of the point R where T intersects this directrix.

4.1 The cartesian equation of the ellipse

The equation $\frac{x^2}{a^2} + \frac{y^2}{b^2} = 1$, where a and b are positive constants, describes an ellipse.

This equation is given in the FP3 section of the formula booklet.

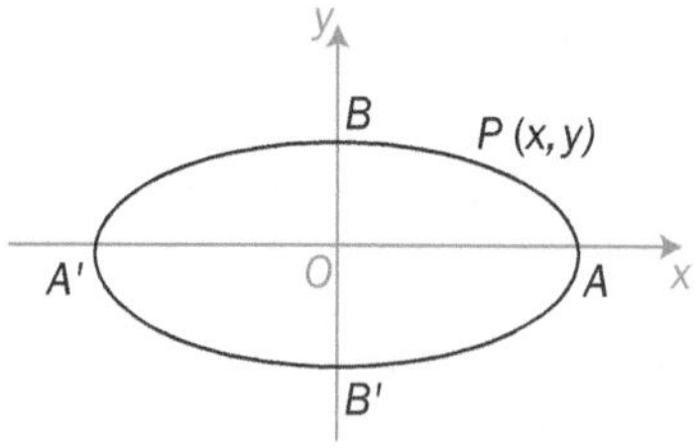

The ellipse with equation $\frac{x^2}{a^2} + \frac{y^2}{b^2} = 1$ crosses the x-axis at points $A(a, 0)$ and $A'(-a, 0)$, and the y-axis at the points $B(0, b)$ and $B'(0, -b)$.

The origin O is the centre of the ellipse.

For example, substituting $y = 0$ into this equation gives $\frac{x^2}{a^2} = 1$ that is, $x = \pm a$

So the ellipse crosses the x-axis at the points $A(a, 0)$ and $A'(-a, 0)$.

The lines AA' and BB' are the axes of the ellipse. The longer line is the major axis, and the shorter line is the minor axis.

For example, if $a < b$ then AA' is the minor axis.

The semi-major (semi-minor) axis is half the major (minor) axis, from the centre to the edge of the ellipse.

For example, if $a > b$ then OA is a semi-major axis.

FP3

EXAMPLE 1

Sketch, on the same diagram, the ellipse E with equation $\frac{x^2}{9}+\frac{y^2}{4}=1$ and the ellipse F with equation $3x^2+y^2=9$

Compare $E: \frac{x^2}{9}+\frac{y^2}{4}=1$ with the general equation $\frac{x^2}{a^2}+\frac{y^2}{b^2}=1$ to find a and b:

$a^2=9$ so $a=3$ $\qquad$ $b^2=4$ so $b=2$

By definition, $a, b > 0$.

E crosses the x-axis at $(\pm 3, 0)$ and the y-axis at $(0, \pm 2)$ and the major axis is horizontal.

For the ellipse E, $a > b$.

Express the equation of F in standard form by dividing all terms by 9:

$3x^2+y^2=9$

so $\quad \frac{x^2}{3}+\frac{y^2}{9}=1$

Compare $\frac{x^2}{3}+\frac{y^2}{9}=1$ with $\frac{x^2}{a^2}+\frac{y^2}{b^2}=1$

Hence $a=\sqrt{3}$, $b=3$

F crosses the x-axis at $(\pm\sqrt{3}, 0)$ and the y-axis at $(0, \pm 3)$ and the major axis is vertical.

For the ellipse F, $a < b$.

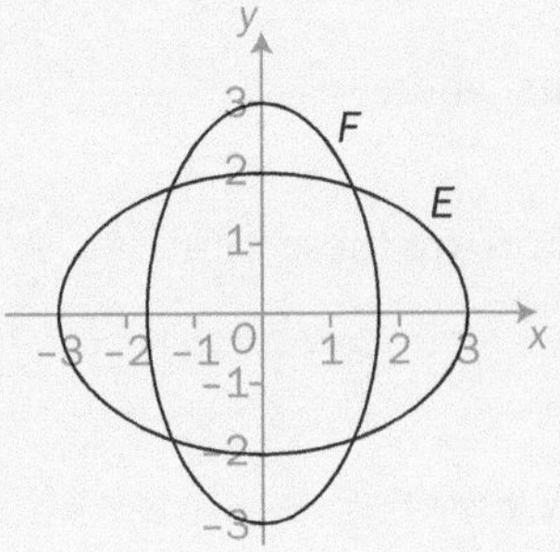

FP3

Exercise 4.1

1 Sketch, on separate diagrams, the ellipses with these equations. Mark the points where each ellipse crosses the x- or y-axis with their coordinates.

a $\frac{x^2}{16}+\frac{y^2}{9}=1$ $\qquad$ **b** $x^2+\frac{y^2}{4}=1$

c $x^2+2y^2=8$ $\qquad$ **d** $9x^2+4y^2=1$

For part **d**, use $9=\frac{1}{\frac{1}{9}}$

2 Verify that the given point P lies on the given ellipse E.

a $P(2, -1)$, $E: \frac{x^2}{8}+\frac{y^2}{2}=1$ $\qquad$ **b** $P\left(1, \frac{3}{2}\right)$, $E: \frac{x^2}{2}+\frac{2y^2}{9}=1$

c $P\left(3\cos\frac{1}{5}\pi, 4\sin\frac{1}{5}\pi\right)$, $E: \frac{x^2}{9}+\frac{y^2}{16}=1$

3 The point $P(\sqrt{2}, -1)$ lies on the ellipse E with equation $kx^2 + y^2 = 9$, where k is a constant.

a Show that $k = 4$

b Hence sketch this ellipse, marking the points where E crosses the x- or y-axes with their coordinates. State the length of the major axis of this ellipse.

4 The ellipse E has equation $\frac{x^2}{4} + \frac{y^2}{9} = 1$. The line l has equation $y = x + 2$

Use algebra to find the coordinates of the points where l intersects E.

5 The ellipse E has equation $\frac{x^2}{9} + y^2 = 1$ and the ellipse F has equation $\frac{x^2}{3} + \frac{y^2}{2} = 1$

a Sketch, on the same diagram, the ellipse E and the ellipse F.

b Find the coordinates of the points where E and F intersect. Give answers in simplified surd form.

6 a Sketch, on the same diagram, the ellipse E with equation $\frac{x^2}{4} + 2y^2 = 1$ and circle C with centre O and radius 1.

b i Find the exact coordinates of the four points where E and C intersect.

ii Show that the area of rectangle whose vertices are these four points is $\frac{8}{7}\sqrt{3}$ square units.

7 The diagram shows the ellipse E with equation $\frac{x^2}{a^2} + \frac{y^2}{b^2} = 1$, where $a, b > 0$. The ellipse crosses the positive x-axis at point A and the positive y-axis at point B.

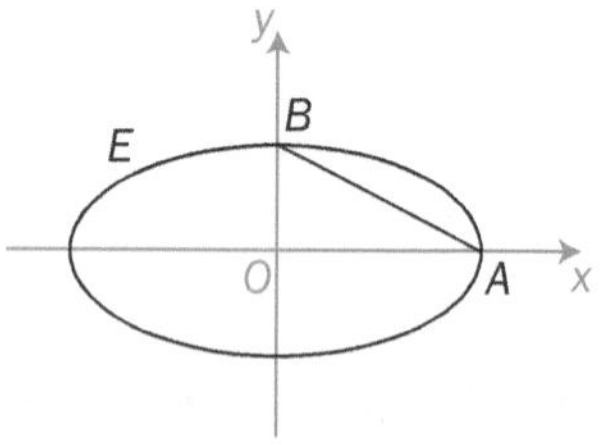

Given that the length $AB = 3$

a show that $a^2 + b^2 = 9$

Given further that E passes through the point $P(2, 1)$

b find the exact values of a and b

c find an equation of the ellipse F which passes through point A and the midpoint of AB.

FP3

8 The ellipse E has equation $\frac{x^2}{5} + \frac{y^2}{4} = 1$

a Sketch E.

b Show that the line l with equation $y = x + 3$ is a tangent to E.

Find the point of intersection of l and E.

The minor axis of this ellipse is QR.

c Find the area of triangle PQR, where P is the point of intersection of l and E.

9 The diagram shows the ellipse E with equation $x^2 + ky^2 = h$, where k and h are constants.

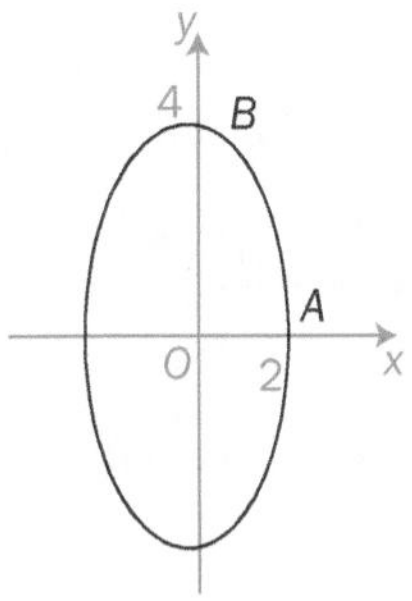

E crosses the positive x-axis at the point $A(2, 0)$ and the positive y-axis at the point $B(0, 4)$.

a Find the value of h and the value of k.

R is the region bounded by the curve AB, and the x- and y-axes.

b Find the exact volume of the solid formed when R is rotated once about the x-axis.

c Using the substitution $x = 2\sin\theta$, or otherwise, show that the exact area of region R is 2π square units.

FP3

10 The diagram shows the ellipse E with equation $\frac{x^2}{4} + \frac{y^2}{3} = 1$,

and which passes through the general point $P(x, y)$. Point Q on the line $x = 4$ is such that the line PQ is horizontal. The fixed point S has coordinates $S(1, 0)$

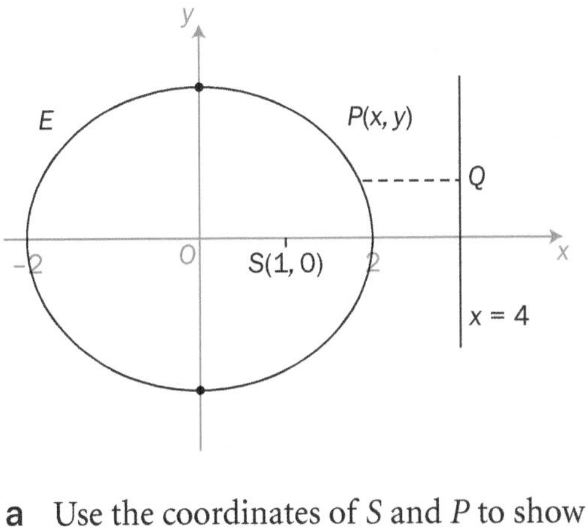

a Use the coordinates of S and P to show that

$4(SP)^2 = x^2 - 8x + 16$

$(SP)^2$ is the square of the distance SP.

b Deduce that $\frac{SP}{PQ} = e$, for e a constant to be determined.

4.2 Further properties of the ellipse

You can measure the extent to which an ellipse deviates from a circle by calculating its eccentricity e, a real number $0 < e < 1$. The smaller the eccentricity, the greater the resemblance the ellipse has to a circle.

Do not confuse e with the number 2.71828...

The eccentricity of the ellipse with equation $\frac{x^2}{a^2} + \frac{y^2}{b^2} = 1$, where $a > b$, is given by

$$e = \left(1 - \frac{b^2}{a^2}\right)^{\frac{1}{2}}$$

e satisfies the equation $b^2 = a^2(1 - e^2)$

$\frac{b^2}{a^2} < 1$ ensures that $\left(1 - \frac{b^2}{a^2}\right) > 0$

and so $e = \left(1 - \frac{b^2}{a^2}\right)^{\frac{1}{2}} \in \mathbb{R}, 0 < e < 1$

When $a < b$, the eccentricity is defined to be $e = \left(1 - \frac{a^2}{b^2}\right)^{\frac{1}{2}}$

and then e satisfies the equation $a^2 = b^2(1 - e^2)$

EXAMPLE 1

Find the eccentricity of the ellipse E with equation

$$\frac{x^2}{8} + \frac{y^2}{6} = 1$$

Compare $\frac{x^2}{8} + \frac{y^2}{6} = 1$ with $\frac{x^2}{a^2} + \frac{y^2}{b^2} = 1$:

$a^2 = 8, b^2 = 6$ so $e = \left(1 - \frac{b^2}{a^2}\right)^{\frac{1}{2}}$

$= \left(1 - \frac{6}{8}\right)^{\frac{1}{2}}$

$= \sqrt{\frac{1}{4}}$

$a > b$ in this example

The eccentricity of the ellipse is $e = \frac{1}{2}$

EXAMPLE 2

The diagram shows the ellipse E with equation $\frac{x^2}{a^2}+\frac{y^2}{b^2}=1$, where $a > b$, and eccentricity e. Also shown are the fixed point $S(ae, 0)$ and the fixed line l with equation $x = \frac{a}{e}$

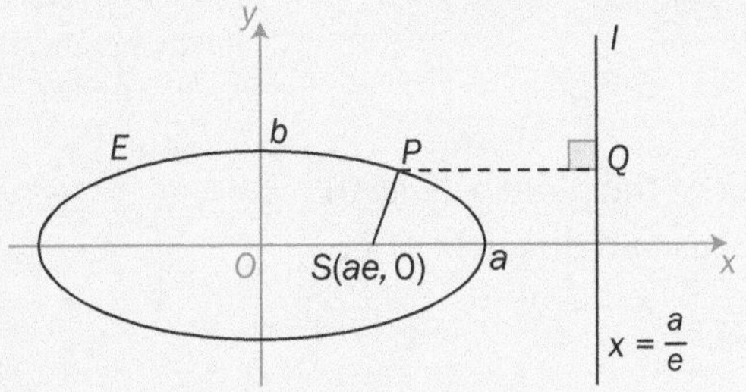

Since $0 < e < 1$, $ae < a < \frac{a}{e}$ that is, the relative positions of S and l are correct.

P is any point on E and point Q, on l, is such that the line PQ is perpendicular to l.
Prove that $PS = ePQ$

S has coordinates $S(ae, 0)$ and P has coordinates $P(x, y)$

So $PS^2 = (x - ae)^2 + y^2$

PS^2 means the square of the length PS. Working with PS^2 rather than the length PS avoids the use of square roots.

Q has coordinates $Q\left(\frac{a}{e}, y\right)$ and so $PQ^2 = \left(\frac{a}{e} - x\right)^2$

Line PQ is horizontal.

Hence $PS^2 - e^2PQ^2 = (x - ae)^2 + y^2 - e^2\left(\frac{a}{e} - x\right)^2$

The required result will follow if it can be shown that $PS^2 - e^2PQ^2 = 0$

$$= x^2 - 2aex + a^2e^2 + y^2 - e^2\left(\frac{a^2}{e^2} - \frac{2ax}{e} + x^2\right)$$

$$= x^2 - 2aex + a^2e^2 + y^2 - a^2 + 2aex - e^2x^2$$

$$= (1 - e^2)x^2 - a^2(1 - e^2) + y^2$$

The terms in x cancel. Gather terms in x^2 and in a^2 and factorise.

$$= \frac{b^2}{a^2}x^2 - b^2 + y^2$$

Using $b^2 = a^2(1 - e^2)$

$$= b^2\left(\frac{x^2}{a^2} + \frac{y^2}{b^2} - 1\right)$$

$$= b^2(1 - 1)$$

$$= 0$$

$P(x, y)$ lies on the ellipse with equation $\frac{x^2}{a^2} + \frac{y^2}{b^2} = 1$

Hence $PS^2 - e^2PQ^2 = 0$

So $PS = ePQ$, as required.

$PS^2 - e^2PQ^2 = 0$ so $PS^2 = e^2PQ^2$, so taking (positive) square roots gives $PS = ePQ$

FP3

For the ellipse E with equation $\frac{x^2}{a^2}+\frac{y^2}{b^2}=1$, where $a > b$ and eccentricity e

1 the point $S(ae, 0)$ is a focus of E

2 the line l with equation $x = \frac{a}{e}$ is a directrix of E

3 if P is any point on the ellipse then $PS = ePQ$

1 and **2** are given in the FP3 section of the formula booklet.

3 is the focus-directrix property. Compare with the parabola in FP1.

By symmetry in the y-axis, the pair consisting of the point $S'(-ae, 0)$ and line l' with equation $x = -\frac{a}{e}$ are also a focus and directrix of E, respectively.

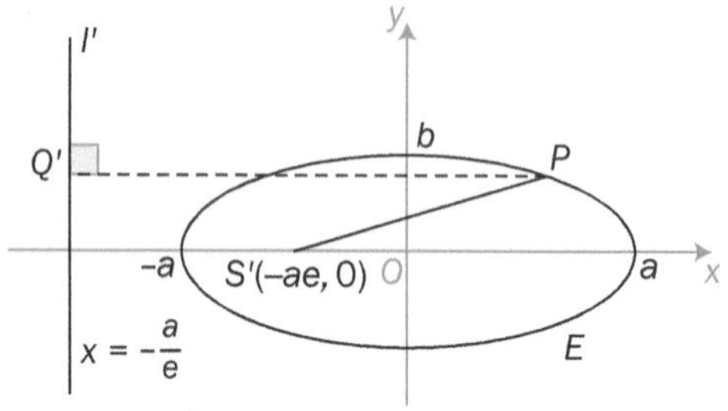

$\frac{S'P}{PQ'} = e$, where P is any point

Exercise 4.2

1 Calculate the eccentricity of each ellipse. Where appropriate, give answers in simplified surd form.

a $\frac{x^2}{9}+\frac{y^2}{8}=1$ b $\frac{x^2}{4}+y^2=1$

c $\frac{x^2}{3}+\frac{y^2}{4}=1$ d $4x^2+9y^2=1$

e $2x^2+3y^2=12$

2 Sketch, on separate diagrams these ellipses. Mark the foci with their coordinates and directrices with their equations.

Foci are always on the major axis. Directrices are always perpendicular to the major axis.

a $\frac{x^2}{25}+\frac{y^2}{21}=1$ b $\frac{x^2}{16}+\frac{y^2}{4}=1$

c $16x^2+9y^2=36$

3 The ellipse E has equation $\frac{x^2}{8}+\frac{y^2}{2}=1$. The ellipse F with equation $\frac{x^2}{16}+\frac{y^2}{b^2}=1$, where b is a positive constant, has the same eccentricity as E.

a Find the eccentricity of E. Give your answer in simplified surd form.

b Find the possible values of b.

4 The ellipse E has equation $\frac{x^2}{9} + \frac{y^2}{5} = 1$

a Find the eccentricity of E.

b Find the coordinates of the foci and the equations of the directrices of E.

Point P on E is such that the distance $PS = \frac{5}{3}$, where S is the focus of E on the positive x-axis.

c Using the focus-directrix property, or otherwise, find the possible coordinates of point P.

5 The ellipse E has equation $\frac{x^2}{9} + \frac{y^2}{6} = 1$. The foci of this ellipse are the points S and S', where S lies on the positive x-axis.

a Find the eccentricity of E. Give your answer in exact form.

b Using the focus-directrix property, or otherwise, find the coordinates of these points on E which lie in the first quadrant. Give answers in simplified surd form.

i the point P such that $PS = \frac{3}{2}$ ii the point R such that $RS' = \frac{13}{4}$

iii the point T such that $TS' = 2TS$

6 The ellipse E has equation $\frac{x^2}{8} + \frac{y^2}{6} = 1$. The ellipse F with equation $\frac{x^2}{a^2} + \frac{y^2}{27} = 1$, where $a > 3\sqrt{3}$, has the same eccentricity as E.

a Find the eccentricity of E and hence show that $a = 6$.

b Sketch, on a single diagram, the ellipse E and the ellipse F.

One of the directrices of E has equation $x = k$, where k is a positive constant.

c Find k and the coordinates of the points where this directrix intersects F. Give answers in exact form.

7 Show that the ellipse E with equation $\frac{x^2}{a^2} + \frac{y^2}{b^2} = 1$, where $a > b > 0$, and the ellipse F with equation $b^2 x^2 + a^2y^2 = 1$ have equal eccentricities.

8 The diagram shows the ellipse with equation $\frac{x^2}{a^2} + \frac{y^2}{b^2} = 1$, where $a > b$, and with eccentricity e. Also shown are the foci S, S' and directrices l and l' of E.

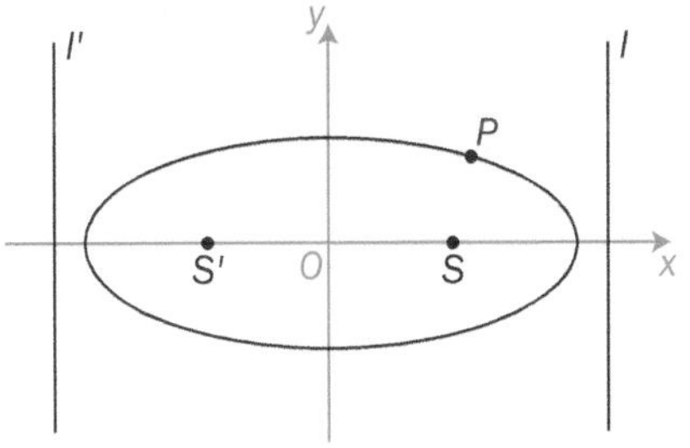

a Use the focus-directrix property to show that $PS + PS' = 2a$

b Hence find an expression involving a and e for the perimeter of triangle SPS'.

c In the case that angle $SPS' = 90°$, show that $PS \times PS' = 2b^2$

4.3 The cartesian equation of the hyperbola

The equation $\frac{x^2}{a^2} - \frac{y^2}{b^2} = 1$, where a and b are positive constants, describes a hyperbola.

This equation is in the FP3 formula booklet.

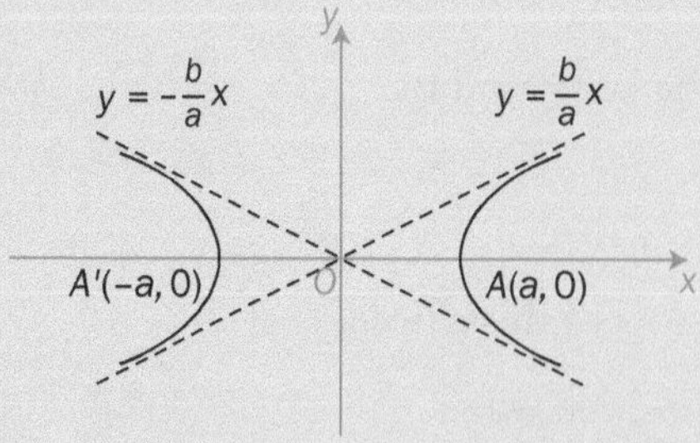

When $|x| < a$, $\frac{x^2}{a^2} < 1$. In this case there are no real values of y for which $\frac{x^2}{a^2} - \frac{y^2}{b^2} = 1$ so the curve is not defined for $|x| < a$

The dotted lines with equations $y = \pm\frac{b}{a}x$ are asymptotes to the curve.
The line AA' is the traverse axis.

The hyperbola approaches these dotted lines but never touches or intersects them.

The hyperbola with equation $\frac{x^2}{a^2} - \frac{y^2}{b^2} = 1$, where $a, b > 0$ has

1 eccentricity $e > 1$ given by $e = \left(1 + \frac{b^2}{a^2}\right)^{\frac{1}{2}}$

2 foci on the traverse axis at the points $(\pm ae, 0)$

3 directrices with equations $x = \pm\frac{a}{e}$

4 asymptotes with equations $y = \pm\frac{b}{a}x$

e satisfies the equation $b^2 = a^2(e^2 - 1)$

For any point P on the hyperbola, $PS = ePQ$

$e = \left(1 + \frac{b^2}{a^2}\right)^{\frac{1}{2}} > (1+0)^{\frac{1}{2}} = 1$

Unlike the ellipse, e is defined this way, regardless of whether $a > b$ or $a \leq b$

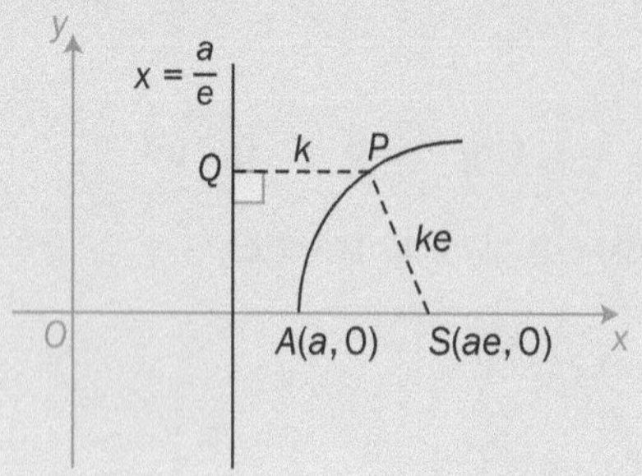

Focus-directrix property
Since $e > 1$, the length PS is greater than the length PQ for any point P on the hyperbola.

EXAMPLE 1

The hyperbola H has equation $\frac{x^2}{4} - \frac{y^2}{5} = 1$

Find the coordinates of

a the focus S of H which lies on the positive x-axis

b the points P on H which lie at a distance of 4 units from S.

---

a Compare $\frac{x^2}{4} - \frac{y^2}{5} = 1$ with $\frac{x^2}{a^2} - \frac{y^2}{b^2} = 1$ to find the eccentricity of H:

$$a^2 = 4, \quad b^2 = 5 \quad \text{so} \quad e = \left(1 + \frac{b^2}{a^2}\right)^{\frac{1}{2}} = \left(1 + \frac{5}{4}\right)^{\frac{1}{2}} = \frac{3}{2}$$

Hence, focus S has coordinates $S(3, 0)$.

$a = 2$ so $ae = 2 \times \frac{3}{2} = 3$

b The directrix that crosses the positive x-axis has equation

$$x = \frac{a}{e} = \left(\frac{2}{\frac{3}{2}}\right) = \frac{4}{3}$$

You must use the directrix which corresponds with the given focus.

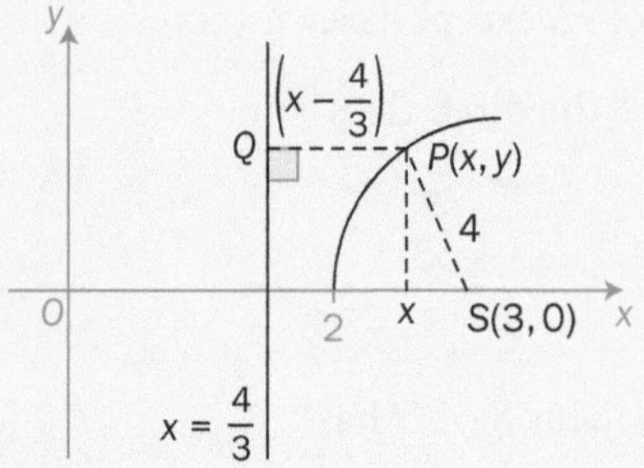

For simplicity, the curve is shown in the first quadrant only.

Use the focus-directrix property $PS = ePQ$ to find the x-coordinate of $P(x, y)$:

$$PS = 4 \text{ so } 4 = \frac{3}{2} \times PQ$$

$$PQ = \frac{8}{3} \text{ units}$$

From the diagram

$$x = \frac{4}{3} + PQ$$

$$= \frac{4}{3} + \frac{8}{3} = 4$$

Substitute $x = 4$ into the equation of H to find the y-coordinate of P:

$$\frac{x^2}{4} - \frac{y^2}{5} = 1 \quad \text{so} \quad \frac{4^2}{4} - \frac{y^2}{5} = 1 \quad \text{so} \quad \frac{y^2}{5} = 3$$

Hence the possible coordinates of P are $P(4 \pm \sqrt{15})$

There are *two* points P on H which lie 4 units from S.

FP3

Exercise 4.3

Where appropriate, give answers in simplified surd form.

1 Calculate the eccentricity of these hyperbolas.

a $\frac{x^2}{3} - \frac{y^2}{9} = 1$ **b** $\frac{x^2}{2} - \frac{y^2}{8} = 1$ **c** $\frac{x^2}{9} - \frac{y^2}{7} = 1$

2 For these hyperbolas, find the coordinates of their foci and the equations of their directrices and asymptotes.

a $\frac{x^2}{4} - \frac{y^2}{12} = 1$ **b** $\frac{x^2}{12} - \frac{y^2}{4} = 1$ **c** $4x^2 - y^2 = 1$

3 The hyperbola H has equation $x^2 - \frac{y^2}{3} = 1$. The line l has equation $y = x + 1$

a Find the coordinates of the points where l intersects H.

b Sketch, on a single diagram, the graph of H and l. Your sketch should include all the important features of H, except its asymptotes.

c Find the area of the trapezium defined by l, the directrices of H and the x-axis.

In the remaining questions, you may assume a and/or b are positive constants.

4 The hyperbola H has equation $\frac{x^2}{a^2} - y^2 = 1$. A focus S of H has coordinates $(3, 0)$.

a Show that $a^2 = 8$ and find e, the eccentricity of H.

Points P_1 and P_2 lie on H at a distance $\sqrt{2}$ units from S.

b Find the coordinates of P_1 and P_2. You may assume P_1 lies in the first quadrant.

c Show that triangle P_1SP_2 is right-angled.

5 The hyperbola H has equation $\frac{x^2}{a^2} - \frac{y^2}{7} = 1$. H passes through the point $P(4, 7)$.

a Show that $a = \sqrt{2}$ and write down the coordinates of the two foci of H.

The hyperbola F crosses the x-axis at the point where $x = \frac{\sqrt{6}}{3}$. F and H share the same directrices.

b Show that an equation for F is $\frac{3}{2}x^2 - 3y^2 = 1$

FP3

6 The hyperbola H has equation $\frac{x^2}{9} - \frac{y^2}{7} = 1$ The points S and S' are the foci of H, where S lies on the positive x-axis. P is a point on H such that $SP = \frac{37}{9}$

a Using the focus-directrix property, or otherwise

i find the coordinates of P (you may assume P lies in the first quadrant)

ii show that $PS' = \frac{91}{9}$

b Find the area of triangle SPS'.

7 The hyperbola H has equation $\frac{x^2}{12} - \frac{y^2}{6} = 1$. An asymptote L to H has equation $y = kx$, where k is a positive constant.

a Show that $k = \frac{1}{\sqrt{2}}$ and find the coordinates of the focus S of H which lies on the positive x-axis.

b Sketch the part of the graph of H which lies in the first quadrant. Show the line L on your sketch.

Line L_1, perpendicular to L, passes through point S.

c Show that the equation of L_1 is $y = 6 - \sqrt{2}x$

d Find the x-coordinates of the points P_1 and P_2 at which L_1 intersects H.

e Using the focus-directrix property, or otherwise, show that the length $P_1P_2 = 4\sqrt{3}$

8 The hyperbola H has equation $\frac{x^2}{a^2} - \frac{y^2}{b^2} = 1$ and eccentricity e. The point S is the focus of H on the positive x-axis. Point A has coordinates $(a, 0)$.

a Write down, in terms of a and e, the distance SA.

b Using the focus-directrix property, or otherwise, prove that if $SA = SP$, where P is a point on H in the first quadrant, then $P \equiv A$

$P \equiv A$ Means that P and A are the same point.

9 The diagram shows part of the hyperbola H with equation $\frac{x^2}{a^2} - \frac{y^2}{b^2} = 1$.

Also shown are the foci S and S', and the two directrices l and l' of H. Point P on H is such that $\angle S'PS = 90°$.

a Show that $(PQ)^2 + (PQ')^2 = 4a^2$, where PQ and PQ' are the perpendicular distances from P to l and l' respectively.

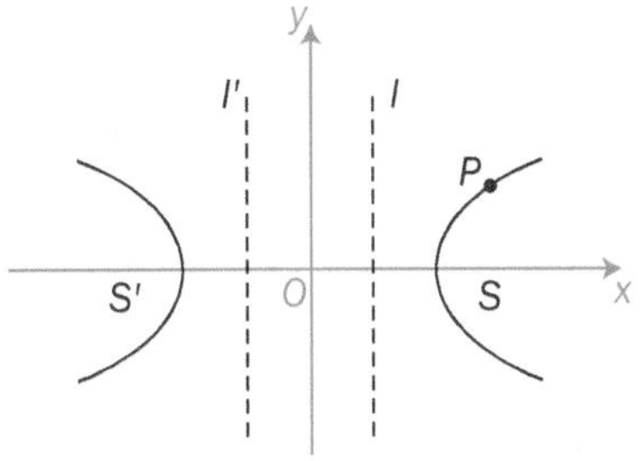

b Show further that the x-coordinate of P is given by $\frac{a}{e}(2e^2 - 1)^{\frac{1}{2}}$, where e is the eccentricity of H.

FP3

4.4 Cartesian equations of tangents and normals

You can find a cartesian equation for a tangent or normal to an ellipse or hyperbola by using implicit differentiation.

EXAMPLE 1

The diagram shows the ellipse E with equation

$$\frac{x^2}{6}+\frac{y^2}{3}=1$$

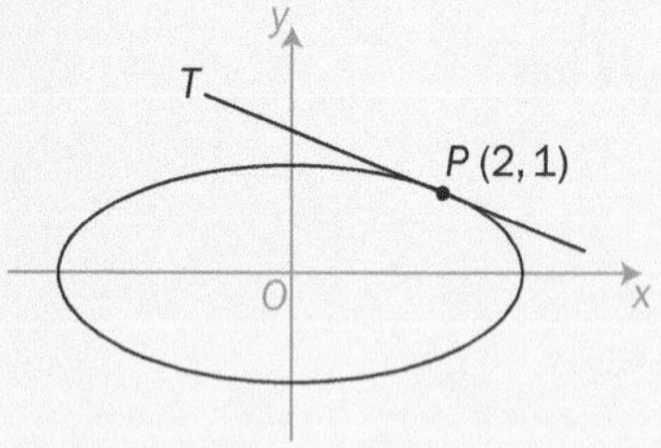

Also shown is the tangent T to E at the point $P(2, 1)$.
Find a cartesian equation for T.

Use implicit differentiation to find the gradient of T:

$$\frac{x^2}{6}+\frac{y^2}{3}=1$$

so $$\frac{1}{3}x+\frac{2}{3}y\frac{dy}{dx}=0$$

$$\frac{dy}{dx}=-\frac{x}{2y}$$

$\frac{d}{dx}(y^2)=2y\frac{dy}{dx}$ Refer to C4.

At point P, $x = 2$, $y = 1$ so the gradient m of T is

$$m=-\frac{2}{2\times1}$$
$$=-1$$

Use the equation $y - y_1 = m(x - x_1)$ to find the equation of T:

An equation for T is $y-1=-(x-2)$

$$y=-x+3$$

You could also use $y = mx + c$

You can use algebra to determine whether the line with equation $y = mx + c$ is a tangent to a given ellipse or hyperbola.

FP3

EXAMPLE 2

A hyperbola H has equation $\frac{x^2}{a^2} - \frac{y^2}{a^2} = 1$, where $a > 0$

Show that the line L with equation $y = mx + c$ is a tangent to H precisely when

$$a^2(m^2 - 1) = c^2$$

This curve is a rectangular hyperbola. The asymptotes are perpendicular.

Multiply the equation of H by a^2 to remove fractions.

$$\frac{x^2}{a^2} - \frac{y^2}{a^2} = 1$$

$$\text{so} \quad x^2 - y^2 = a^2$$

Substitute the equation of L into this equation for H:

That is, force L to intersect H.

$$\text{Since } y = mx + c$$

$$y^2 = (mx + c)^2$$

$$\text{so} \quad x^2 - (mx + c)^2 = a^2$$

Expand brackets and simplify:

$$x^2 - m^2x^2 - 2mcx - c^2 = a^2$$

$$\text{that is, } (1 - m^2)x^2 - 2mcx - (c^2 + a^2) = 0$$

The roots of this quadratic correspond to the intersection points of L and H.
For L to be a tangent to H, this quadratic must have one (repeated) root and so its discriminant must be 0.

Equate the discriminant of this quadratic to zero:

$$(-2mc)^2 - 4(1 - m^2) \times -(c^2 + a^2) = 0$$

$$\text{Hence} \quad 4m^2c^2 + 4(1 - m^2)(c^2 + a^2) = 0$$

Discriminant of $ax^2 + bx + c = 0$ is $b^2 - 4ac$

Divide all terms by 4 and expand brackets:

$$m^2c^2 + c^2 + a^2 - m^2c^2 - m^2a^2 = 0$$

$$c^2 + a^2 - m^2a^2 = 0$$

$$c^2 = a^2(m^2 - 1)$$

Hence L is a tangent if, and only if, $a^2(m^2 - 1) = c^2$, as required.

$c^2 + a^2 - m^2a^2 = 0$ provided
$c^2 = m^2a^2 - a^2$
that is, if $c^2 = (m^2 - 1)a^2$

The line with equation $y = mx + c$ is a tangent to the ellipse with equation $\frac{x^2}{a^2} + \frac{y^2}{b^2} = 1$ precisely when $a^2m^2 + b^2 = c^2$

The line with equation $y = mx + c$ is a tangent to the hyperbola with equation $\frac{x^2}{a^2} - \frac{y^2}{b^2} = 1$ precisely when $a^2m^2 - b^2 = c^2$

You need to remember these two results. They are not in the formula booklet.

FP3

Exercise 4.4

1 Use implicit differentiation to find a cartesian equation of the tangent to these curves at the given point P.

a The hyperbola with equation $\frac{x^2}{8}-\frac{y^2}{4}=1$ at the point P (4, 2).

b The ellipse with equation $\frac{x^2}{5}+\frac{y^2}{4}=1$, at the point $P\left(\frac{5}{3},\frac{4}{3}\right)$.

2 Use implicit differentiation to find a cartesian equation of the normal to these curves at the given point P. Give each answer in the form $px+qy+r=0$, where p, q and r are integers to be stated.

a The hyperbola with equation $\frac{x^2}{4}-\frac{y^2}{7}=1$ at the point $P\left(-\frac{8}{3},\frac{7}{3}\right)$.

b The ellipse with equation $2x^2+4y^2=1$, at the point $P\left(\frac{2}{3},-\frac{1}{6}\right)$.

3 The ellipse E has equation $\frac{x^2}{9}+\frac{y^2}{7}=1$. The line L has equation $y=\frac{7}{3}$

a Find the coordinates of the point P in the first quadrant where L intersects E. Give your answer in exact form.

b Show that an equation for the tangent to E at point P is $3y+\sqrt{2}x=9$

4 The hyperbola H has equation $\frac{x^2}{3}-\frac{y^2}{2}=1$. Point P on H lies in the first quadrant and has x-coordinate $\frac{9}{5}$.

a Show that an equation for the normal to H at point P is $3y+x=3$

b Find the coordinates of the point Q where this normal intersects H again.

5 Determine which of these lines is a tangent to the ellipse with equation $\frac{x^2}{5}+\frac{y^2}{9}=1$

a $L_1: y=2x+5$

b $L_2: 2y=3x+9$

c $L_3: y=2\sqrt{2}x-7$

Use the condition for a line to be a tangent to an ellipse.

6 **a** Given that the line L with equation $y=2x+c$, where c is a constant, is a tangent to the hyperbola with equation $\frac{x^2}{7}-\frac{y^2}{3}=1$ find the possible values of c.

b Given that the line L with equation $y=mx-8$ where m is a constant, is a tangent to the ellipse with equation $\frac{x^2}{6}+\frac{y^2}{10}=1$ find the possible values of m.

FP3

7 The ellipse E has equation

$$\frac{x^2}{a^2}+\frac{y^2}{b^2}=1$$

where a > b > 0, and eccentricity e.

It is given that the point $S(\sqrt{2}, 0)$ is a focus of E.

a Show that $a^2 - b^2 = 2$

Given further that the line L with equation $y = x + 4$ is a tangent to E

b find the value of a and the exact value of b

c find the coordinates of the point P at which L is a tangent to E.

8 Use algebra to prove that the line with equation $y = mx + c$ is a tangent to the ellipse with equation

$$\frac{x^2}{a^2}+\frac{y^2}{b^2}=1$$

precisely when $a^2m^2 + b^2 = c^2$

9 The hyperbola H has equation $\frac{x^2}{a^2}-\frac{y^2}{b^2}=1$ where $a, b > 0$. It is given that the line with equation $2y = \sqrt{11}x$ is an asymptote to H, and that the line with equation $y = 3x + 10$ is a tangent to H.

a Find the value of a and the exact value of b.

Point P on H lies in the second quadrant and has y-coordinate $\frac{11}{2}$

b Show that an equation for the tangent to H at P is

$$2y + 3\sqrt{3}x + 16 = 0$$

10 Prove that the equation of the tangent to the hyperbola with equation $\frac{x^2}{a^2}-\frac{y^2}{b^2}=1$, where $a, b > 0$, at the point $P(x_1, y_1)$ can be expressed as $\frac{xx_1}{a^2}-\frac{yy_1}{b^2}=1$

FP3

Parametric equations for the ellipse

You can describe an ellipse using parametric equations.

Refer to C4.

EXAMPLE 1

Verify that the point $P(3\cos\theta, 2\sin\theta)$ lies on the ellipse with cartesian equation

$$\frac{x^2}{9}+\frac{y^2}{4}=1$$

Substitute the coordinates of point P into the ellipse equation:

At point P, $x = 3\cos\theta$ and $y = 2\sin\theta$

$$\text{So}\quad \frac{x^2}{9}+\frac{y^2}{4}=\frac{(3\cos\theta)^2}{9}+\frac{(2\sin\theta)^2}{4}$$

$$=\frac{9\cos^2\theta}{9}+\frac{4\sin^2\theta}{4}$$

$$=\cos^2\theta+\sin^2\theta$$

$$=1$$

Hence the point $P(3\cos\theta, 2\sin\theta)$ lies on this ellipse.

The ellipse given by the equation

$$\frac{x^2}{a^2}+\frac{y^2}{b^2}=1$$

where a and b are positive constants has parametric equations

$$x = a\cos\theta,\ y = b\sin\theta,\ -\pi < \theta \leqslant \pi$$

This result is in the FP3 section of the formula booklet.

The restriction $-\pi < \theta \leqslant \pi$ means the coordinates of any point P on the ellipse can be written uniquely in the form $P(a\cos\theta, b\sin\theta)$.

You can use parametric differentiation to find the gradient of an ellipse at any of its points.

EXAMPLE 2

An ellipse E is given by the parametric equations

$$x=\sqrt{8}\cos\theta,\ y=\sqrt{2}\sin\theta$$

Find the gradient of E at the point P corresponding to $\theta=\frac{1}{4}\pi$

Find an expression for $\frac{dy}{dx}$ in terms of θ:

$$y=\sqrt{2}\sin\theta \quad \text{so} \quad \frac{dy}{d\theta}=\sqrt{2}\cos\theta$$

$$x=\sqrt{8}\cos\theta \quad \text{so} \quad \frac{dx}{d\theta}=-\sqrt{8}\sin\theta$$

$$\text{Hence} \quad \frac{dy}{dx}=-\frac{\sqrt{2}\cos\theta}{\sqrt{8}\sin\theta}$$

Chain rule: $\frac{dy}{dx}=\frac{\frac{dy}{d\theta}}{\frac{dx}{d\theta}}$ Refer to C3

$$=-\frac{1}{2}\cot\theta$$

$\frac{\cos\theta}{\sin\theta}=\cot\theta$

Substitute the given value of θ into $\frac{dy}{dx}$ to find the required gradient:

$$\text{At } P,\ \theta=\frac{1}{4}\pi \quad \text{so} \quad m=-\frac{1}{2}\cot\left(\frac{1}{4}\pi\right)$$

$$=-\frac{1}{2}$$

So the ellipse E has gradient $-\frac{1}{2}$ at point P.

Exercise 4.5

1 Write down parametric equations for the ellipses with these cartesian equations.

a $\frac{x^2}{16}+\frac{y^2}{9}=1$ **b** $\frac{x^2}{9}+\frac{y^2}{3}=1$ **c** $2x^2+y^2=8$

2 Find cartesian equations for the ellipses given by these parametric equations.

a $x=5\cos\theta, y=3\sin\theta$ **b** $x=\sqrt{5}\cos\theta,\ y=\sqrt{2}\sin\theta$

c $x=\frac{1}{3}\cos\theta,\ y=\frac{2}{3}\sin\theta$

3 An ellipse E is defined by the parametric equations

$x=4\cos\theta, y=5\sin\theta$

By calculating their x- and y-coordinates, or otherwise, find the quadrants in which the points corresponding to these values of θ lie.

a $\theta=\frac{4}{5}\pi$ **b** $\theta=-\frac{1}{3}\pi$ **c** $\theta=2.5^c$ **d** $\theta=-\frac{5}{8}\pi$

FP3

4 An ellipse E is defined by the parametric equations

$x = 4\cos\theta, y = k\sin\theta$ where $-\pi < \theta \leqslant \pi$ and $k > 0$ is a constant.

Point $P(2\sqrt{3}, 1)$ on E corresponds to the value θ_1

a Find the value of θ_1. Give your answer in terms of π.

b Hence show that $k = 2$

c Find the exact gradient of E at point P

d Hence show that an equation for the normal to E at point P is $\sqrt{3}y = 2x - 3\sqrt{3}$

5 An ellipse E is given by the parametric equations

$x = 2\cos\theta, \quad y = 3\sin\theta, \quad -\pi < \theta \leqslant \pi$

a Show that $\frac{dy}{dx} = -\frac{3}{2}\cot\theta$

b Find the gradient of E at the point P on E corresponding to $\theta = \frac{5}{6}\pi$

c Find the exact coordinates of the point Q on E in the first quadrant where the gradient of E is -3.

Use trigonometric identities.

6 The ellipse E is defined by the parametric equations

$x = 3\cos\theta, \ y = \sqrt{5}\sin\theta$ where $-\pi < \theta \leqslant \pi$

Point P on E in the first quadrant has x-coordinate 2.

a Show that the y-coordinate of P is $\frac{5}{3}$

b Find an equation for the tangent T to E at point P.

c Show that the eccentricity e of E is $\frac{2}{3}$

d Hence show that T intersects one of the directrices of E on the x-axis. State the equation of this directrix.

7 The ellipse E has equation $\frac{x^2}{9} + \frac{y^2}{4} = 1$

Point P on E has coordinates $(3\cos\theta, 2\sin\theta)$

Show that the tangent to E at the point $P(3\cos\theta, 2\sin\theta)$ has equation

$(2\cos\theta)\,x + (3\sin\theta)\,y = 6$

FP3

8 The point $P(\sqrt{3}\cos\theta, \sqrt{2}\sin\theta)$ on the ellipse E with equation

$$\frac{x^2}{3} + \frac{y^2}{2} = 1$$

a Show that the normal to E at the point P has equation
$\sqrt{2}y = (\sqrt{3}\tan\theta)x - \sin\theta$

For a particular point P on E in the first quadrant, the normal to E at P has y-intercept $-\frac{1}{2}$

b Find the exact coordinates of point P.

9 The ellipse E is defined by the parametric equations

$x = a\cos\theta,\ y = \sqrt{a}\sin\theta$ where $-\pi < \theta \leqslant \pi$

and a is a positive constant.

It is given that E passes through the point $P\left(\frac{3}{2}, \frac{3}{2}\right)$

a Show that $a = 3$

b Find an equation for the normal to E at point P.

c Find the coordinates of point Q where this normal intersects E again.

10 An ellipse E has equation

$$\frac{x^2}{a^2} + \frac{y^2}{b^2} = 1$$

where a and b are positive constants.

a Show that an equation for the tangent T to E at the point $P(a\cos\theta, b\sin\theta)$ is

$(a\sin\theta)\,y + (b\cos\theta)\,x = ab$

You may be asked to prove this type of result in the exam.

The tangent T crosses the x-axis at point U and the y-axis at point V.

b Show that the area of the triangle OUV, where O is the origin, is equal to

$ab|\text{cosec } 2\theta|$

4.6 Parametric equations for the hyperbola

You can describe a hyperbola using parametric equations.

Refer to C4.

EXAMPLE 1

Verify that the point $P(a\sec\theta, b\tan\theta)$ lies on the hyperbola with cartesian equation

$\frac{x^2}{a^2} - \frac{y^2}{b^2} = 1$ where $a, b > 0$ are constants.

Substitute the coordinates of point P into the hyperbola equation:

At point P, $x = a\sec\theta$ and $y = b\tan\theta$

$$\text{So } \frac{x^2}{a^2} - \frac{y^2}{b^2} = \frac{(a\sec\theta)^2}{a^2} - \frac{(b\tan\theta)^2}{b^2}$$

$$= \frac{a^2\sec^2\theta}{a^2} - \frac{b^2\tan^2\theta}{b^2}$$

$$= \sec^2\theta - \tan^2\theta$$

$$= 1$$

$\sec^2\theta = \tan^2\theta + 1$ Refer to C3.

Hence the point $P(a\sec\theta, b\tan\theta)$ lies on the given hyperbola.

The hyperbola given by the equation

$$\frac{x^2}{a^2} - \frac{y^2}{b^2} = 1$$

where $a, b > 0$ are constants, has parametric equations

$$x = a\sec\theta, \quad y = b\tan\theta$$

Neither $\sec\theta$ nor $\tan\theta$ can be evaluated for $\theta = \frac{1}{2}\pi, \frac{3}{2}\pi$

Unless stated otherwise, it can be assumed that

$0 \leqslant \theta < 2\pi, \theta \neq \frac{1}{2}\pi, \frac{3}{2}\pi$

An alternative set of parametric equations for this hyperbola is

$$x = \pm a\cosh\theta, y = b\sinh\theta, \theta \in \mathbb{R}$$

$\cosh^2\theta - \sinh^2\theta \equiv 1$
Refer to Section 1.4.

Both sets of these parametric equations are in the FP3 section of the formula book.

EXAMPLE 2

The hyperbola H has equation $\frac{x^2}{3} - \frac{y^2}{9} = 1$, where $a, b > 0$ are constants.
Find the coordinates of the point $P\left(\sqrt{3}\sec\theta, 3\tan\theta\right)$ on H in the first quadrant where the gradient of H is 2.

Find an expression for $\frac{dy}{dx}$ in terms of θ:

$$y = 3\tan\theta \quad \text{so} \quad \frac{dy}{d\theta} = 3\sec^2\theta$$

$$x = \sqrt{3}\sec\theta \quad \text{so} \quad \frac{dx}{d\theta} = \sqrt{3}\sec\theta\tan\theta$$

$\frac{d}{d\theta}(\tan\theta) = \sec^2\theta$

$\frac{d}{d\theta}(\sec\theta) = \sec\theta\tan\theta$

Refer to C4.

$$\text{Hence } \frac{dy}{dx} = \frac{3\sec^2\theta}{\sqrt{3}\sec\theta\tan\theta}$$

$$= \frac{\sqrt{3}\sec\theta}{\tan\theta}$$

$$= \frac{\sqrt{3}}{\cos\theta} \times \frac{\cos\theta}{\sin\theta}$$

$$= \sqrt{3}\operatorname{cosec}\theta$$

Chain rule: $\frac{dy}{dx} = \frac{\frac{dy}{d\theta}}{\frac{dx}{d\theta}}$ Refer to C3.

At point P the gradient of H is 2

$$\text{so} \quad \sqrt{3}\operatorname{cosec}\theta = 2$$

$$\frac{\sqrt{3}}{\sin\theta} = 2$$

$$\sin\theta = \frac{\sqrt{3}}{2}$$

$$\text{so} \quad \theta = \frac{1}{3}\pi$$

$P\left(\sqrt{3}\sec\theta, 3\tan\theta\right)$, where $0 < \theta < 2\pi$, lies in the first quadrant. Hence $\sec\theta > 0$ and $\tan\theta > 0$, so θ is acute.

When $\theta = \frac{1}{3}\pi$, $x = \sqrt{3}\sec\left(\frac{1}{3}\pi\right)$ and $y = 3\tan\left(\frac{1}{3}\pi\right)$

$$= 2\sqrt{3} \qquad\qquad = 3\sqrt{3}$$

$\sec\left(\frac{1}{3}\pi\right) = \frac{1}{\cos\left(\frac{1}{3}\pi\right)} = \frac{1}{\left(\frac{1}{2}\right)} = 2$

The coordinates of P are $\left(2\sqrt{3}, 3\sqrt{3}\right)$.

FP3

Exercise 4.6

1 Write down parametric equations involving sec θ and tan θ for the hyperbolas with these cartesian equations.

a $\frac{x^2}{25} - \frac{y^2}{9} = 1$

b $x^2 - \frac{y^2}{4} = 1$

c $3x^2 - 4y^2 = 12$

2 Find cartesian equations for the hyperbolas given by these parametric equations.

a $x = 3\sec\theta, y = 4\tan\theta$

b $x = \pm 4\cosh\theta, y = \sinh\theta$

c $x = \frac{1}{\sqrt{2}}\sec\theta, y = \sqrt{2}\tan\theta$

3 The hyperbola H has cartesian equation $\frac{x^2}{3} - \frac{y^2}{6} = 1.$
Point $P(a\sec\theta, b\tan\theta)$, where a and b are positive constants, is any point on H.

a State the exact values of a and b.

Point P on H corresponds to $\theta = \frac{1}{6}\pi$

b Find the exact coordinates of P.

The line l passes through P and is parallel to an asymptote to H.

c Find the possible equations for l. Give answers in the form $y = \sqrt{2}(px + q)$, where p and q are integers to be stated.

4 The hyperbola H has cartesian equation $\frac{x^2}{9} - \frac{y^2}{4} = 1$
Point $P(3\sec\theta, 2\tan\theta)$ is any point on H.

a Show that the gradient of the normal to H at point $P(3\sec\theta, 2\tan\theta)$ is $-\frac{3}{2}\sin\theta$

Given that $\sin\theta = \frac{4}{5}$, where $\frac{1}{2}\pi < \theta < \pi$

b find an equation for the normal to H at point P. Give your answer in the form $py + qx + r = 0$ for integers p, q and r.

FP3

5 The diagram shows part of the hyperbola H with equation

$$\frac{x^2}{4} - \frac{y^2}{12} = 1$$

Point S is a focus of H and the line l is a directrix of H.

Point P on H has coordinates $P(2\sec\theta, 2\sqrt{3}\tan\theta)$

The line l passes through the positive x-axis at point R.

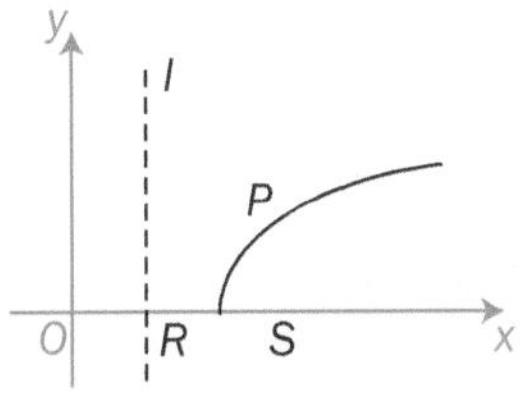

a Find the eccentricity of H.

b Using the focus-directrix property of H, or otherwise, show that

$$PS = 2(2\sec\theta - 1)$$

For a particular point P on this part of H, the triangle PSR is equilateral.

c Find the exact coordinates of point P.

6 The hyperbola H has cartesian equation

$$\frac{x^2}{16} - \frac{y^2}{9} = 1$$

Point $P(4\sec\theta, 3\tan\theta)$ is any point on H.

a Show that an equation for the normal to H at point P is

$$3y + 4x\sin\theta = 25\tan\theta$$

H has a focus S on the positive x-axis.

b Find the coordinates of S.

The normal to H at P cuts the x-axis at point R.

c Show that $\frac{PS}{RS}$ is a constant, stating its value.

7 The hyperbola H has equation $\frac{x^2}{a^2} - \frac{y^2}{b^2} = 1$ where a and b are positive constants.

a Show that an equation for the tangent T to H at the point $P(a\sec\theta, b\tan\theta)$ is

$$bx\sec\theta - ay\tan\theta = ab$$

The tangent T crosses the x-axis at point D.

b Show that the area of the triangle ODP, where O is the origin, is $\frac{1}{2}ab|\sin\theta|$

FP3

4.7 Loci problems

A locus is a path followed by a point subject to a given rule. You can find the locus of points associated with a parabola, ellipse or hyperbola.

In the exam, you could be set a locus question involving a parabola or rectangular hyperbola. Refer to FP1.

EXAMPLE 1

The diagram shows the parabola C with equation $y^2 = 8x$
Point $P(2t^2, 4t)$ is any point on C. Point M is the midpoint of the line OP.

Show that, as t varies, the locus of M is a parabola, stating the coordinates of its focus.

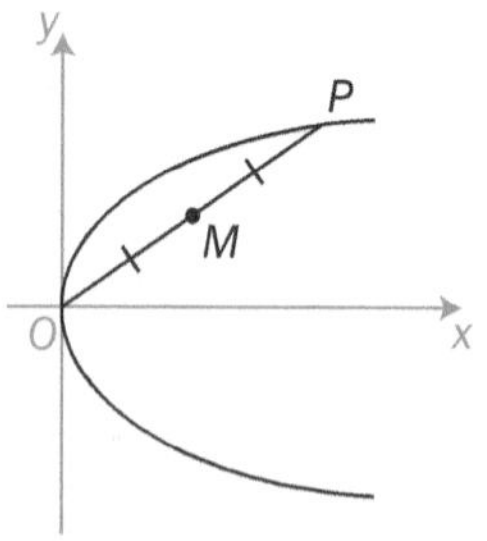

Find an expression in terms of t for the coordinates of M:

P has coordinates $P(2t^2, 4t)$ so the midpoint of OP has coordinates $\left(\frac{2t^2+0}{2}, \frac{4t+0}{2}\right)$

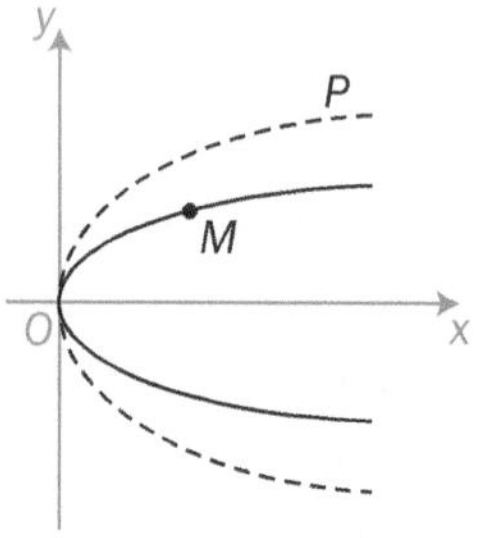

That is, M has coordinates $M(t^2, 2t)$
$x = t^2, y = 2t, t \in \mathbb{R}$ are the parametric equations of a parabola, so the locus of M is a parabola with focus at $(1, 0)$

Refer to FP1 or the FP1 section of the formula book.

Exercise 4.7

1 The ellipse E has equation $\frac{x^2}{36} + \frac{y^2}{9} = 1$. For any point $P(6\cos\theta, 3\sin\theta)$ on E, the point R divides the line OP internally in the ratio $1:2$.

a Show that, as P varies, the locus of R is an ellipse.

b Show that the eccentricities of these two ellipses are equal.

c Sketch, on the same diagram, these two ellipses.

2 The hyperbola H has equation $\frac{x^2}{4} - \frac{y^2}{16} = 1$. For any point $P(2\sec\theta, 4\tan\theta)$ on H, the point R divides the line OP externally in the ratio 2:1.

a Show that, as P varies, the locus of R is a hyperbola K.

b Find the exact distance ST, where S and T are the foci on the positive x-axis, of H and K respectively. Simplify your answer as far as possible.

Using a torch to generate a cone of light, investigate the transition from circle to ellipse through parabola to hyperbola as the angle of the section through a cone is increased.

3 The diagram shows part of an ellipse E with equation

$$\frac{x^2}{9}+\frac{y^2}{4}=1$$

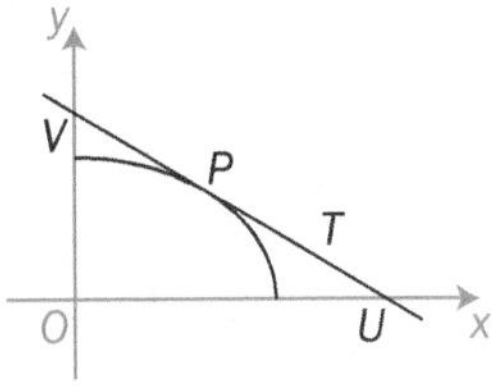

Point $P(3\cos\theta, 2\sin\theta)$ is any point on this curve, such that

$0<\theta<\frac{1}{2}\pi$

Also shown is the tangent T to E at point P, which intersects the x-axis at point U and the y-axis at point V.

Given that an equation for T is $2x\cos\theta+3y\sin\theta=6$

a find, in terms of θ, the coordinates of point U and the point V.

Point M is the midpoint of the line UV.

b Show that a cartesian equation for the locus of M as θ varies, is

$$y^2=\frac{4x^2}{4x^2-9}$$

Use the identity $\cos^2\theta+\sin^2\theta=1$

4 **a** Prove that $t+\frac{1}{t}\geqslant 2$ for all $t\in\mathbb{R}, t>0$

Multiply through by t

The parabola C has equation $y^2=4x$. $P(t^2, 2t)$, where $t>0$, is any point on the upper half of C. The point $Q\left(\frac{1}{t^2}, \frac{2}{t}\right)$, where $t>0$, also lies on C.

b Show that an equation for the tangent T to C at P is

$$ty-x=t^2$$

c Hence find the equation of the tangent T' to C at the point Q.

The tangents T and T' intersect at point R.

d Give the equation of the locus of R as t varies.

Use the result of part a.

5 The rectangular hyperbola H has equation $xy=c^2$, where c is a positive constant.

Point $P\left(ct, \frac{c}{t}\right)$, where $t\in\mathbb{R}, t\neq 0$, is any point on H.

a Show that an equation for the tangent to H at the point P is

$$t^2y+x=2ct$$

Point $Q\left(2ct, \frac{c}{2t}\right)$ also lies on this curve.

b Find an equation for the tangent to H at point Q.

These tangents intersect at point R.

c As t varies, show that the locus of R is a rectangular hyperbola.

6 The ellipse E has equation $\frac{x^2}{4}+\frac{y^2}{3}=1$. Point $P\left(2\cos\theta, \sqrt{3}\sin\theta\right)$ lies on E.

a Show that an equation for the normal to E at P is $\sqrt{3}y-2x\tan\theta+\sin\theta=0$

Point R is the y-intercept of this normal. Point M is the midpoint of the line PR.

b Show that, as P varies, the locus of M is an ellipse.
Find, in exact form, the eccentricity of this ellipse.

7 The parabola C has equation $y^2 = 4ax$ where $a > 0$ is constant.
$P(at^2, 2at)$ is any point on C.

a Show that an equation for the tangent T to C at P is

$$yt - x = at^2$$

The point $Q\left(\frac{1}{2}at^2, \sqrt{2}at\right)$ also lies on C.

b Find the equation of the tangent T' to C at the point Q.
Give coefficients in exact form.

T crosses the y-axis at point A. T' crosses the x-axis at point B.
M is the reflection in the y-axis of the midpoint of AB.

c Show that the locus of M is a parabola, D.

d Sketch, on a single diagram, the parabola C and the parabola D.

8 The hyperbola H has equation $\frac{x^2}{a^2}-\frac{y^2}{b^2}=1$, where a and b are positive constants.
Point $P(a\sec\theta, b\tan\theta)$ is any point on H, where $0<\theta<\frac{1}{2}\pi$
An equation for the normal to H at point on P is $by + ax\sin\theta = (a^2 + b^2)\tan\theta$
This normal crosses the y-axis at the point C and the x-axis at the point D.

a Find expressions for the coordinates of points C and D.

Point M is the midpoint of the line CD.

b Show that, as P varies, the locus of M is part of a hyperbola F.

c Show further that the eccentricity f of F satisfies the equation

$$f^2=\frac{e^2}{e^2-1}$$

where e is the eccentricity of H.

FP3

9 The diagram shows the ellipse E with equation $\frac{x^2}{a^2} + \frac{y^2}{b^2} = 1$ where $a > b > 0$, and the line l with equation $y = x + c$

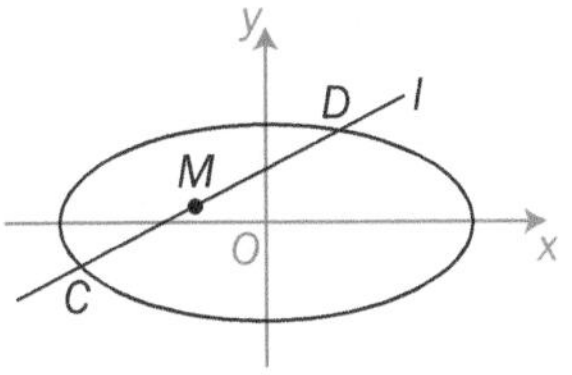

The line l intersects the ellipse at points C and D.

Point M (x_0, y_0) is the midpoint of the line CD.

a Show that $x_0 = -\frac{a^2c}{a^2 + b^2}$ and find, in terms of a, b and c, an expression for y_0.

If α, β are the roots of the equation $ax^2 + bx + c = 0$ then $\alpha + \beta = -\frac{b}{a}$

As c varies, the locus of M is part of a straight line p.

b Find a cartesian equation for the line p.

c Write down a cartesian equation for the hyperbola which has the line p as one of its asymptotes.

10 The hyperbola H has equation $\frac{x^2}{a^2} - \frac{y^2}{b^2} = 1$ and focus S, where the x-coordinate of S is positive. The diagram shows the part of H in the first quadrant.

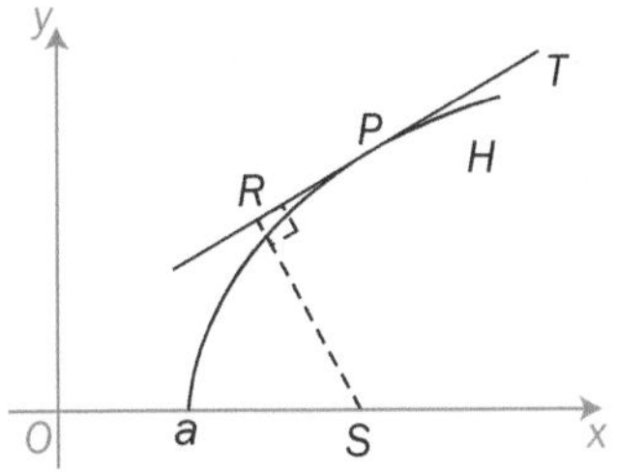

Also shown is the tangent T to H at the point P. The equation of T is $y = mx + c$.

Point $R(x_0, y_0)$ is the foot of the perpendicular from S to T.

Refer to Section 4.4

a Write down an equation connecting m, a, b and c.

b Show that

i $(y_0 - mx_0)^2 = a^2m^2 - b^2$ **ii** $(my_0 + x_0)^2 = a^2e^2$

c Hence show that, as P varies, the locus of R is the circle with equation

$$x^2 + y^2 = a^2$$

d Find, in terms of a and e, the coordinates of the point P_1 on H such that the corresponding point R_1 has coordinates $(0, a)$.

1 The ellipse E has equation $\frac{x^2}{4}+\frac{y^2}{2}=1$

a Find the exact value of the eccentricity e of this ellipse.

b Write down an equation for each of the directrices of E.

Point P on E is such that $OS = SP$, where O is the origin and S is the focus of E on the positive x-axis.

c Find the exact x-coordinate of P.

2 The hyperbola H has cartesian equation $\frac{x^2}{4}-\frac{y^2}{9}=1$
$P(2\sec t, 3\tan t)$ is any point on H such that $\cos t \neq 0$

a Show that an equation for the tangent T to H at P is
$$2y\sin t = 3(x - 2\cos t)$$

The line l is an asymptote to H.

b Given that the gradient of l is positive, show that the x-coordinate of the point where T and l intersect is $2(\sec t + \tan t)$.

3 The hyperbola H has equation $\frac{x^2}{2}-\frac{y^2}{b^2}=1$, where $b > 0$.
The eccentricity of H is 2.

a Find the exact value of b.

Point S is the focus of H on the positive x-axis. An ellipse E passes through S and the point $B(0, b)$

b Find a cartesian equation for E.

c On a single diagram, sketch H and E.

d Find the area of the rectangle whose vertices are the points where H and E intersect.

4 The ellipse E has equation $\frac{x^2}{a^2}+\frac{y^2}{b^2}=1$ where $a > b$ are positive constants. The points S and S' are the foci of E.

a Show that an equation for the normal N to E at the point $P(a\cos\theta, b\sin\theta)$ is
$$by - (a\tan\theta)\,x + (a^2 - b^2)\sin\theta = 0$$

Point R is where N intersects the x-axis. The eccentricity of E is e.

b Show that the coordinates of R are $R(ae^2\cos\theta, 0)$.

c Deduce that R lies strictly between S and S'.

5 The ellipse E has equation $\frac{x^2}{9}+\frac{y^2}{5}=1$, with foci at S and S'.

The line l, which has equation $3y = 2x + k$ where $k > 0$, is a tangent to E at the point P.

a Show that $k = 9$

b Find the coordinates of P

c Show that the area of triangle SPS' is $\frac{10}{3}$ square units.

6 The diagram shows the hyperbola H with equation

$$\frac{x^2}{4}-\frac{y^2}{5}=1$$

Also shown are the two foci S, S′ of H and its directrices.
Point P on H lies in the first quadrant.

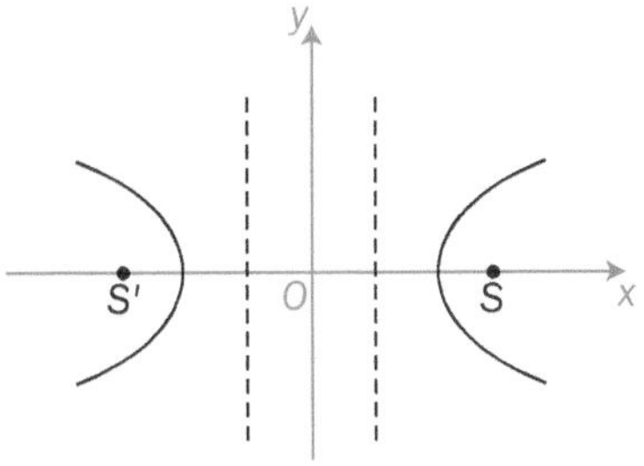

a Find
  i the coordinates of the foci
  ii the equation of each directrix of H.

b Use the focus-directrix property to show that $S'P - SP = 4$

c Given that angle $SPS' = 90°$
  i show that the distance $SP = \sqrt{14} - 2$
  ii find the exact coordinates of P.

7 The ellipse E has equation $\frac{x^2}{9}+\frac{y^2}{25}=1$.

Point $P(3\cos\theta, 5\sin\theta)$ is any point on E.

a Sketch E, showing the coordinates of the foci.

b Show that an equation for the tangent T to E at point P is

$$(3\sin\theta)\,y + (5\cos\theta)x = 15$$

N is the normal to E at point P. T and N intersect the y-axis at the points Q and R, respectively.

c Show that $OQ \times OR$ is a constant, stating its value.

8 The hyperbola H has equation $\frac{x^2}{a^2}-\frac{y^2}{b^2}=1$, where $a, b > 0$ are constants.

The hyperbola has eccentricity e. Point $P(a\cosh t, b\sinh t)$ lies on H.

a Show that an equation for the normal N to H at point P is

$$by + (a\tanh t)\,x = a^2e^2\sinh t$$

N intersects the x-axis at the point Q. M is the midpoint of PQ.

b Show that, as P varies, the locus of M is part of a hyperbola H'.

c Express, in terms of e only, equations for the asymptotes of H'.

FP3

4 Exit

Summary

Refer to

- You can define the equation of an ellipse in either cartesian or parametric form.

  Cartesian: $\frac{x^2}{a^2}+\frac{y^2}{b^2}=1$ Parametric: $x=a\cos\theta,\ y=b\sin\theta,\ -\pi<\theta\leqslant\pi$ — 4.1, 4.5

- You can define the equation of a hyperbola in either cartesian or parametric form.

  Cartesian: $\frac{x^2}{a^2}-\frac{y^2}{b^2}=1$ Parametric: $x=a\sec\theta,\ y=b\tan\theta\quad 0\leqslant\theta<2\pi,\ \theta\neq\frac{1}{2}\pi,\frac{3}{2}\pi$

  Or $x=\pm a\cosh\theta,\ y=b\sinh\theta,\ \theta\in\mathbb{R}$ — 4.3, 4.6

- The ellipse $\frac{x^2}{a^2}+\frac{y^2}{b^2}=1$, where $a>b$, has

  eccentricity $e=\left(1-\frac{b^2}{a^2}\right)^{\frac{1}{2}}$ [$0<e<1$ satisfies the equation $b^2=a^2(1-e^2)$]

  foci $S(\pm ae,0)$ directrices $x=\pm\frac{a}{e}$ — 4.1, 4.2

- The hyperbola $\frac{x^2}{a^2}-\frac{y^2}{b^2}=1$ has

  eccentricity $e=\left(1+\frac{b^2}{a^2}\right)^{\frac{1}{2}}$ [$e>1$ satisfies the equation $b^2=a^2(e^2-1)$]

  foci $S(\pm ae,0)$ directrices $x=\pm\frac{a}{e}$ asymptotes $y=\pm\frac{b}{a}x$ — 4.3

- For any ellipse or hyperbola, $PS=ePQ$ where P is any point on the curve, S is a focus and Q the foot of the perpendicular from P to the corresponding directrix [focus-directrix property] — 4.2, 4.3
- You can use algebra to show that $y=mx+c$ is a tangent to the
  - ellipse $\frac{x^2}{a^2}+\frac{y^2}{b^2}=1$ precisely when $a^2m^2+b^2=c^2$
  - hyperbola $\frac{x^2}{a^2}-\frac{y^2}{b^2}=1$ precisely when $a^2m^2-b^2=c^2$ — 4.4

Links

Circles, ellipses, parabolas and hyperbolas are all related to one another as plane slices through a cone at different angles. Isaac Newton used these *conic sections* in his treatment of gravity. Circles and ellipses describe the closed orbits of planets and comets with the sun placed at one of the foci. Hyperbolas give open 'fly-by' orbits, often used in sling-shot manoeuvres to boost satellite trajectories. Whilst parabolas provide the boundary case where escape to infinity is just possible.

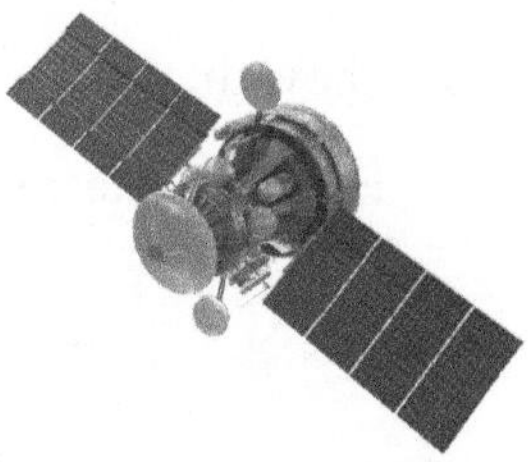

5 Matrices

This chapter will show you how to

- manipulate 3 × 3 matrices
- calculate the determinant and inverse (if non-singular) of a 3 × 3 matrix
- find eigenvalues and eigenvectors of 2 × 2 and 3 × 3 matrices
- diagonalise a 3 × 3 matrix

See Section 0.4. W
See FP1 for revision.

Before you start

You should know how to:

1 Manipulate 2 × 2 matrices.

e.g. if $\mathbf{A} = \begin{pmatrix} 1 & 3 \\ 2 & 1 \end{pmatrix}$ and $\mathbf{B} = \begin{pmatrix} 4 & 0 \\ -2 & -3 \end{pmatrix}$ find **AB**

Multiply the rows in **A** with the columns in **B**:

$$\mathbf{AB} = \begin{pmatrix} 1 & 3 \\ 2 & 1 \end{pmatrix}\begin{pmatrix} 4 & 0 \\ -2 & -3 \end{pmatrix} = \begin{pmatrix} -2 & -9 \\ 6 & -3 \end{pmatrix}$$

2 Find the transpose, determinant and inverse of a matrix.

e.g. Find $\mathbf{M}^\mathrm{T}$, det **M** and $\mathbf{M}^{-1}$ where

$$\mathbf{M} = \begin{pmatrix} 2 & 1 \\ 3 & -1 \end{pmatrix}$$

Swap rows for columns to find $\mathbf{M}^\mathrm{T}$:

$$\mathbf{M} = \begin{pmatrix} 2 & 1 \\ 3 & -1 \end{pmatrix} \quad \text{so} \quad \mathbf{M}^\mathrm{T} = \begin{pmatrix} 2 & 3 \\ 1 & -1 \end{pmatrix}$$

$$\det \mathbf{M} = \begin{vmatrix} 2 & 1 \\ 3 & -1 \end{vmatrix} = 2 \times (-1) - 3 \times 1 = -5$$

$$\mathbf{M}^{-1} = -\frac{1}{5}\begin{pmatrix} -1 & -1 \\ -3 & 2 \end{pmatrix} = \frac{1}{5}\begin{pmatrix} 1 & 1 \\ 3 & -2 \end{pmatrix}$$

Check in:

1 Given that $\mathbf{A} = \begin{pmatrix} 2 & -1 \\ 3 & 4 \end{pmatrix}$ and $\mathbf{B} = \begin{pmatrix} 1 & 1 \\ -1 & 0 \end{pmatrix}$ find

a **AB**

b **BA**

c $\mathbf{AB}^2\mathbf{A}$

d $(\mathbf{A}+\mathbf{B})^2$

2 a Find $\mathbf{M}^\mathrm{T}$ and det **M** given that $\mathbf{M} = \begin{pmatrix} 5 & 3 \\ 7 & 6 \end{pmatrix}$

b Given that $\mathbf{N} = \begin{pmatrix} 2 & k+1 \\ k & 3 \end{pmatrix}$ is singular, where $k \in \mathbb{R}$, find the possible values of k.

c Find the inverse of the these matrices.

i $\mathbf{A} = \begin{pmatrix} 2 & 3 \\ 4 & 1 \end{pmatrix}$ ii $\mathbf{B} = \begin{pmatrix} k & 1 \\ -1 & k \end{pmatrix}$, $k \in \mathbb{R}$

5.1 Calculations with 3 × 3 matrices

You can multiply two 3 × 3 matrices together. The result is another 3 × 3 matrix.

> The element in the ith row and jth column of **AB** is the scalar product of the ith row of **A** with the jth column of **B**.

Refer to C4 for scalar products.

EXAMPLE 1

Find **AB** if $\mathbf{A} = \begin{pmatrix} 2 & 4 & 1 \\ 3 & -1 & 2 \\ 0 & 1 & 3 \end{pmatrix}$ and $\mathbf{B} = \begin{pmatrix} 1 & 0 & 3 \\ 3 & 2 & 0 \\ 5 & 1 & 2 \end{pmatrix}$

The element in the first row and first column of **AB** is the scalar product of the first row of **A** with the first column of **B**.

$$\begin{pmatrix} 2 & 4 & 1 \end{pmatrix}\begin{pmatrix} 1 \\ 3 \\ 5 \end{pmatrix} = 2 \times 1 + 4 \times 3 + 1 \times 5$$

$$= 19$$

$$\begin{pmatrix} 2 & 4 & 1 \\ 3 & -1 & 2 \\ 0 & 1 & 3 \end{pmatrix}\begin{pmatrix} 1 & 0 & 3 \\ 3 & 2 & 0 \\ 5 & 1 & 2 \end{pmatrix}$$

The element in the first row and second column of **AB** is the scalar product of the first row of **A** with the second column of **B**.

$$\begin{pmatrix} 2 & 4 & 1 \end{pmatrix}\begin{pmatrix} 0 \\ 2 \\ 1 \end{pmatrix} = 2 \times 0 + 4 \times 2 + 1 \times 1$$

$$= 9$$

$$\begin{pmatrix} 2 & 4 & 1 \\ 3 & -1 & 2 \\ 0 & 1 & 3 \end{pmatrix}\begin{pmatrix} 1 & 0 & 3 \\ 3 & 2 & 0 \\ 5 & 1 & 2 \end{pmatrix}$$

Other elements in the product are calculated in a similar way.

$$\mathbf{AB} = \begin{pmatrix} 19 & 9 & 8 \\ 10 & 0 & 13 \\ 18 & 5 & 6 \end{pmatrix}$$

Check each entry of this product for yourself.

> Given a 3 × 3 matrix **A**, its transpose is the matrix whose ith row is the ith column of **A**, where $i = 1, 2, 3$. The transpose of **A** is written as $\mathbf{A}^{\mathrm{T}}$
> For any two 3 × 3 matrices **A** and **B**,
> $(\mathbf{AB})^{\mathrm{T}} = \mathbf{B}^{\mathrm{T}}\mathbf{A}^{\mathrm{T}}$

The transpose can be defined for a matrix of *any* order.

EXAMPLE 2

For the matrices defined in Example 1

a write down $\mathbf{A}^T$

b find $\mathbf{B}^T\mathbf{A}^T$

a $\mathbf{A} = \begin{pmatrix} 2 & 4 & 1 \\ 3 & -1 & 2 \\ 0 & 1 & 3 \end{pmatrix}$ so $\mathbf{A}^T = \begin{pmatrix} 2 & 3 & 0 \\ 4 & -1 & 1 \\ 1 & 2 & 3 \end{pmatrix}$

You find the elements of $\mathbf{A}^T$ by reflecting the elements of **A** in its main diagonal.

b Use a standard result regarding transposes:

$$\mathbf{B}^T\mathbf{A}^T = (\mathbf{AB})^T$$

$$= \begin{pmatrix} 19 & 9 & 8 \\ 10 & 0 & 13 \\ 18 & 5 & 6 \end{pmatrix}^T = \begin{pmatrix} 19 & 10 & 18 \\ 9 & 0 & 5 \\ 8 & 13 & 6 \end{pmatrix}$$

Using the result from Example 1.

Exercise 5.1

1 Find the products **AB** and **BA** for these matrices.

a $\mathbf{A} = \begin{pmatrix} 1 & 2 & 0 \\ 2 & 3 & 2 \\ 1 & 4 & 1 \end{pmatrix}, \mathbf{B} = \begin{pmatrix} 2 & 2 & 4 \\ 3 & 1 & 5 \\ 4 & 3 & 2 \end{pmatrix}$

b $\mathbf{A} = \begin{pmatrix} 2 & 0 & 3 \\ -1 & 4 & 3 \\ 3 & -2 & 2 \end{pmatrix}, \mathbf{B} = \begin{pmatrix} 1 & -2 & 2 \\ 1 & 3 & 0 \\ 0 & -1 & 3 \end{pmatrix}$

Defining the exponential of a matrix by the power series, show that

$$\exp\left(\theta\begin{pmatrix} 0 & -1 \\ 1 & 0 \end{pmatrix}\right) = \begin{pmatrix} \cos\theta & -\sin\theta \\ \sin\theta & \cos\theta \end{pmatrix}$$

2 $\mathbf{A} = \begin{pmatrix} a & b & c \\ 2 & 4 & c \\ c & 2 & 2 \end{pmatrix}$ and $\mathbf{B} = \begin{pmatrix} 2 & 2 & 0 \\ a & c & b \\ -3 & 0 & b \end{pmatrix}$, where a, b and c are constants.

Given that the first column of **AB** is $\begin{pmatrix} 6 \\ 15 \\ 10 \end{pmatrix}$

a find the values of a, b and c

b find $\mathbf{B}^T\mathbf{A}^T$.

3 Simplify these expressions. **A** and **B** are any pair of 3×3 matrices.

a $(\mathbf{A}^T)^T$

b $(\mathbf{B}^T\mathbf{A}^T)^T$

c $(\mathbf{B}^T\mathbf{A})^T - \mathbf{A}^T\mathbf{B}$

4 A matrix **M** is called symmetric if $\mathbf{M}^T = \mathbf{M}$

See Section 5.7 for symmetric matrices.

a Prove that if **A** is any square matrix then $\mathbf{AA}^T$ is a symmetric matrix.

b Prove that if **A** is a symmetric non-singular matrix then $\mathbf{A}^{-1}$ is symmetric.

Consider $\mathbf{A}(\mathbf{A}^{-1})^T$

5 For any 3×3 matrix **A**, prove by induction that $(\mathbf{A}^T)^n = (\mathbf{A}^n)^T$ for all $n \in \mathbb{N}$

FP3

5.2 Matrices and linear transformations

You can use matrix multiplication to transform vectors.

If $\mathbf{A}$ is a 3×3 matrix and $\mathbf{v}$ is any 3×1 vector, then the product $\mathbf{Av}$ is also a 3×1 vector.
$\mathbf{A}$ represents the linear transformation $T: \mathbb{R}^3 \to \mathbb{R}^3$, where $T(\mathbf{v}) = \mathbf{Av}$
The vector $\mathbf{Av}$ is the image of $\mathbf{v}$ under the transformation T.

T is a function from the set of 3×1 vectors $\mathbb{R}^3$ to itself.

EXAMPLE 1

A transformation $T: \mathbb{R}^3 \to \mathbb{R}^3$ is represented by the matrix

$$\mathbf{A} = \begin{pmatrix} 2 & 0 & 4 \\ 3 & 2 & 0 \\ 0 & 3 & 5 \end{pmatrix}$$

Find the image of the vector $\mathbf{v} = \begin{pmatrix} 1 \\ 2 \\ 3 \end{pmatrix}$ under this transformation. Interpret your answer.

Calculate the product $\mathbf{Av}$:

$$\mathbf{Av} = \begin{pmatrix} 2 & 0 & 4 \\ 3 & 2 & 0 \\ 0 & 3 & 5 \end{pmatrix}\begin{pmatrix} 1 \\ 2 \\ 3 \end{pmatrix}$$

$$= \begin{pmatrix} 2 \times 1 + 0 \times 2 + 4 \times 3 \\ 3 \times 1 + 2 \times 2 + 0 \times 3 \\ 0 \times 1 + 3 \times 2 + 5 \times 3 \end{pmatrix}$$

$$= \begin{pmatrix} 14 \\ 7 \\ 21 \end{pmatrix}$$

Hence the image of $\mathbf{v}$ under T is the vector $\begin{pmatrix} 14 \\ 7 \\ 21 \end{pmatrix}$

$\mathbf{Av}$ is also referred to as the image of $\mathbf{v}$ under $\mathbf{A}$.

This means T maps the point with coordinates $P(1,2,3)$ to the point $P'(14, 7, 21)$.

You can apply a transformation to a straight line.

EXAMPLE 2

The transformation $T: \mathbb{R}^2 \to \mathbb{R}^2$ is represented by the matrix

$$\mathbf{A} = \begin{pmatrix} 2 & -1 \\ 1 & 1 \end{pmatrix}$$

Find the image of the line l with equation $y = x + 1$ under T.

Let T map $\begin{pmatrix} x \\ y \end{pmatrix}$ to $\begin{pmatrix} x' \\ y' \end{pmatrix}$ where $\begin{pmatrix} x \\ y \end{pmatrix}$ is the position vector of any

point $P(x, y)$ on l.

Then
$$\begin{pmatrix} x' \\ y' \end{pmatrix} = T \begin{pmatrix} x \\ y \end{pmatrix}$$

$$= T \begin{pmatrix} x \\ x+1 \end{pmatrix}$$

$$= \begin{pmatrix} 2 & -1 \\ 1 & 1 \end{pmatrix} \begin{pmatrix} x \\ x+1 \end{pmatrix}$$

$$= \begin{pmatrix} x-1 \\ 2x+1 \end{pmatrix}$$

so $x' = x - 1, \quad y' = 2x + 1$

In terms of x, the y-coordinate of P is $x + 1$ because P lies on the line l with equation $y = x + 1$

$$\begin{pmatrix} 2 & -1 \\ 1 & 1 \end{pmatrix} \begin{pmatrix} x \\ x+1 \end{pmatrix} = \begin{pmatrix} 2x - (x+1) \\ x + (x+1) \end{pmatrix}$$

$$= \begin{pmatrix} x-1 \\ 2x+1 \end{pmatrix}$$

Express y' in terms of x' to find the image of l under T:

$$x' = x - 1 \quad \text{so} \quad x = x' + 1$$
$$y' = 2x + 1$$
$$= 2(x' + 1) + 1$$
$$= 2x' + 3$$

So the image of l under T is a line with equation $y = 2x + 3$

The dashes on x and y are no longer needed.

The transformation represented by **BA** is the transformation represented by **A** followed by the transformation represented by **B**.

Refer to FP1

FP3

Exercise 5.2

1 Find the image of each vector **v** under the transformation represented by the matrix **A**.

a $\mathbf{v} = \begin{pmatrix} 2 \\ 1 \\ 3 \end{pmatrix}$, $\mathbf{A} = \begin{pmatrix} 1 & 3 & 4 \\ 2 & 0 & 2 \\ 1 & 2 & 1 \end{pmatrix}$

b $\mathbf{v} = \begin{pmatrix} 3 \\ -1 \\ 0 \end{pmatrix}$, $\mathbf{A} = \begin{pmatrix} 0 & 2 & -4 \\ 3 & 5 & 3 \\ -1 & 1 & 2 \end{pmatrix}$

2 $\mathbf{A} = \begin{pmatrix} 4 & 0 & 2 \\ 1 & 3 & 2 \\ 2 & 1 & 3 \end{pmatrix}$

The image of the vector $\mathbf{v} = \begin{pmatrix} 3 \\ p \\ q \end{pmatrix}$ under the transformation represented by **A** is $\begin{pmatrix} 14 \\ 11 \\ 11 \end{pmatrix}$

a Find the value of p and the value of q.

b Hence find the image of **v** under the transformation represented by $\mathbf{A}^{\mathrm{T}}$.

3 $\mathbf{A} = \begin{pmatrix} p & q & 0 \\ 2 & 5 & 1 \\ 1 & q & p \end{pmatrix}$ $\quad p, q \in \mathbb{R}$

The image of the vector $\begin{pmatrix} 1 \\ 2 \\ 2 \end{pmatrix}$ under the transformation represented by **A** is $\begin{pmatrix} 6 \\ r \\ 11 \end{pmatrix}$, for r a constant.

a Show that $r = 14$

b Find the value of p and the value of q.

c Find the image of the vector $\begin{pmatrix} 3 \\ -1 \\ 2 \end{pmatrix}$ under **A**.

FP3

4 The transformation $T: \mathbb{R}^2 \to \mathbb{R}^2$ is represented by

the matrix $\mathbf{A} = \begin{pmatrix} 3 & 4 \\ 1 & 2 \end{pmatrix}$

Under T, the vector $\mathbf{v} = \begin{pmatrix} a \\ b \end{pmatrix}$, where a, $b \in \mathbb{R}$, has image $\begin{pmatrix} 24 \\ 10 \end{pmatrix}$

a Find $\mathbf{A}^{-1}$

b Hence, or otherwise, find the vector **v**.

The transformation $S: \mathbb{R}^2 \to \mathbb{R}^2$ is represented by the matrix $\mathbf{A}^{\mathrm{T}}$.

c Find the image of **v** under the combined transformation of T followed by S.

5 The transformation $T: \mathbb{R}^2 \to \mathbb{R}^2$ is represented

by the matrix $\mathbf{A} = \begin{pmatrix} 3 & -1 \\ 2 & 1 \end{pmatrix}$

Find the images under T of the lines l with these equations.

a $l: y = 2x + 1$ b $l: y = 4x - 1$ c $l: y = x - 1$

Give each answer in the form $y = mx + c$

6 The transformation $T: \mathbb{R}^2 \to \mathbb{R}^2$ is represented

by the matrix $\mathbf{A} = \begin{pmatrix} 4 & 1 \\ 2 & 1 \end{pmatrix}$

The line l has equation $y = 2 - 3x$

a Show that the image under T of the line l is the line l_1 with equation $y = 4 - x$

b Hence, or otherwise, find a matrix under which the image of l is the line l_2 with equation $y = x + 4$

Consider how l_1 and l_2 are related geometrically.

7 The transformation $T: \mathbb{R}^2 \to \mathbb{R}^2$ is represented by the matrix **A**.

a Find the image under T of the line l with equation $y = 2x - 3$ when

i $\mathbf{A} = \begin{pmatrix} 1 & 1 \\ 2 & 0 \end{pmatrix}$

ii $\mathbf{A} = \begin{pmatrix} -4 & 2 \\ -2 & 1 \end{pmatrix}$

Under the transformation represented by the matrix $\mathbf{M} = \begin{pmatrix} 3 & 6 \\ 1 & 2 \end{pmatrix}$

the line l with equation $y = mx + c$ is mapped to the point $P(3, 1)$.

b Find the value of m and the value of c.

FP3

5.3 3 × 3 determinants

You can find the determinant of a 3 × 3 matrix using its **minor** values.

Refer to FP1 for 2 × 2 determinants.

If $\mathbf{P} = \begin{pmatrix} a_1 & a_2 & a_3 \\ b_1 & b_2 & b_3 \\ c_1 & c_2 & c_3 \end{pmatrix}$ then the minor of the element a_1 is the

determinant of the 2 × 2 matrix formed by deleting the row and column of **P** containing a_1.

$$\begin{pmatrix} b_2 & b_3 \\ c_2 & c_3 \end{pmatrix}$$

that is, $A_1 = \begin{vmatrix} b_2 & b_3 \\ c_2 & c_3 \end{vmatrix} = b_2c_3 - c_2b_3$

Similarly, the minor of b_2 is $B_2 = \begin{vmatrix} a_1 & a_3 \\ c_1 & c_3 \end{vmatrix} = a_1c_3 - c_1a_3$

$$\begin{vmatrix} a & b \\ c & d \end{vmatrix} = ad - cb$$

For example, in the matrix $\mathbf{P} = \begin{pmatrix} 2 & 4 & 3 \\ 2 & 4 & 1 \\ 1 & 5 & 2 \end{pmatrix}$, $c_2 = 5$ and the minor

of this element is $C_2 = \begin{vmatrix} 2 & 3 \\ 2 & 1 \end{vmatrix} = -4$

Given that for square matricies det(AB) = det(A)det(B) show that premultiplying a square matrix by

$$\begin{pmatrix} 1 & 1 & 0 \\ 0 & 1 & 0 \\ 0 & 0 & 1 \end{pmatrix}$$

leaves its determinant unchanged. What is the effect on the rows of the original matrix?

The determinant of the matrix $\mathbf{P} = \begin{pmatrix} a_1 & a_2 & a_3 \\ b_1 & b_2 & b_3 \\ c_1 & c_2 & c_3 \end{pmatrix}$ is the expression $a_1A_1 - a_2A_2 + a_3A_3$

To form this expression

- write down each element in the first row of P multiplied with its minor:

  $a_1A_1 \qquad a_2A_2 \qquad a_3A_3$

- insert the signs shown in the first row of the sign matrix $\begin{pmatrix} + & - & + \\ - & + & - \\ + & - & + \end{pmatrix}$:

  $+a_1A_1 \quad - \quad a_2A_2 \quad + \quad a_3A_3$

det **P** can be calculated by expanding along any row of **P** or down any column of **P**.

Make sure that you use the correct signs from the sign matrix.

EXAMPLE 1

$\mathbf{P} = \begin{pmatrix} 2 & 4 & 3 \\ 3 & 1 & 2 \\ 2 & 0 & 5 \end{pmatrix}$ Find det **P** by expanding

a along the first row of **P**

b down the second column of **P**.

---

a Write down each element in the first row of **P** multiplied with its minor:

$$2\begin{vmatrix} 1 & 2 \\ 0 & 5 \end{vmatrix} \quad 4\begin{vmatrix} 3 & 2 \\ 2 & 5 \end{vmatrix} \quad 3\begin{vmatrix} 3 & 1 \\ 2 & 0 \end{vmatrix}$$

Insert the signs shown in the first row of the sign matrix $\begin{pmatrix} + & - & + \\ - & + & - \\ + & - & + \end{pmatrix}$:

$$\text{so } \det \mathbf{P} = +\ 2\begin{vmatrix} 1 & 2 \\ 0 & 5 \end{vmatrix} - 4\begin{vmatrix} 3 & 2 \\ 2 & 5 \end{vmatrix} + 3\begin{vmatrix} 3 & 1 \\ 2 & 0 \end{vmatrix}$$

$$= 2(1 \times 5 - 0 \times 2) - 4(3 \times 5 - 2 \times 2) + 3(3 \times 0 - 2 \times 1)$$
$$= 10 - 44 + (-6)$$
$$= -40$$

Hence det **P** = −40

This can also be written as $|\mathbf{P}| = -40$

b Write down each element in the second column of **P** multiplied with its minor:

$$4\begin{vmatrix} 3 & 2 \\ 2 & 5 \end{vmatrix} \quad 1\begin{vmatrix} 2 & 3 \\ 2 & 5 \end{vmatrix} \quad 0\begin{vmatrix} 2 & 3 \\ 3 & 2 \end{vmatrix}$$

Insert the signs shown in the second column of the sign matrix

$\begin{pmatrix} + & - & + \\ - & + & - \\ + & - & + \end{pmatrix}$:

$$\text{so } \det \mathbf{P} = -4\begin{vmatrix} 3 & 2 \\ 2 & 5 \end{vmatrix} + 1\begin{vmatrix} 2 & 3 \\ 2 & 5 \end{vmatrix} - 0\begin{vmatrix} 2 & 3 \\ 3 & 2 \end{vmatrix}$$

$$= -4(3 \times 5 - 2 \times 2) + 1(2 \times 5 - 2 \times 3)$$
$$- 0(2 \times 2 - 3 \times 3)$$
$$= -44 + 4 - 0$$
$$= -40$$

Hence det **P** = −40

The zero in the second column of **P** makes the calculation easier than expanding along the first row.

The answers to parts a and b agree.

FP3

Exercise 5.3

1 Find the determinants of these matrices.

a $\mathbf{P}=\begin{pmatrix}3 & 1 & 4\\ 1 & 2 & 3\\ 2 & 3 & 2\end{pmatrix}$ **b** $\mathbf{Q}=\begin{pmatrix}4 & 0 & 2\\ 2 & 1 & 3\\ 1 & 4 & 1\end{pmatrix}$ **c** $\mathbf{R}=\begin{pmatrix}1 & 4 & 0\\ 3 & 2 & 3\\ 2 & 3 & 0\end{pmatrix}$

d $\mathbf{S}=\begin{pmatrix}1 & -2 & 3\\ -2 & 0 & 2\\ 3 & 4 & -1\end{pmatrix}$ **e** $\mathbf{T}=\begin{pmatrix}0 & 2 & 3\\ -1 & 5 & -2\\ -2 & 3 & 0\end{pmatrix}$ **f** $\mathbf{U}=\begin{pmatrix}2 & 0 & 3\\ 0 & 4 & 0\\ -1 & -3 & 0\end{pmatrix}$

2 Express these determinants in terms of x. Factorise each answer over the real numbers as far as possible.

a $\begin{vmatrix}x & 4 & 3\\ 3 & 1 & 2\\ 0 & 4 & 1\end{vmatrix}$ **b** $\begin{vmatrix}5 & 2 & 1\\ x & x & 4\\ 3 & 2 & 1\end{vmatrix}$ **c** $\begin{vmatrix}1 & x & -1\\ 0 & 2 & 1\\ x & -4 & x\end{vmatrix}$

d $\begin{vmatrix}x & -2 & 1\\ x & x & 4\\ 1 & 1 & x\end{vmatrix}$ **e** $\begin{vmatrix}x+1 & 1 & 0\\ -3 & x-1 & -1\\ x & -1 & x\end{vmatrix}$ **f** $\begin{vmatrix}x+1 & x & 1\\ x^2-1 & 3 & 2\\ 0 & 1 & 1\end{vmatrix}$

3 $\mathbf{A}=\begin{pmatrix}3 & 6 & 0\\ x & 3 & 1\\ 2 & x & x\end{pmatrix}$, where $x \in \mathbb{R}$

Find the values of x for which $\mathbf{A}$ is a singular matrix.

'Singular' means det $\mathbf{A} = 0$
Refer to FP1.

4 $\mathbf{A}=\begin{pmatrix}1 & 3 & 1\\ 1 & p & 3\\ p & 4 & 1\end{pmatrix}$, where $p \in \mathbb{R}$

a In the case when det $\mathbf{A} = 5$, find the possible values of p.

b Find the possible values of p for which $\mathbf{A}$ is singular.
Give answers in simplified surd form.

5 $\mathbf{P}=\begin{pmatrix}x & x & 1\\ 2 & 3 & 3\\ -1 & -1 & x\end{pmatrix}$, where $x \in \mathbb{R}$.

a Show that $\mathbf{P}$ is a non-singular matrix for all real values of x.

b State the minimum value of det $\mathbf{P}$ and the value of x which gives this minimum.

6 $\mathbf{A} = \begin{pmatrix} 4 & 2 & 1 \\ 1 & 2 & 3 \\ 1 & 3 & 3 \end{pmatrix}$, $\mathbf{B} = \begin{pmatrix} 5 & 0 & 6 \\ k & 2k & 3 \\ 1 & k & 1 \end{pmatrix}$, $k \in \mathbb{R}$

det **AB** = det **A** × det **B**
Refer to FP1.

a Find det **A**.

b In the case when det **AB** = 110, find the possible values of k.

c Find the possible values of k for which **B** – **A** is a singular matrix.

7 $\mathbf{P} = \begin{pmatrix} 1 & 3 & k \\ x & 3 & 2 \\ 2 & 2 & 1 \end{pmatrix}$ where k is a constant and x is any real number.

Given that det **P** does not depend on x, find the value of k and the value of the determinant.

8 Solve exactly each of these determinant equations.

a $\begin{vmatrix} x & 1 & 2 \\ 3 & x & 1 \\ 2 & 1 & x \end{vmatrix} = 0$

b $\begin{vmatrix} x-1 & 3 & x \\ 2 & 1 & x \\ 1 & x & 4 \end{vmatrix} + 10 = 0$

9 For any 3 × 3 matrix $\mathbf{A} = \begin{pmatrix} a_1 & a_2 & a_3 \\ b_1 & b_2 & b_3 \\ c_1 & c_2 & c_3 \end{pmatrix}$ prove that

a $\mathbf{A} - \mathbf{A}^\mathrm{T}$ is a singular matrix

b det $\mathbf{A}^\mathrm{T}$ = det **A**.

10 For any 3 × 3 matrix $\mathbf{A} = \begin{pmatrix} a_1 & a_2 & a_3 \\ b_1 & b_2 & b_3 \\ c_1 & c_2 & c_3 \end{pmatrix}$ prove that

a if the first two rows of **A** are identical then **A** is singular

b interchanging the first two columns of **A** gives a matrix whose determinant is –det **A**.

11 The determinant of a 4 × 4 matrix is defined in terms of its 3 × 3 minors and the sign matrix $\begin{pmatrix} + & - & + & - \\ - & + & - & + \\ + & - & + & - \\ - & + & - & + \end{pmatrix}$. Find det **A** for $\mathbf{A} = \begin{pmatrix} 2 & 0 & 1 & 0 \\ 2 & 3 & 4 & 0 \\ 3 & 1 & 2 & 3 \\ 1 & 2 & 2 & 4 \end{pmatrix}$

FP3

5.4 The inverse of a 3 × 3 matrix

You can find the inverse of a non-singular 3 × 3 matrix **A**.

Refer to FP1 for 2 × 2 inverses.

If $\mathbf{A} = \begin{pmatrix} a_1 & a_2 & a_3 \\ b_1 & b_2 & b_3 \\ c_1 & c_2 & c_3 \end{pmatrix}$ is non-singular, then you can calculate its inverse, $\mathbf{A}^{-1}$, as follows.

- Form a new matrix consisting of the minors of each element of **A**.

$$\begin{pmatrix} A_1 & A_2 & A_3 \\ B_1 & B_2 & B_3 \\ C_1 & C_2 & C_3 \end{pmatrix}$$

Refer to Section 5.3 for the definition of minors.

- Change the sign of the minors whose positions in this matrix correspond to the positions of the minus signs in the matrix $\begin{pmatrix} + & - & + \\ - & + & - \\ + & - & + \end{pmatrix}$.

$$\begin{pmatrix} A_1 & -A_2 & A_3 \\ -B_1 & B_2 & -B_3 \\ C_1 & -C_2 & C_3 \end{pmatrix}$$

This is called the matrix of **cofactors** of **A**.

- Transpose this matrix to form the **adjoint** matrix of **A**.

$$\begin{pmatrix} A_1 & -B_1 & C_1 \\ -A_2 & B_2 & -C_2 \\ A_3 & -B_3 & C_3 \end{pmatrix}$$

- Multiply the adjoint matrix by $\frac{1}{\det \mathbf{A}}$ to find $\mathbf{A}^{-1}$.

A valid step, as **A** is non-singular, that is, $\det \mathbf{A} \neq 0$.

$$\mathbf{A}^{-1} = \frac{1}{\det \mathbf{A}} \begin{pmatrix} A_1 & -B_1 & C_1 \\ -A_2 & B_2 & -C_2 \\ A_3 & -B_3 & C_3 \end{pmatrix}$$

If $\mathbf{A} = \begin{pmatrix} a_1 & a_2 & a_3 \\ b_1 & b_2 & b_3 \\ c_1 & c_2 & c_3 \end{pmatrix}$ is non-singular then

$$\mathbf{A}^{-1} = \frac{1}{\det \mathbf{A}} \begin{pmatrix} A_1 & -B_1 & C_1 \\ -A_2 & B_2 & -C_2 \\ A_3 & -B_3 & C_3 \end{pmatrix}$$

where A_1 is the minor of a_1, B_2 is the minor of b_2 etc.

When a matrix **A** has an inverse, **A** is called an **invertible** matrix.

EXAMPLE 1

Given that $\mathbf{A} = \begin{pmatrix} 0 & 1 & 3 \\ 1 & 0 & 1 \\ 2 & 3 & 2 \end{pmatrix}$ is non-singular, find $\mathbf{A}^{-1}$.

$\begin{pmatrix} 0 & 1 & 3 \\ 1 & 0 & 1 \\ 2 & 3 & 2 \end{pmatrix} = \begin{pmatrix} a_1 & a_2 & a_3 \\ b_1 & b_2 & b_3 \\ c_1 & c_2 & c_3 \end{pmatrix}$

i Calculate the minor of each element of **A**.

$$\mathbf{A} = \begin{pmatrix} 0 & 1 & 3 \\ 1 & 0 & 1 \\ 2 & 3 & 2 \end{pmatrix}$$

so $A_1 = \begin{vmatrix} 0 & 1 \\ 3 & 2 \end{vmatrix} = -3 \quad A_2 = \begin{vmatrix} 1 & 1 \\ 2 & 2 \end{vmatrix} = 0 \quad A_3 = \begin{vmatrix} 1 & 0 \\ 2 & 3 \end{vmatrix} = 3$

$$B_1 = \begin{vmatrix} 1 & 3 \\ 3 & 2 \end{vmatrix} = -7 \quad B_2 = \begin{vmatrix} 0 & 3 \\ 2 & 2 \end{vmatrix} = -6 \quad B_3 = \begin{vmatrix} 0 & 1 \\ 2 & 3 \end{vmatrix} = -2$$

$$C_1 = \begin{vmatrix} 1 & 3 \\ 0 & 1 \end{vmatrix} = 1 \quad C_2 = \begin{vmatrix} 0 & 3 \\ 1 & 1 \end{vmatrix} = -3 \quad C_3 = \begin{vmatrix} 0 & 1 \\ 1 & 0 \end{vmatrix} = -1$$

ii Find the matrix of cofactors of **A**.

$$\begin{pmatrix} -3 & 0 & 3 \\ 7 & -6 & 2 \\ 1 & 3 & -1 \end{pmatrix}$$

Remember to apply the sign matrix $\begin{pmatrix} + & - & + \\ - & + & - \\ + & - & + \end{pmatrix}$.

iii Find the adjoint of **A**.

$$\begin{pmatrix} -3 & 7 & 1 \\ 0 & -6 & 3 \\ 3 & 2 & -1 \end{pmatrix}$$

The adjoint is the transpose of the matrix of cofactors.

iv Calculate det **A** and multiply the adjoint of **A** by $\frac{1}{\det \mathbf{A}}$.

Expand along the first row of **A**:

$$\begin{aligned} \det \mathbf{A} &= a_1A_1 - a_2A_2 + a_3A_3 \\ &= (0 \times -3) - (1 \times 0) + (3 \times 3) \\ &= 9 \end{aligned}$$

Use the minors A_1, A_2 and A_3 calculated in part **i**.

Hence $\mathbf{A}^{-1} = \frac{1}{9}\begin{pmatrix} -3 & 7 & 1 \\ 0 & -6 & 3 \\ 3 & 2 & -1 \end{pmatrix}$

Check that $\mathbf{AA}^{-1} = \mathbf{I}$, where **I** is the 3 x 3 identity matrix.

Many scientific calculators have a matrix mode which you can use to check the inverse is correct.

If **A** and **B** are non-singular, then **AB** is non-singular and $(\mathbf{AB})^{-1} = \mathbf{B}^{-1}\mathbf{A}^{-1}$

If the transformation S is represented by the non-singular matrix **A** then the inverse transformation of S is represented by $\mathbf{A}^{-1}$.

Refer to FP1.

FP3

Exercise 5.4

1 Find the inverse of these non-singular matrices.

a $\mathbf{A}=\begin{pmatrix}2 & 0 & 1\\ 3 & 1 & 0\\ 1 & 3 & 2\end{pmatrix}$ b $\mathbf{B}=\begin{pmatrix}-2 & 1 & 1\\ 3 & 0 & -1\\ -1 & 2 & 3\end{pmatrix}$ c $\mathbf{C}=\begin{pmatrix}4 & -4 & 3\\ 0 & -2 & 2\\ 1 & 3 & 1\end{pmatrix}$

2 $\mathbf{A}=\begin{pmatrix}1 & -1 & 1\\ 2 & 3 & 1\\ 5 & 4 & 3\end{pmatrix}$

a Show that $\mathbf{A}$ is non-singular.

b Hence find $\mathbf{A}^{-1}$.

3 Find, where possible, the inverse of these matrices.

a $\mathbf{P}=\begin{pmatrix}6 & 2 & 9\\ -1 & 5 & 2\\ 3 & 1 & 1\end{pmatrix}$ b $\mathbf{Q}=\begin{pmatrix}4 & 1 & 5\\ 2 & 0 & 2\\ 3 & 3 & 6\end{pmatrix}$ c $\mathbf{R}=\begin{pmatrix}3 & \frac{1}{2} & 2\\ 2 & 3 & 4\\ 0 & \frac{1}{4} & 0\end{pmatrix}$

4 $\mathbf{A}=\begin{pmatrix}k & 3 & 1\\ 1 & 0 & 0\\ 2 & 1 & 2\end{pmatrix}$, where k is a constant.

a Find det $\mathbf{A}$. b Find, in terms of k, $\mathbf{A}^{-1}$.

c Verify that $\mathbf{A}^{-1}\mathbf{A}=\mathbf{I}$, where $\mathbf{I}$ is the 3×3 identity matrix.

5 $\mathbf{P}=\begin{pmatrix}x & 1 & -2\\ 2 & 4 & 0\\ 3 & x & 1\end{pmatrix}$, where x is any integer.

a Show that $\mathbf{P}$ is non-singular.

b Find, in terms of x, an expression for $\mathbf{P}^{-1}$.

For a given value of x, one of the columns of $\mathbf{P}^{-1}$ is parallel to the vector $\begin{pmatrix}4\\ -2\\ 1\end{pmatrix}$

c Find this value of x.

6 $\mathbf{P}=\begin{pmatrix}6 & 2 & 1\\ 0 & 2 & 1\\ 1 & 5 & 2\end{pmatrix}$

Refer to Section 5.2

a Find $\mathbf{P}^{-1}$

The image of the vector $\begin{pmatrix}a\\ b\\ c\end{pmatrix}$ under $\mathbf{P}$ is $\begin{pmatrix}-2\\ 1\\ 2\end{pmatrix}$

b Find each of the values a, b and c.

FP3

7 The transformation T is represented by the non-singular matrix $\mathbf{A} = \begin{pmatrix} -9 & 1 & 15 \\ 3 & 0 & -5 \\ 1 & 0 & -2 \end{pmatrix}$

a Find the matrix which represents the inverse transformation to T.

The transformation S is represented by the non-singular matrix **B**

where $\mathbf{AB} = \begin{pmatrix} 1 & 0 & 1 \\ 0 & 1 & 1 \\ 0 & 2 & 1 \end{pmatrix}$

b Find matrix **B**.

c Find the matrix **C** which represents the combined transformation of the inverse transformation of T followed by the inverse transformation of S.

Use $\mathbf{B}^{-1}\mathbf{A}^{-1} = (\mathbf{AB})^{-1}$

d Find the vector **v** whose image under **A** is the same as the image of the vector $\begin{pmatrix} 1 \\ -2 \\ -1 \end{pmatrix}$ under **C**.

8 Consider the system of simultaneous equations

$$x + 3y - z = 4 \quad (1)$$
$$2x + y + z = 6 \quad (2)$$
$$x - y + 2z = 3 \quad (3)$$

a Express this system of equations in the form $\mathbf{A}\begin{pmatrix} x \\ y \\ z \end{pmatrix} = \begin{pmatrix} a \\ b \\ c \end{pmatrix}$

giving the 3×3 matrix **A** and the values of a, b and c.

b Find $\mathbf{A}^{-1}$ and hence solve the given system of equations.

c Solve the given system of equations by eliminating z.

Consider the equations (1) + (2) and 2 × (1) + (3)

9 Solve these systems of equations using

a an inverse matrix

b elimination of a variable.

i
$$2x + 3y + z = 5$$
$$4x - y + z = 15$$
$$3x - 2y + 3z = 17$$

ii
$$4x - 3y + 2z = -5$$
$$5x + 2y - 3z = 0$$
$$6x - 4y + 5z = -2$$

FP3

5.5 Eigenvalues and eigenvectors of a 2 × 2 matrix

Given a matrix **A**, an eigenvector of **A** is a non-zero vector **v** such that $\mathbf{Av} = \lambda\mathbf{v}$ for some $\lambda \in \mathbb{R}$.
λ is an eigenvalue of **A**.

The direction of **v** is preserved under the transformation **A**.

EXAMPLE 1

$\mathbf{A} = \begin{pmatrix} 2 & 2 \\ 1 & 3 \end{pmatrix}$

Verify that $\mathbf{v} = \begin{pmatrix} a \\ a \end{pmatrix}$, where $a \in \mathbb{R}$, $a \neq 0$, is an eigenvector of **A** and hence write down an eigenvalue of **A**.

$$\mathbf{Av} = \begin{pmatrix} 2 & 2 \\ 1 & 3 \end{pmatrix}\begin{pmatrix} a \\ a \end{pmatrix} = \begin{pmatrix} 4a \\ 4a \end{pmatrix} = 4\begin{pmatrix} a \\ a \end{pmatrix}$$

so $\mathbf{Av} = 4\mathbf{v}$

Hence $\mathbf{v} = \begin{pmatrix} a \\ a \end{pmatrix}$ is an eigenvector of **A**.

$\lambda = 4$ is an eigenvalue of **A**.

For example, the parallel vectors $\begin{pmatrix} 1 \\ 1 \end{pmatrix}$ and $\begin{pmatrix} -2 \\ -2 \end{pmatrix}$ are eigenvectors **corresponding to** the eigenvalue $\lambda = 4$.

The eigenvalues **v** of a 2×2 matrix $\mathbf{A} = \begin{pmatrix} a & b \\ c & d \end{pmatrix}$ satisfy the equation $\mathbf{Av} = \lambda\mathbf{v}$, that is $(\mathbf{A} - \lambda\mathbf{I})\,\mathbf{v} = 0$, where $\mathbf{I} = \begin{pmatrix} 1 & 0 \\ 0 & 1 \end{pmatrix}$ and $\mathbf{0} = \begin{pmatrix} 0 \\ 0 \end{pmatrix}$

The eigenvalues λ of **A** are the roots of equation $|\mathbf{A} - \lambda\mathbf{I}| = 0$, that is $\begin{vmatrix} a-\lambda & b \\ c & d-\lambda \end{vmatrix} = 0$

This follows from the general result that the matrix equation $\mathbf{Bv} = 0$ has a non-zero solution **v** if, and only if, $\det \mathbf{B} = 0$

The equation $|\mathbf{A} - \lambda\mathbf{I}| = 0$ is the **characteristic** equation of **A**.

EXAMPLE 2

$\mathbf{A} = \begin{pmatrix} 2 & 2 \\ 1 & 3 \end{pmatrix}$

a Find the eigenvalues of **A**.

b Hence find an eigenvector corresponding to each eigenvalue of **A**.

EXAMPLE 2 (CONT.)

a Solve the characteristic equation $|\mathbf{A} - \lambda\mathbf{I}| = 0$:

$$\mathbf{A} - \lambda\mathbf{I} = \begin{pmatrix} 2 & 2 \\ 1 & 3 \end{pmatrix} - \begin{pmatrix} \lambda & 0 \\ 0 & \lambda \end{pmatrix} = \begin{pmatrix} 2-\lambda & 2 \\ 1 & 3-\lambda \end{pmatrix}$$

$$|\mathbf{A}-\lambda\mathbf{I}| = (2-\lambda)(3-\lambda) - 1 \times 2 = \lambda^2 - 5\lambda + 4$$

When $|\mathbf{A} - \lambda\mathbf{I}| = 0$

$$\lambda^2 - 5\lambda + 4 = 0$$

so $(\lambda - 1)(\lambda - 4) = 0$

$$\lambda = 1, 4$$

For a 2×2 matrix, the characteristic equation will always be a quadratic in λ.

Hence the eigenvalues of **A** are $\lambda_1 = 1$, $\lambda_2 = 4$

b Use the equation $\mathbf{Av} = \lambda\mathbf{v}$ to find eigenvectors $\mathbf{v} = \begin{pmatrix} x \\ y \end{pmatrix}$ of A:

For $\lambda_1 = 1$

Take each eigenvalue in turn.

$\mathbf{Av} = 1 \times \mathbf{v}$

$$\begin{pmatrix} 2 & 2 \\ 1 & 3 \end{pmatrix}\begin{pmatrix} x \\ y \end{pmatrix} = \begin{pmatrix} x \\ y \end{pmatrix}$$

$$\begin{pmatrix} 2x+2y \\ x+3y \end{pmatrix} = \begin{pmatrix} x \\ y \end{pmatrix}$$

Equate top components:

$$2x + 2y = x$$

so $\quad x = -2y$

Equating the bottom components gives the equation $x + 3y = y$, which leads to the same relationship $x = -2y$

Hence $\mathbf{v} = \begin{pmatrix} x \\ y \end{pmatrix} = \begin{pmatrix} -2y \\ y \end{pmatrix} = y\begin{pmatrix} -2 \\ 1 \end{pmatrix}$

$\begin{pmatrix} -2 \\ 1 \end{pmatrix}$ is an eigenvector corresponding to $\lambda_1 = 1$

Eigenvectors are not unique. Any multiple of $\begin{pmatrix} -2 \\ 1 \end{pmatrix}$ is also an eigenvector of **A** corresponding to this eigenvalue.

Similarly, for $\lambda_2 = 4$

$\mathbf{Av} = 4\mathbf{v} \qquad \begin{pmatrix} 2 & 2 \\ 1 & 3 \end{pmatrix}\begin{pmatrix} x \\ y \end{pmatrix} = 4\begin{pmatrix} x \\ y \end{pmatrix}$

Equate top components:

$$2x + 2y = 4x$$

$$x = y$$

$$\mathbf{v} = \begin{pmatrix} x \\ y \end{pmatrix} = x\begin{pmatrix} 1 \\ 1 \end{pmatrix}$$

so $\begin{pmatrix} 1 \\ 1 \end{pmatrix}$ is an eigenvector corresponding to $\lambda_2 = 4$

Compare this result with Example 1.

Hence $\mathbf{v}_1 = \begin{pmatrix} -2 \\ 1 \end{pmatrix}$ and $\mathbf{v}_2 = \begin{pmatrix} 1 \\ 1 \end{pmatrix}$ are eigenvectors of **A**

corresponding to the eigenvalues $\lambda_1 = 1$ and $\lambda_2 = 4$ respectively.

Exercise 5.5

1 Find the eigenvalues of these matrices. For each eigenvalue, find a corresponding eigenvector of the matrix.

a $\mathbf{A}=\begin{pmatrix}1 & 3\\3 & 1\end{pmatrix}$ b $\mathbf{B}=\begin{pmatrix}3 & 2\\4 & 1\end{pmatrix}$ c $\mathbf{C}=\begin{pmatrix}2 & -1\\-4 & 5\end{pmatrix}$

2 $\mathbf{Q}=\begin{pmatrix}4 & 7\\1 & k\end{pmatrix}$, where k is a constant. It is given that $\mathbf{v}=\begin{pmatrix}1\\-1\end{pmatrix}$ is an eigenvector of $\mathbf{Q}$ corresponding to the eigenvalue λ.

a Starting with the equation $\mathbf{Qv}=\lambda\mathbf{v}$, find the value of λ.

b Hence show that $k=-2$

c Find the other eigenvalue, and a corresponding eigenvector, of $\mathbf{Q}$.

3 $\mathbf{A}=\begin{pmatrix}4 & 6\\1 & -1\end{pmatrix}$

a Find the eigenvalues of $\mathbf{A}$.

b Verify that

i the sum of these eigenvalues equals the sum of the elements on the main diagonal of $\mathbf{A}$.

ii the product of these eigenvalues equals det $\mathbf{A}$.

These results are generally true. You can use them to check that your eigenvalues are correct.

4 $\mathbf{A}=\begin{pmatrix}4 & 2\\2 & 1\end{pmatrix}$

a Find the eigenvalues λ_1 and λ_2 of $\mathbf{A}$, where $\lambda_1<\lambda_2$.

b Find two non-parallel eigenvectors of $\mathbf{A}$ and show that these vectors are perpendicular.

Refer to C4 for perpendicular vectors.

5 A line which is mapped to itself under a transformation T represented by a matrix $\mathbf{M}$ is called an invariant line of T.

The matrix $\mathbf{M} = \begin{pmatrix} -1 & 2 \\ 4 & 1 \end{pmatrix}$ represents the transformation T.

You may be asked a question about invariant lines in the exam.

a By finding its image under T, show that the line l with equation $y = 2x$ is an invariant line of T.

b Hence write down an eigenvalue and corresponding eigenvector of $\mathbf{M}$.

c i Find the other eigenvalue, and a corresponding eigenvector, of $\mathbf{M}$.

ii Hence write down a cartesian equation of another invariant line of T which passes through the origin.

6 Find cartesian equations for the invariant lines through the origin under the transformations represented by these matrices.

a $\begin{pmatrix} 6 & 1 \\ -2 & 3 \end{pmatrix}$ b $\begin{pmatrix} 0 & 2 \\ 1 & -\frac{1}{6} \end{pmatrix}$

Find the eigenvectors of each matrix – see question 5.

7 $\mathbf{A} = \begin{pmatrix} a & 2 \\ 3 & 5 \end{pmatrix}$, where a is a constant.

Given that 3 is an eigenvalue of $\mathbf{A}$

a find the value of a

b find an eigenvector of $\mathbf{A}$ corresponding to the eigenvalue 3.

c Find the other eigenvalue of $\mathbf{A}$.

8 $\mathbf{M} = \begin{pmatrix} 4 & 4 \\ p & q \end{pmatrix}$ where p and q are constants.

Given that $\mathbf{v}_1 = \begin{pmatrix} 1 \\ -2 \end{pmatrix}$ and $\mathbf{v}_2 = \begin{pmatrix} 4 \\ 1 \end{pmatrix}$ are eigenvectors of $\mathbf{M}$

a find the eigenvalues of $\mathbf{M}$

b find the value of p and the value of q.

If $\mathbf{N} = \mathbf{M}^{-1}$

c verify that $\mathbf{v}_1$ and $\mathbf{v}_2$ are eigenvectors of $\mathbf{N}$ and state the eigenvalue corresponding to each of these eigenvectors of $\mathbf{N}$.

Eigenvalues and eigenvectors of a 3 × 3 matrix

You can extend the method shown in Section 5.5 to find eigenvalues and eigenvectors of a 3 × 3 matrix.

For a 3 × 3 matrix, the characteristic equation will be a **cubic** in λ.

The eigenvalues of the matrix **A** are the roots of the equation

$$|\mathbf{A} - \lambda\mathbf{I}| = 0$$

where **I** is the 3 × 3 identity matrix.

EXAMPLE 1

$$\mathbf{A} = \begin{pmatrix} 3 & 2 & 0 \\ 1 & 0 & 2 \\ 1 & 1 & 1 \end{pmatrix}$$

a Find the eigenvalues of **A**.

b Hence find an eigenvector corresponding to the greatest eigenvalue of **A**.

---

a Solve the characteristic equation $|\mathbf{A} - \lambda\mathbf{I}| = 0$:

$$\mathbf{A} - \lambda\mathbf{I} = \begin{pmatrix} 3 & 2 & 0 \\ 1 & 0 & 2 \\ 1 & 1 & 1 \end{pmatrix} - \begin{pmatrix} \lambda & 0 & 0 \\ 0 & \lambda & 0 \\ 0 & 0 & \lambda \end{pmatrix} = \begin{pmatrix} 3-\lambda & 2 & 0 \\ 1 & -\lambda & 2 \\ 1 & 1 & 1-\lambda \end{pmatrix}$$

$$\begin{vmatrix} 3-\lambda & 2 & 0 \\ 1 & -\lambda & 2 \\ 1 & 1 & 1-\lambda \end{vmatrix} = 0$$

so $(3-\lambda)\begin{vmatrix} -\lambda & 2 \\ 1 & 1-\lambda \end{vmatrix} - 2\begin{vmatrix} 1 & 2 \\ 1 & 1-\lambda \end{vmatrix} = 0$

Make use of the zero element. Expand along the first row.

so $(3-\lambda)\,[-\lambda\,(1-\lambda) - 2] - 2\,((1-\lambda) - 2) = 0$

Hence $(3-\lambda)\,(\lambda^2 - \lambda - 2) + 2(\lambda + 1) = 0$

$(3-\lambda)\,(\lambda + 1)\,(\lambda - 2) + 2\,(\lambda + 1) = 0$

$(\lambda + 1)\,[(3-\lambda)\,(\lambda - 2) + 2] = 0$

Where possible, look for common factors rather than expand brackets. E.g. $\lambda^2 - \lambda - 2 \equiv (\lambda + 1)(\lambda - 2)$

Hence $(\lambda + 1)\,(1-\lambda)\,(\lambda - 4) = 0$

$(3-\lambda)(\lambda-2) + 2 \equiv -\lambda^2 + 5\lambda - 4 \equiv (1-\lambda)(\lambda - 4)$

So the eigenvalues of **A** are $\lambda_1 = -1$, $\lambda_2 = 1$ and $\lambda_3 = 4$

b The greatest eigenvalue of **A** is $\lambda_3 = 4$

For $\lambda_3 = 4$, $\mathbf{Av} = \lambda\mathbf{v}$ means $\begin{pmatrix} 3 & 2 & 0 \\ 1 & 0 & 2 \\ 1 & 1 & 1 \end{pmatrix}\begin{pmatrix} x \\ y \\ z \end{pmatrix} = 4\begin{pmatrix} x \\ y \\ z \end{pmatrix}$

Equate top components: $3x + 2y = 4x$ so $2y = x$

Equate middle components: $x + 2z = 4y$ so $z = y$

Using the relationship $2y = x$

Hence $\mathbf{v} = \begin{pmatrix} x \\ y \\ z \end{pmatrix} = \begin{pmatrix} 2y \\ y \\ y \end{pmatrix}$ So $\begin{pmatrix} 2 \\ 1 \\ 1 \end{pmatrix}$ is an eigenvector corresponding to $\lambda_3 = 4$

Exercise 5.6

1 Find the eigenvalues of these matrices. For each eigenvalue, find a corresponding eigenvector of the matrix, giving components as integers.

a $\mathbf{A}=\begin{pmatrix}1&0&1\\0&2&2\\0&1&1\end{pmatrix}$ **b** $\mathbf{B}=\begin{pmatrix}1&2&3\\2&1&1\\0&0&1\end{pmatrix}$

c $\mathbf{C}=\begin{pmatrix}2&3&3\\2&1&2\\1&0&2\end{pmatrix}$ **d** $\mathbf{D}=\begin{pmatrix}1&-3&-3\\0&2&4\\-1&1&-1\end{pmatrix}$

2 $\mathbf{A}=\begin{pmatrix}2&0&0\\0&1&3\\0&3&1\end{pmatrix}$

a Find the eigenvalues of **A**.

b Find an eigenvector corresponding to each eigenvalue of **A**.

c Show that the eigenvectors found in part **b** are pairwise perpendicular.

In **c**, consider the three possible pairings.

3 $\mathbf{A}=\begin{pmatrix}2&0&2\\1&2&0\\0&4&2\end{pmatrix}$

a Show that **A** has exactly one eigenvalue.

b Find two unit vectors, each of which is an eigenvector of **A**.

4 $\mathbf{A}=\begin{pmatrix}7&-4&4\\4&-1&2\\-4&4&-3\end{pmatrix}$

a Verify that $\begin{pmatrix}1\\1\\0\end{pmatrix}$ is an eigenvector of **A** and state the eigenvalue, λ_1, to which this eigenvector corresponds.

λ_2 is an eigenvalue of **A** with corresponding eigenvector $\begin{pmatrix}1\\0\\k\end{pmatrix}$, where k is a constant.

b Show that $k=-2$ and find the value of λ_2

Given further that 1 is an eigenvalue of **A**

c find an eigenvector of **A** corresponding to this eigenvalue.

FP3

5 $\mathbf{P} = \begin{pmatrix} 1 & 1 & -2 \\ 2 & 3 & 0 \\ 1 & 1 & 1 \end{pmatrix}$. It is given that 3 is an eigenvalue of **P**.

a Find an eigenvector of **P** corresponding to this eigenvalue.

b Show that **P** has exactly one other eigenvalue and find a corresponding eigenvector. Express your answer as a unit vector.

6 $\mathbf{A} = \begin{pmatrix} -1 & 2 & -2 \\ 0 & 0 & 2 \\ 1 & a & 4 \end{pmatrix}$, where a is a constant. It is given that $\begin{pmatrix} 2 \\ 1 \\ 0 \end{pmatrix}$ is an eigenvector of **A**.

a Show that $a = -2$

b Find two non-parallel eigenvectors of **A**, giving each answer in the form $\begin{pmatrix} p \\ q \\ 1 \end{pmatrix}$ for integers p and q.

c Find the acute angle, in degrees, between these two eigenvectors.

7 $\mathbf{Q} = \begin{pmatrix} 4 & -3 & 3 \\ 2 & -3 & 2 \\ -4 & 2 & -3 \end{pmatrix}$

a Show that an eigenvalue λ of **Q** satisfies the equation

$$\lambda^3 + 2\lambda^2 - \lambda - 2 = 0$$

b Hence find an eigenvector of **Q** corresponding to the smallest eigenvalue of **Q**.

8 Find the eigenvalues and corresponding eigenvectors of these matrices.

a $\mathbf{A} = \begin{pmatrix} 4 & 1 & -3 \\ 1 & 4 & -3 \\ 1 & 5 & -4 \end{pmatrix}$

b $\mathbf{B} = \begin{pmatrix} 9 & 10 & -3 \\ -5 & -6 & 3 \\ 3 & 6 & -1 \end{pmatrix}$

9 $\mathbf{A} = \begin{pmatrix} 3 & 1 & -1 \\ -1 & 1 & 1 \\ 1 & 1 & 1 \end{pmatrix}$

Given that 1 is an eigenvalue of **A**

a find an eigenvector of **A** corresponding to this eigenvalue

b show that **A** has exactly one other eigenvalue, λ, and state its value.

$\mathbf{v} = \begin{pmatrix} x \\ y \\ z \end{pmatrix}$ is an eigenvector of **A** corresponding to λ.

c Show that $z = x + y$ and hence find two non-parallel eigenvectors of **A** corresponding to λ.

10 $\mathbf{M} = \begin{pmatrix} 1 & -4 & 4 \\ -3 & 0 & 6 \\ -1 & 1 & 5 \end{pmatrix}$

Given that 3 is an eigenvalue of **M**

a find the other two eigenvalues of **M**

b find an eigenvector corresponding to each eigenvalue of **M**.

(λ - 3) is a factor of the characteristic equation.

Relative to the origin O, points P and Q have coordinates $P(1, p, 0)$ and $Q(q, 1, 1)$, where p and q are constants. P and Q have position vectors **p** and **q**, respectively.

Given that **p** and **q** are eigenvectors of **M**

c state the value of p and the value of q

d show that triangle OPQ has area $\frac{1}{2}\sqrt{3}$ square units

e hence find the area of the image, under **M**, of this triangle. Give your answer in simplified surd form.

11 $\mathbf{M} = \begin{pmatrix} 0 & 3 & 6 \\ -2 & 5 & -2 \\ 4 & -4 & -2 \end{pmatrix}$

a Find the eigenvalues of **A**.

The line with vector equation vector $\mathbf{r} = t\begin{pmatrix} a \\ 2 \\ b \end{pmatrix}, t \in \mathbb{R}$ where

a and b are constants and $b \neq 0$, is invariant under the transformation represented by **A**.

b Find the value of a and the value of b.

5.7 Special types of matrices

A diagonal matrix is a square matrix in which elements not on the main diagonal are zero.

E.g. $\begin{pmatrix} 2 & 0 \\ 0 & 3 \end{pmatrix}$ and $\begin{pmatrix} 3 & 0 & 0 \\ 0 & 0 & 0 \\ 0 & 0 & -1 \end{pmatrix}$ are diagonal matrices.

Elements on the main diagonal may be zero.

A square matrix $\mathbf{A}$ is symmetric if $\mathbf{A}^T = \mathbf{A}$

E.g. $\mathbf{A} = \begin{pmatrix} 3 & 4 & 1 \\ 4 & 2 & 0 \\ 1 & 0 & 1 \end{pmatrix}$ is a symmetric matrix.

A^T is the transpose of A. Refer to Section 5.1.

A matrix is orthogonal if its columns are unit vectors which are pairwise perpendicular.

$\begin{pmatrix} 1 & 0 & 0 \\ 0 & 0 & 1 \\ 0 & -1 & 0 \end{pmatrix}$ is a simple example of an orthogonal matrix.

The column vectors $\mathbf{v}_1 = \begin{pmatrix} 1 \\ 0 \\ 0 \end{pmatrix}$, $\mathbf{v}_2 = \begin{pmatrix} 0 \\ 0 \\ -1 \end{pmatrix}$ and $\mathbf{v}_3 = \begin{pmatrix} 0 \\ 1 \\ 0 \end{pmatrix}$ of this matrix are unit vectors, and are pairwise perpendicular i.e. $\mathbf{v}_i \cdot \mathbf{v}_j = 0$ for any pair of vectors $\mathbf{v}_i, \mathbf{v}_j, i \neq j$

E.g. $\mathbf{v}_1.\mathbf{v}_2 = \begin{pmatrix} 1 \\ 0 \\ 0 \end{pmatrix} . \begin{pmatrix} 0 \\ 0 \\ -1 \end{pmatrix}$

$= 1 \times 0 + 0 \times 0 + 0 \times (-1)$

$= 0$

so $\mathbf{v}_1$ and $\mathbf{v}_2$ are perpendicular. Refer to C4.

EXAMPLE 1

Given that $\mathbf{A} = \begin{pmatrix} \frac{1}{\sqrt{2}} & 0 & -\frac{1}{\sqrt{2}} \\ \frac{1}{\sqrt{2}} & 0 & \frac{1}{\sqrt{2}} \\ 0 & 1 & 0 \end{pmatrix}$, show that

a $\mathbf{A}$ is an orthogonal matrix

b $\mathbf{A}^{-1} = \mathbf{A}^T$

a Calculate 3 pairs of scalar products:

If $\mathbf{v}_1 = \begin{pmatrix} \frac{1}{\sqrt{2}} \\ \frac{1}{\sqrt{2}} \\ 0 \end{pmatrix}$, $\mathbf{v}_2 = \begin{pmatrix} 0 \\ 0 \\ 1 \end{pmatrix}$ and $\mathbf{v}_3 = \begin{pmatrix} -\frac{1}{\sqrt{2}} \\ \frac{1}{\sqrt{2}} \\ 0 \end{pmatrix}$ then

$\mathbf{v}_1 \cdot \mathbf{v}_2 = 0 \quad \mathbf{v}_2 \cdot \mathbf{v}_3 = 0 \quad$ and $\quad \mathbf{v}_1 \cdot \mathbf{v}_3 = 0$

Hence the column vectors of **A** are pairwise perpendicular.

E.g. $\mathbf{v}_1 \cdot \mathbf{v}_3 = \begin{pmatrix} \frac{1}{\sqrt{2}} \\ \frac{1}{\sqrt{2}} \\ 0 \end{pmatrix} \cdot \begin{pmatrix} -\frac{1}{\sqrt{2}} \\ \frac{1}{\sqrt{2}} \\ 0 \end{pmatrix}$

$= -\frac{1}{2} + \frac{1}{2} + 0$

$= 0$

EXAMPLE 1 (CONT.)

Calculate the magnitude of each column vector:

$$\mathbf{v}_1 = \begin{pmatrix} \frac{1}{\sqrt{2}} \\ \frac{1}{\sqrt{2}} \\ 0 \end{pmatrix} \text{ so } |\mathbf{v}_1| = \sqrt{\tfrac{1}{2}+\tfrac{1}{2}+0} = 1 \text{ so } \mathbf{v}_1 \text{ is a unit vector.}$$

Similarly $|\mathbf{v}_2| = 1$ and $|\mathbf{v}_3| = 1$

So the columns of **A** are unit vectors which are pairwise perpendicular.
Therefore **A** is an orthogonal matrix.

b Calculate $A^T A$:

$$\mathbf{A} = \begin{pmatrix} \frac{1}{\sqrt{2}} & 0 & -\frac{1}{\sqrt{2}} \\ \frac{1}{\sqrt{2}} & 0 & \frac{1}{\sqrt{2}} \\ 0 & 1 & 0 \end{pmatrix} \quad \text{so} \quad \mathbf{A}^T = \begin{pmatrix} \frac{1}{\sqrt{2}} & \frac{1}{\sqrt{2}} & 0 \\ 0 & 0 & 1 \\ -\frac{1}{\sqrt{2}} & \frac{1}{\sqrt{2}} & 0 \end{pmatrix}$$

$$\text{Hence } \mathbf{A}^T\mathbf{A} = \begin{pmatrix} \frac{1}{\sqrt{2}} & \frac{1}{\sqrt{2}} & 0 \\ 0 & 0 & 1 \\ -\frac{1}{\sqrt{2}} & \frac{1}{\sqrt{2}} & 0 \end{pmatrix} \begin{pmatrix} \frac{1}{\sqrt{2}} & 0 & -\frac{1}{\sqrt{2}} \\ \frac{1}{\sqrt{2}} & 0 & \frac{1}{\sqrt{2}} \\ 0 & 1 & 0 \end{pmatrix}$$

$$= \begin{pmatrix} \frac{1}{2}+\frac{1}{2} & 0 & -\frac{1}{2}+\frac{1}{2} \\ 0 & 1 & 0 \\ -\frac{1}{2}+\frac{1}{2} & 0 & \frac{1}{2}+\frac{1}{2} \end{pmatrix} = \begin{pmatrix} 1 & 0 & 0 \\ 0 & 1 & 0 \\ 0 & 0 & 1 \end{pmatrix}$$

$\mathbf{A}^T\mathbf{A} = \mathbf{I}$ and so $\mathbf{A}^{-1} = \mathbf{A}^T$, as required.

If $A^T A = I$ then A^T must be the inverse of A i.e. $A^{-T} = A^T$

In 3-D a general rotation matrix can be written in terms of 3 angles, θ_1, θ_2, θ_3 as

$$R = \begin{pmatrix} c_2 & -s_2 s_3 & -s_2 c_3 \\ -s_1 s_2 & c_1 c_3 - s_1 c_2 s_3 & -c_1 s_3 - s_1 c_2 c_3 \\ c_1 s_2 & s_1 c_3 + c_1 c_2 s_3 & -s_1 s_3 + c_1 c_2 c_3 \end{pmatrix}$$

where $s_1 = \sin\theta_1$, $c_3 = \cos\theta_3$ etc.
Show that R is orthogonal.

If **A** is an orthogonal matrix then $\mathbf{A}^{-1} = \mathbf{A}^T$

EXAMPLE 2

It is given that the vectors $\mathbf{v}_1 = \begin{pmatrix} 2 \\ 1 \\ 2 \end{pmatrix}$, $\mathbf{v}_2 = \begin{pmatrix} 1 \\ 0 \\ -1 \end{pmatrix}$ and $\mathbf{v}_3 = \begin{pmatrix} 1 \\ -4 \\ 1 \end{pmatrix}$ are pairwise perpendicular.

Use these vectors to find an orthogonal matrix.

The matrix **A** whose columns are unit vectors $\hat{\mathbf{v}}_1$, $\hat{\mathbf{v}}_2$ and $\hat{\mathbf{v}}_3$, parallel to $\mathbf{v}_1$, $\mathbf{v}_2$ and $\mathbf{v}_3$, respectively, will be orthogonal.

$$\mathbf{v}_1 = \begin{pmatrix} 2 \\ 1 \\ 2 \end{pmatrix} \quad \text{so} \quad |\mathbf{v}_1| = \sqrt{4+1+4} = 3 \quad \text{so } \hat{\mathbf{v}}_1 = \begin{pmatrix} \frac{2}{3} \\ \frac{1}{3} \\ \frac{2}{3} \end{pmatrix}$$

A unit vector has magnitude 1 unit. Refer to C4.

FP3

EXAMPLE 2 (CONT.)

Similarly, $\hat{\mathbf{v}}_2 = \begin{pmatrix} \frac{1}{\sqrt{2}} \\ 0 \\ -\frac{1}{\sqrt{2}} \end{pmatrix}$ and $\hat{\mathbf{v}}_3 = \begin{pmatrix} \frac{1}{3\sqrt{2}} \\ -\frac{4}{3\sqrt{2}} \\ \frac{1}{3\sqrt{2}} \end{pmatrix}$

So $\begin{pmatrix} \frac{2}{3} & \frac{1}{\sqrt{2}} & \frac{1}{3\sqrt{2}} \\ \frac{1}{3} & 0 & -\frac{4}{3\sqrt{2}} \\ \frac{2}{3} & -\frac{1}{\sqrt{2}} & \frac{1}{3\sqrt{2}} \end{pmatrix}$ is an orthogonal matrix.

E.g. $|\mathbf{v}_3| = \sqrt{18}$ so the top component of $\hat{\mathbf{v}}_3$ is $\frac{1}{\sqrt{18}}$, i.e. $\frac{1}{3\sqrt{2}}$

Given a non-zero vector $\mathbf{v}$, a normalised vector is the unit vector $\hat{\mathbf{v}} = \frac{1}{|\mathbf{v}|}\mathbf{v}$

Exercise 5.7

1 Classify these matrices as diagonal, symmetric and/or orthogonal.

a $\begin{pmatrix} 1 & 0 \\ 0 & 0 \end{pmatrix}$ **b** $\begin{pmatrix} 0 & 0 & 1 \\ 0 & -1 & 0 \\ 1 & 0 & 0 \end{pmatrix}$ **c** $\begin{pmatrix} \frac{1}{\sqrt{2}} & -\frac{1}{\sqrt{2}} \\ -\frac{1}{\sqrt{2}} & \frac{1}{\sqrt{2}} \end{pmatrix}$

2 Normalise (that is, find $\hat{\mathbf{v}}$) for these vectors $\mathbf{v}$. Give components in simplified surd form where appropriate.

a $\mathbf{v} = \begin{pmatrix} -2 \\ 1 \\ 2 \end{pmatrix}$ **b** $\mathbf{v} = \begin{pmatrix} \sqrt{2} \\ \sqrt{3} \\ 2 \end{pmatrix}$ **c** $\mathbf{v} = \begin{pmatrix} \sqrt{2} \\ 4 \\ 0 \end{pmatrix}$ **d** $\mathbf{v} = \begin{pmatrix} \sqrt{2} \\ 3 \\ -1 \end{pmatrix}$

3 $\mathbf{A} = \begin{pmatrix} 2 & 1 & a \\ b & 0 & c \\ 3 & -1 & 3 \end{pmatrix}$ for constants a, b and c. Given that $\mathbf{A}^2$ is a diagonal matrix

a show that $a = 2$ and find the value of b and c.

b find $\mathbf{A}^2$

c hence, or otherwise, find $\mathbf{A}^{-1}$

4 Show that these matrices are orthogonal.

a $\mathrm{A} = \frac{1}{7}\begin{pmatrix} 2 & 6 & -3 \\ 3 & 2 & 6 \\ 6 & -3 & -2 \end{pmatrix}$ **b** $\mathbf{B} = \begin{pmatrix} \frac{\sqrt{5}}{3} & \frac{\sqrt{15}}{6} & \frac{1}{6} \\ \frac{1}{3} & -\frac{\sqrt{3}}{3} & \frac{2\sqrt{5}}{6} \\ \frac{\sqrt{3}}{3} & -\frac{1}{2} & -\frac{\sqrt{15}}{6} \end{pmatrix}$

5 **a** Show that the vectors $\mathbf{v}_1 = \begin{pmatrix} \sqrt{3} \\ 0 \\ 1 \end{pmatrix}$, $\mathbf{v}_2 = \begin{pmatrix} \sqrt{2} \\ 4 \\ -\sqrt{6} \end{pmatrix}$ and $\mathbf{v}_3 = \begin{pmatrix} 1 \\ -\sqrt{2} \\ -\sqrt{3} \end{pmatrix}$ are pairwise perpendicular.

b Use these vectors to find an orthogonal matrix. Where appropriate, give elements in simplified surd form.

6 The 2×2 matrices $\mathbf{A} = \begin{pmatrix} 1 & 4 \\ 2 & -1 \end{pmatrix}$ and $\mathbf{B} = \begin{pmatrix} a & b \\ c & d \end{pmatrix}$ are such that

$\mathbf{A} + \mathbf{B}$ is a diagonal matrix.

a Show that $b = -4$ and that $c = -2$

Given further that $\mathbf{AB}$ is a diagonal matrix

b find the value of a and the value of d.

Transformations S and T are represented by matrices $\mathbf{A}$ and $\mathbf{B}$ respectively.

c Give a complete description of the transformation T followed by S in terms of a rotation about O and an enlargement centre O.

7 $\mathbf{A} = \begin{pmatrix} \frac{1}{\sqrt{3}} & \frac{1}{\sqrt{2}} & q \\ -\frac{1}{\sqrt{3}} & 0 & r \\ -\frac{1}{\sqrt{3}} & p & s \end{pmatrix}$, where p, q, r and s are constants.

Given that $\mathbf{A}$ is an orthogonal matrix

a show that $p = \frac{1}{\sqrt{2}}$ **b** $s = -q$

c Find the possible values of q, r and s. Give answers in simplified surd form.

8 **a** If $\mathbf{A}$ and $\mathbf{B}$ are two symmetric matrices, prove that $\mathbf{AB}$ is symmetric if and only if $\mathbf{AB} = \mathbf{BA}$

Consider $(\mathbf{AB})^{\mathrm{T}}$

b Give an example of two 2×2 symmetric matrices $\mathbf{A}$ and $\mathbf{B}$ for which $\mathbf{AB}$ is not symmetric.

9 $\mathbf{A} = \begin{pmatrix} a & b \\ c & d \end{pmatrix}$ is an orthogonal matrix.

a Prove that $\mathbf{A}^{-1} = \mathbf{A}^{\mathrm{T}}$

b Show further that $a^2 = d^2$ and that $b^2 = c^2$. State the possible values of det $\mathbf{A}$.

FP3

5.8 Diagonalising a 3 × 3 matrix

If **A** is a symmetric matrix with eigenvalues $\lambda_1, \lambda_2, \lambda_3$, and corresponding normalised eigenvectors $\hat{\mathbf{v}}_1, \hat{\mathbf{v}}_2, \hat{\mathbf{v}}_3$
then $\mathbf{P}^T\mathbf{A}\mathbf{P} = \mathbf{D}$

where $\mathbf{D} = \begin{pmatrix} \lambda_1 & 0 & 0 \\ 0 & \lambda_2 & 0 \\ 0 & 0 & \lambda_3 \end{pmatrix}$ and **P** is the orthogonal matrix whose columns are the vectors $\hat{\mathbf{v}}_1, \hat{\mathbf{v}}_2, \hat{\mathbf{v}}_3$ taken in that order.

Normalised vectors have unit length.
The process of finding **P** and **D** is called **diagonalisation**.
The matrix **P diagonalises A**. Every symmetric matrix with real elements can be diagonalised.

EXAMPLE 1

$\mathbf{A} = \begin{pmatrix} 2 & 1 & 0 \\ 1 & 3 & -1 \\ 0 & -1 & 2 \end{pmatrix}$. The eigenvalues of **A** are $\lambda_1 = 1, \lambda_2 = 2$ and $\lambda_3 = 4$. Eigenvectors of **A** corresponding to these eigenvalues are $\mathbf{v}_1 = \begin{pmatrix} -1 \\ 1 \\ 1 \end{pmatrix}, \mathbf{v}_2 = \begin{pmatrix} 1 \\ 0 \\ 1 \end{pmatrix}$ and $\mathbf{v}_3 = \begin{pmatrix} 1 \\ 2 \\ -1 \end{pmatrix}$, respectively.

Find an orthogonal matrix **P** and a diagonal matrix **D** such that $\mathbf{P}^T\mathbf{A}\mathbf{P} = \mathbf{D}$

Normalise the given eigenvectors:

$$\hat{\mathbf{v}}_1 = \begin{pmatrix} -\frac{1}{\sqrt{3}} \\ \frac{1}{\sqrt{3}} \\ \frac{1}{\sqrt{3}} \end{pmatrix} \qquad \hat{\mathbf{v}}_2 = \begin{pmatrix} \frac{1}{\sqrt{2}} \\ 0 \\ \frac{1}{\sqrt{2}} \end{pmatrix} \qquad \hat{\mathbf{v}}_3 = \begin{pmatrix} \frac{1}{\sqrt{6}} \\ \frac{2}{\sqrt{6}} \\ -\frac{1}{\sqrt{6}} \end{pmatrix}$$

$|\mathbf{v}_1| = \sqrt{1+1+1} = \sqrt{3}$

$|\mathbf{v}_2| = \sqrt{1+0+1} = \sqrt{2}$

$|\mathbf{v}_3| = \sqrt{1+4+1} = \sqrt{6}$

Form suitable matrices **D** and **P**:

$$\mathbf{D} = \begin{pmatrix} 1 & 0 & 0 \\ 0 & 2 & 0 \\ 0 & 0 & 4 \end{pmatrix} \quad \text{and} \quad \mathbf{P} = \begin{pmatrix} -\frac{1}{\sqrt{3}} & \frac{1}{\sqrt{2}} & \frac{1}{\sqrt{6}} \\ \frac{1}{\sqrt{3}} & 0 & \frac{2}{\sqrt{6}} \\ \frac{1}{\sqrt{3}} & \frac{1}{\sqrt{2}} & -\frac{1}{\sqrt{6}} \end{pmatrix}$$

Matrix theory guarantees that
i **P** is an orthogonal matrix
ii $\mathbf{P}^T\mathbf{A}\mathbf{P} = \mathbf{D}$
Unless asked to, you need not verify either of these properties.

Note that if, instead, **D** is taken to be $\begin{pmatrix} 2 & 0 & 0 \\ 0 & 4 & 0 \\ 0 & 0 & 1 \end{pmatrix}$ then the required matrix **P** which diagonalises **A** is

$$\mathbf{P} = \begin{pmatrix} \frac{1}{\sqrt{2}} & \frac{1}{\sqrt{6}} & -\frac{1}{\sqrt{3}} \\ 0 & \frac{2}{\sqrt{6}} & \frac{1}{\sqrt{3}} \\ \frac{1}{\sqrt{2}} & -\frac{1}{\sqrt{6}} & \frac{1}{\sqrt{3}} \end{pmatrix}$$

For the method to work, the columns of **P** must correspond to those of **D**.

Exercise 5.8

1 $\mathbf{A}=\begin{pmatrix}1 & 2 & 0\\ 2 & 3 & -2\\ 0 & -2 & 1\end{pmatrix}$

The vectors $\mathbf{v}_1=\begin{pmatrix}1\\0\\1\end{pmatrix}$, $\mathbf{v}_2=\begin{pmatrix}-1\\1\\1\end{pmatrix}$ and $\mathbf{v}_3=\begin{pmatrix}1\\2\\-1\end{pmatrix}$ are eigenvectors of $\mathbf{A}$ corresponding to the eigenvalues λ_1, λ_2 and λ_3, respectively.

a Show that the vectors $\mathbf{v}_1$, $\mathbf{v}_2$ and $\mathbf{v}_3$ are pairwise perpendicular.

b Find each of the values of λ_1, λ_2 and λ_3

c Hence find an orthogonal matrix $\mathbf{P}$ and a diagonal matrix $\mathbf{D}$ such that $\mathbf{P}^{\mathrm{T}}\mathbf{AP}=\mathbf{D}$

2 $\mathbf{A}=\begin{pmatrix}-1 & 1 & 1\\ 1 & 0 & -2\\ 1 & -2 & 0\end{pmatrix}$. The eigenvalues of $\mathbf{A}$ are $\lambda_1=-3$, $\lambda_2=0$ and $\lambda_3=2$

a Show that $\mathbf{v}_1=\begin{pmatrix}-1\\1\\1\end{pmatrix}$ is an eigenvector corresponding to the eigenvalue $\lambda_1=-3$

b Find an eigenvector corresponding to each of the eigenvalues $\lambda_2=0$ and $\lambda_3=2$

c Hence find an orthogonal matrix $\mathbf{P}$ and a diagonal matrix $\mathbf{D}$ such that $\mathbf{P}^{\mathrm{T}}\mathbf{AP}=\mathbf{D}$.

3 For these matrices $\mathbf{A}$, find an orthogonal matrix $\mathbf{P}$ and a diagonal matrix $\mathbf{D}$ such that $\mathbf{P}^{\mathrm{T}}\mathbf{AP}=\mathbf{D}$

a $\mathbf{A}=\begin{pmatrix}3 & 2 & 0\\ 2 & -1 & 1\\ 0 & 1 & 3\end{pmatrix}$ b $\mathbf{A}=\begin{pmatrix}2 & 1 & 1\\ 1 & 3 & 0\\ 1 & 0 & 3\end{pmatrix}$ c $\mathbf{A}=\begin{pmatrix}2 & 1 & -1\\ 1 & 2 & -1\\ -1 & -1 & 4\end{pmatrix}$

4 $\mathbf{A}=\begin{pmatrix}1 & k & \sqrt{3}\\ k & 3 & k\\ \sqrt{3} & k & -1\end{pmatrix}$, where k is a constant. It is given that $\begin{pmatrix}0\\1\\0\end{pmatrix}$ is an eigenvector of $\mathbf{A}$.

a Show that $k=0$ and find the eigenvalue to which this eigenvector corresponds.

b Find the other eigenvalues of $\mathbf{A}$.

c Find an orthogonal matrix $\mathbf{P}$ and a diagonal matrix $\mathbf{D}$ such that $\mathbf{P}^{\mathrm{T}}\mathbf{AP}=\mathbf{D}$

FP3

5 $\mathbf{A} = \begin{pmatrix} 1 & 0 & -1 \\ 0 & 1 & 0 \\ -1 & 0 & 1 \end{pmatrix}$

a Find a symmetric orthogonal matrix **P** and a diagonal matrix **D** such that $\mathbf{P}^T\mathbf{AP} = \mathbf{D}$

b Without calculating its inverse, show that matrix **P** is self-inverse.

c Hence, or otherwise, find $(\mathbf{PA})^2$

6 $\mathbf{A} = \begin{pmatrix} -1 & 2 & 2 \\ 2 & 0 & p \\ 2 & q & 0 \end{pmatrix}$, where p and q are constants. $\begin{pmatrix} 1 \\ 1 \\ 1 \end{pmatrix}$ is an eigenvector of **A**.

a Find the eigenvalue to which this eigenvector corresponds and show that **A** is a symmetric matrix.

b Find an orthogonal matrix **P** and a diagonal matrix **D** such that $\mathbf{AP} = \mathbf{PD}$

The transformations S and T are represented by the matrices **P** and **D**, respectively.

The image of the vector **u** under S is $\begin{pmatrix} 1 \\ -2 \\ 3 \end{pmatrix}$

c Find the image of **u** under the composite transformation of T followed by S.

7 Find an orthogonal matrix which diagonalises the matrix

a $\mathbf{A} = \begin{pmatrix} 2 & 1 & 1 \\ 1 & 4 & -1 \\ 1 & -1 & 4 \end{pmatrix}$ **b** $\mathbf{B} = \begin{pmatrix} 1 & 3 & -6 \\ 3 & -2 & 3 \\ -6 & 3 & 1 \end{pmatrix}$

8 $\mathbf{A} = \begin{pmatrix} 5 & 1 & -1 \\ 1 & 5 & 1 \\ -1 & 1 & 5 \end{pmatrix}$. $\mathbf{v}_1 = \begin{pmatrix} 1 \\ 1 \\ 0 \end{pmatrix}$ and $\mathbf{v}_2 = \begin{pmatrix} 1 \\ -1 \\ a \end{pmatrix}$, where a is a constant,

are eigenvectors of **A** corresponding to a common eigenvalue λ.

a Show that $\lambda = 6$ and find the value of a.

Given that 3 is also an eigenvalue of **A**

b find an orthogonal matrix **P** and a diagonal matrix **D** such that $\mathbf{P}^T\mathbf{AP} = \mathbf{D}$

FP3

9 $\mathbf{A} = \begin{pmatrix} 0 & 2 & -1 \\ 2 & 1 & 2 \\ -1 & 2 & 4 \end{pmatrix}$

It is given that $\begin{pmatrix} -\sqrt{5} \\ -2 \\ 1 \end{pmatrix}$ is an eigenvector of **A** corresponding to the eigenvalue λ.

a Find the exact value of λ.

b Find an orthogonal matrix **P** which diagonalises **A**. When not exact, give the elements of **P** in simplified surd form.

10 $\mathbf{A} = \begin{pmatrix} 0 & 0 & 0 \\ 0 & 0 & 1 \\ -1 & -2 & 0 \end{pmatrix}$ and $\mathbf{B} = \mathbf{A}^T\mathbf{A}$

a Find matrix **B** and verify that **B** is symmetric.

b Find an orthogonal matrix **P** and a diagonal matrix **D** such that $\mathbf{P}^T\mathbf{B}\mathbf{P} = \mathbf{D}$.

c Hence, or otherwise, find, for this matrix **D**, a matrix **X** such that $\mathbf{X}^T\mathbf{X} = \mathbf{D}$. Give the elements of **X** in simplified surd form.

11 Given that $\mathbf{P}^T\mathbf{A}\mathbf{P} = \mathbf{D}$, where **P** is an orthogonal matrix and **D** a diagonal matrix

a show that $\mathbf{A} = \mathbf{P}\mathbf{D}\mathbf{P}^T$

b deduce that **A** is a symmetric matrix

c prove by induction that $\mathbf{A}^n = \mathbf{P}\mathbf{D}^n\mathbf{P}^T$ for all positive integers n.

For a, use $\mathbf{P}^{-1} = \mathbf{P}^T$

For b, use $(\mathbf{XY})^T = \mathbf{Y}^T\mathbf{X}^T$

12 In this question, **A** is a 3×3 matrix with real elements.

a Show that if $\mathbf{P}^T\mathbf{A}\mathbf{P} = \mathbf{D}$, where **P** is an orthogonal matrix and **D** is a diagonal matrix, then λ is an eigenvalue of **A** if and only if λ is an eigenvalue of **D**.

b Deduce that if **A** is a symmetric matrix and has a unique eigenvalue, λ, then $\mathbf{A} = \lambda\mathbf{I}$, where **I** is the 3×3 identity matrix.

Use the fact that **A** can be diagonalised.

FP3

1 $\mathbf{P} = \begin{pmatrix} x & 1 & -2 \\ 2 & 4 & 2 \\ 3 & x & 0 \end{pmatrix}$, $x \in \mathbb{R}$

a Find the values of x for which $\mathbf{P}$ is singular.

b Find the minimum possible value of det $\mathbf{P}$.

2 The transformation T is represented by the matrix $\mathbf{A} = \begin{pmatrix} 3 & 2 & 4 \\ 0 & 1 & -1 \\ 1 & 0 & 2 \end{pmatrix}$.

The image under T of $\mathbf{v} = \begin{pmatrix} 1 \\ k \\ 1 \end{pmatrix}$, where k is a constant, is parallel to the vector $\begin{pmatrix} 1 \\ -1 \\ 1 \end{pmatrix}$

a Find the value of k.

The transformation S is represented by the matrix $\mathbf{B} = \begin{pmatrix} 1 & 1 & -2 \\ 4 & 3 & 0 \\ 1 & 2 & -1 \end{pmatrix}$

b Find the image of $\mathbf{v}$ under the combined transformation of T followed by S.

3 The transformation T is represented by the matrix $\mathrm{A} = \begin{pmatrix} 6 & 2 \\ -1 & 1 \end{pmatrix}$

The line l has equation $y = 1 - 2x$

a Find the image under T of l. Give your answer as an equation in the form $ay + bx = 8$ where a and b are integers to be stated.

The line l_1 passes through the origin. The image of l_1 under T is a horizontal line.

b Find the equation of l_1.

4 The transformation T is represented by the matrix $\mathbf{P} = \begin{pmatrix} 3 & 4 \\ 2 & 5 \end{pmatrix}$

a Find the eigenvalues of $\mathbf{P}$.

b Find an eigenvector of $\mathbf{P}$ corresponding to each of these eigenvalues.

c Hence write down a cartesian equation for each of the two lines passing through the origin which are invariant under T.

5 $\mathbf{A} = \begin{pmatrix} 1 & 0 & 2 \\ 1 & p & -2 \\ 2 & 0 & -2 \end{pmatrix}$, where p is a constant. It is given that $\begin{pmatrix} 6 \\ -5 \\ -12 \end{pmatrix}$ is an eigenvector of **A**.

a Find the eigenvalue of **A** corresponding to this eigenvector.

b Show that $p = 3$

c Find the other two eigenvalues of **A**.

d Verify that the product of these three eigenvalues is equal to det **A**.

6 $\mathbf{M} = \begin{pmatrix} 3 & 0 & 1 \\ 2 & 1 & 1 \\ 1 & -1 & 2 \end{pmatrix}$

a Show that $\begin{pmatrix} 1 \\ 1 \\ -1 \end{pmatrix}$ is an eigenvector of **A** and write down the eigenvalue to which this eigenvector corresponds.

b Find the other eigenvalues of **A**.

c Find two eigenvectors of **A** which are perpendicular.

7 Given that $\mathbf{A} = \begin{pmatrix} 2 & 2 & 1 \\ 0 & 1 & 2 \\ 3 & 3 & 1 \end{pmatrix}$ and $\mathbf{B} = \begin{pmatrix} 1 & 2 & 1 \\ 3 & 0 & 1 \\ 1 & -1 & 2 \end{pmatrix}$

a find the matrix $\mathbf{BA}^{\mathrm{T}}$

The transformations S and T are represented by the matrices **A** and $\mathbf{B}^{\mathrm{T}}$ respectively.

b Using your answer to part **a**, or otherwise, find the image of the vector $\mathbf{u} = \begin{pmatrix} 2 \\ -1 \\ 0 \end{pmatrix}$ under the combined transformation of T followed by S.

FP3

8 $\mathbf{A}=\begin{pmatrix}4 & -1 & 0\\ -3 & 2 & 1\\ 0 & 0 & 1\end{pmatrix}$

a Show that **A** has exactly two eigenvalues, λ_1 and λ_2, where $\lambda_1 < \lambda_2$

b Find an eigenvector of **A** corresponding to the eigenvalue λ_1

Given that $\mathbf{v}=\begin{pmatrix}1\\ a\\ b\end{pmatrix}$ is an eigenvector of **A** corresponding to the eigenvalue λ_2, where a and b are constants,

c find the value of a and the value of b

d find the image of the vector **v** under the transformation represented by $\mathbf{A}^2$

9 $\mathbf{A}=\begin{pmatrix}3 & 1 & k\\ 2 & 2 & 0\\ 1 & -2 & 1\end{pmatrix}$, where k is a constant, $k < 0$

a Show that **A** is non-singular.

b Find, in terms of k, $\mathbf{A}^{-1}$

The transformation T is represented by **A**. The image of the vector

$\mathbf{v}=\begin{pmatrix}1\\ 0\\ -1\end{pmatrix}$ under T has magnitude $2\sqrt{5}$.

c Find the value of k.

T maps **u** to the vector **v**.

d Show that **u** is a unit vector and state the coordinate axis to which **u** is parallel.

10 $\mathbf{A}=\begin{pmatrix}a & 1 & 2\\ 2 & 1 & -1\\ 2 & 1 & a\end{pmatrix}$, where a is a positive constant.

It is given that det $\mathbf{A} = a + 1$

a Show that $a = 3$

Given that 1 is an eigenvalue of **A**

b find an eigenvector **v** of **A** corresponding to this eigenvalue.

The matrices **B** and **C** are such $\mathbf{CA} = \mathbf{B}$

c Show that $(\mathbf{C} - \mathbf{B})\,\mathbf{v} = \mathbf{0}$, where $\mathbf{0}$ is the zero vector.

d Deduce that $\mathbf{C} - \mathbf{B}$ is a singular matrix.

11 $\mathbf{A} = \begin{pmatrix} 3 & 0 & -1 \\ 0 & 3 & 1 \\ -1 & 1 & 2 \end{pmatrix}$. The eigenvalues of **A** are λ_1, λ_2 and λ_3, where $\lambda_1 < \lambda_2 < \lambda_3$

a Find the values of λ_1, λ_2 and λ_3

b Find an eigenvector of **A** corresponding to λ_3

Given that $\begin{pmatrix} 1 \\ -1 \\ 2 \end{pmatrix}$ and $\begin{pmatrix} 1 \\ 1 \\ 0 \end{pmatrix}$ are eigenvectors of **A** corresponding to λ_1 and λ_2, respectively

c find an orthogonal matrix **P** and a diagonal matrix **D** such that $\mathbf{P}^{\mathrm{T}}\mathbf{AP} = \mathbf{D}$

12 $\mathbf{A} = \begin{pmatrix} 0 & 1 & 2 \\ 1 & -1 & -1 \\ 2 & -1 & 0 \end{pmatrix}$. It is given that $\mathbf{v}_1 = \begin{pmatrix} 1 \\ 2 \\ p \end{pmatrix}$, where p, a non-zero constant, is an eigenvector of **A** corresponding to the eigenvalue λ_1

a Show that $\lambda_1 = 0$ and find the value of p.

Given further that the two other eigenvalues of **A** are 2 and -3

b find an eigenvector of **A** corresponding to each of these eigenvalues

c hence find an orthogonal matrix **P** and a diagonal matrix **D** such that

$$\mathbf{P}^{\mathrm{T}}\mathbf{AP} = \mathbf{D}$$

The transformations S and T are represented by the matrices **P** and **D** respectively, found in part **c**. The vector **u** is mapped to the vector $\mathbf{v}_1$ under S.

d Show that the image of **u** under the transformation T is the zero vector.

13 $\mathbf{P} = \begin{pmatrix} 2 & 1 & 2 \\ 3 & 0 & k \\ k & 1 & 2 \end{pmatrix}$, where k is a constant. It is given that **P** is non-singular.

a Show that $\det \mathbf{P} = k(k-2)$

b Find, in terms of k, an expression for $\mathbf{P}^{-1}$

For a particular value of k, the sum of the elements of $\mathbf{P}^{-1}$ is 2.

c Find this value of k.

d For this value of k

i show that **P** has exactly one real eigenvalue, stating its value
ii find an eigenvector corresponding to this eigenvalue.

FP3

5 Exit

Summary

Refer to

- For 3×3 matrices **A** and **B**, the element in the ith row and jth column of **AB** is the scalar product of the ith row of **A** with the jth column of **B**. 5.1
- Given two 3×3 matrices **A** and **B**, $(\mathbf{AB})^{\mathrm{T}} = \mathbf{B}^{\mathrm{T}}\mathbf{A}^{\mathrm{T}}$
- The matrix **A** represents the linear transformation $T : \mathbb{R}^3 \to \mathbb{R}^3$, where $T(\mathbf{v}) = \mathbf{Av}$
  The vector **Av** is the image of **v** under the transformation T. 5.2
- The transformation represented by **BA** is the transformation represented by **A** followed by the transformation represented by **B**.
- You can use 2×2 determinants to define the determinant of a 3×3 matrix **P**.
  You can calculate det **P** by expanding along any row of **P** or down any column of **P** and using the change of sign matrix. 5.3
- The inverse of a non-singular 3×3 matrix $\mathbf{A} = \begin{pmatrix} a_1 & a_2 & a_3 \\ b_1 & b_2 & b_3 \\ c_1 & c_2 & c_3 \end{pmatrix}$ is

$$\mathbf{A}^{-1} = \frac{1}{\det \mathbf{A}} \begin{pmatrix} A_1 & -B_1 & C_1 \\ -A_2 & B_2 & -C_2 \\ A_3 & -B_3 & C_3 \end{pmatrix}, \text{ where } A_1 = \begin{vmatrix} b_2 & b_3 \\ c_2 & c_3 \end{vmatrix} \text{ etc}$$ 5.4

- If **A** and **B** are non-singular, then **AB** is non-singular and $(\mathbf{AB})^{-1} = \mathbf{B}^{-1}\mathbf{A}^{-1}$
  If the transformation S is represented by the non-singular matrix **A** then the inverse transformation of S is represented by $\mathbf{A}^{-1}$.
- An eigenvector of a matrix **A** is a non-zero vector **v** such that $\mathbf{Av} = \lambda\mathbf{v}$ for some $\lambda \in \mathbb{R}$. λ is an eigenvalue of **A**. 5.5, 5.6
- A diagonal matrix is a square matrix whose elements off the maindiagonal are 0
- A square matrix **A** is symmetric if $\mathbf{A}^{\mathrm{T}} = \mathbf{A}$
- A matrix **P** is orthogonal if its columns are unit vectors which are pairwise perpendicular. In this case, $\mathbf{P}^{-1} = \mathbf{P}^{\mathrm{T}}$
  Every symmetric matrix **A** can be diagonalised that is, there exists an orthogonal matrix **P** and a diagonal matrix **D** such that $\mathbf{P}^{\mathrm{T}}\mathbf{AP} = \mathbf{D}$ 5.7, 5.8

Links

Matrices and determinants grew out of studying how to solve systems of simultaneous linear equations. They now have many applications throughout Mathematics and Physics. For example, they provide a natural language for describing the extraordinary world of quantum mechanics.

The strange multiplication rule for matrices is ideal for representing symmetries and transformations. This is exploited in computer graphics where matrices are used to rotate and manipulate the images found in computer games, films, CAD/CAM systems, etc.

6 Vectors

This chapter will show you how to
- calculate a vector product
- find the equation of a plane
- calculate the area of a plane shape in 3-dimensional space
- calculate the volumes of certain types of solid shapes
- express the equation of a line in vector product or cartesian form
- find the equation of a line where two planes intersect
- calculate the shortest distance from a point to a plane, or between two lines.

See Section 0.5. W
See C4 for revision.

Before you start

You should know how to:

1 Find parallel or perpendicular vectors.
e.g. $\mathbf{u} = 2\mathbf{i} + 3\mathbf{j} - \mathbf{k}$, $\mathbf{v} = 4\mathbf{i} + p\mathbf{j} - q\mathbf{k}$ and $\mathbf{w} = 3\mathbf{i} + \mathbf{j} + r\mathbf{k}$ where p, q and r are constants.
   a Find p and q given that $\mathbf{u}$ and $\mathbf{v}$ are parallel.
   b Find r given that $\mathbf{u}$ and $\mathbf{w}$ are perpendicular.

   a $\mathbf{u}$ and $\mathbf{v}$ are parallel so $\mathbf{v} = \lambda\mathbf{u}$ for $\lambda \in \mathbb{R}$.
   Compare $\mathbf{i}$ components: $4 = 2\lambda$, so $\lambda = 2$
   Hence $p = 6$, $q = -2$
   b $\mathbf{u}$ and $\mathbf{w}$ are perpendicular so $\mathbf{u}.\mathbf{w} = 0$
   so $2 \times 3 + 3 \times 1 + (-1)r = 0$ Hence $r = 9$

2 Find the magnitude of a vector.
e.g. If $\mathbf{a} = 2\mathbf{i} + 4\mathbf{j} - 3\mathbf{k}$ find $|\mathbf{a}|$, giving the answer in simplified surd form.

$$|\mathbf{a}| = \sqrt{2^2 + 4^2 + (-3)^2} = \sqrt{29}$$

3 Find the vector equation of a line.
e.g Find a vector equation for the line l which passes through the points $A(3, 2, 0)$ and $B(1, 4, 1)$.
A direction vector $\mathbf{d}$ of l is $\mathbf{d} = \overrightarrow{AB} = \overrightarrow{OB} - \overrightarrow{OA}$
$\mathbf{d} = (\mathbf{i} + 4\mathbf{j} + \mathbf{k}) - (3\mathbf{i} + 2\mathbf{j}) = -2\mathbf{i} + 2\mathbf{j} + \mathbf{k}$
Hence a vector equation for l is
$\mathbf{r} = (3\mathbf{i} + 2\mathbf{j}) + t(-2\mathbf{i} + 2\mathbf{j} + \mathbf{k})$, $t \in \mathbb{R}$

Check in:

1 $\mathbf{u} = \mathbf{i} + 3\mathbf{j} + 2\mathbf{k}$
   a Given that $\mathbf{v} = 3\mathbf{i} + q\mathbf{j} + 3\mathbf{k}$ is perpendicular to $\mathbf{u}$, find the value of the constant q.
   b Show that any vector parallel to $\mathbf{w} = 4\mathbf{i} - 2\mathbf{j} + \mathbf{k}$ is perpendicular to $\mathbf{u}$.

   The vector $\mathbf{p} = a\mathbf{i} - 2\mathbf{j} + b\mathbf{k}$, for constants a and b is parallel to $\mathbf{u}$.
   c Find the values of a and b.

2 $\mathbf{a} = 3\mathbf{i} - 4\mathbf{j} + 5\mathbf{k}$ and $\mathbf{b} = 2\mathbf{i} - 4\mathbf{j} + 2\mathbf{k}$
Find, in simplified surd form,
   a $|\mathbf{a}|$ b $|\mathbf{b}|$ c $|\mathbf{a} - \mathbf{b}|$

3 The line l_1 passes through the points $A(1, 1, 2)$ and $B(7, -1, 6)$. The line l_2 passes through the point $C(7, 5, -12)$ and is parallel to $\mathbf{d} = 3\mathbf{i} + \mathbf{j} - 4\mathbf{k}$
   a Find vector equations for l_1 and l_2.
   b Find the coordinates of the point P where these lines intersect.
   c Show that l_1 and l_2 are perpendicular.
   d Hence find the shortest distance from C to l_1.

6.1 Vector products

You can define the vector product of two vectors by using a 3×3 determinant.

Refer to Section 5.3 for 3×3 determinants.

Given vectors $\mathbf{a} = a_1\mathbf{i} + a_2\mathbf{j} + a_3\mathbf{k}$ and $\mathbf{b} = b_1\mathbf{i} + b_2\mathbf{j} + b_3\mathbf{k}$, the vector product $\mathbf{a} \times \mathbf{b}$ is

$$\mathbf{a} \times \mathbf{b} = \begin{vmatrix} \mathbf{i} & \mathbf{j} & \mathbf{k} \\ a_1 & a_2 & a_3 \\ b_1 & b_2 & b_3 \end{vmatrix}$$

In component form

$$\mathbf{a} \times \mathbf{b} = (a_2b_3 - a_3b_2)\mathbf{i} - (a_1b_3 - a_3b_1)\mathbf{j} + (a_1b_2 - a_2b_1)\mathbf{k}$$

A vector product is also called a **cross product**.

These results are in the FP3 section of the formula booklet.

$\mathbf{a} \times \mathbf{b}$ is itself a vector. You will see the geometrical significance of this definition in later sections.

EXAMPLE 1

Given that $\mathbf{a} = 2\mathbf{i} + 3\mathbf{j} + \mathbf{k}$ and $\mathbf{b} = 4\mathbf{i} + 2\mathbf{j} + 3\mathbf{k}$

a find the vector product $\mathbf{a} \times \mathbf{b}$

b verify that $\mathbf{b} \times \mathbf{a} = -\mathbf{a} \times \mathbf{b}$

---

a Calculate the appropriate determinant using the components of a and b:

$\mathbf{a} = 2\mathbf{i} + 3\mathbf{j} + \mathbf{k}$ and $\mathbf{b} = 4\mathbf{i} + 2\mathbf{j} + 3\mathbf{k}$ so

$$\mathbf{a} \times \mathbf{b} = \begin{vmatrix} \mathbf{i} & \mathbf{j} & \mathbf{k} \\ 2 & 3 & 1 \\ 4 & 2 & 3 \end{vmatrix}$$

$$= \mathbf{i}(3 \times 3 - 2 \times 1) - \mathbf{j}(2 \times 3 - 4 \times 1) + \mathbf{k}(2 \times 2 - 4 \times 3)$$
$$= 7\mathbf{i} - 2\mathbf{j} - 8\mathbf{k}$$

Expand along the first row, treating the unit vectors **i**, **j** and **k** as constants.

b Calculate the appropriate determinant:

$$\mathbf{b} \times \mathbf{a} = \begin{vmatrix} \mathbf{i} & \mathbf{j} & \mathbf{k} \\ 4 & 2 & 3 \\ 2 & 3 & 1 \end{vmatrix}$$

The second and third rows are the components of **b** and **a**, respectively.

$$= \mathbf{i}(2 \times 1 - 3 \times 3) - \mathbf{j}(4 \times 1 - 2 \times 3) + \mathbf{k}(4 \times 3 - 2 \times 2)$$
$$= -7\mathbf{i} + 2\mathbf{j} + 8\mathbf{k}$$
$$= -(7\mathbf{i} - 2\mathbf{j} - 8\mathbf{k})$$
$$= -\mathbf{a} \times \mathbf{b} \text{ as required.}$$

In general $\mathbf{a} \times \mathbf{b} \neq \mathbf{b} \times \mathbf{a}$

EXAMPLE 2

Show that if **a** and **b** are parallel vectors, then $\mathbf{a} \times \mathbf{b} = \mathbf{0}$

Use the definition of parallel vectors $\mathbf{a} = \lambda\mathbf{b}$, $\lambda \in \mathbb{R}$, $\lambda \neq 0$:

Let $\mathbf{a} = a_1\mathbf{i} + a_2\mathbf{j} + a_3\mathbf{k}$ and $\mathbf{b} = b_1\mathbf{i} + b_2\mathbf{j} + b_3\mathbf{k}$ be parallel vectors.

Then, for some value of λ, $b_1 = \lambda a_1$, $b_2 = \lambda a_2$ and $b_3 = \lambda a_3$

Hence $\mathbf{a} \times \mathbf{b} = \begin{vmatrix} \mathbf{i} & \mathbf{j} & \mathbf{k} \\ a_1 & a_2 & a_3 \\ \lambda a_1 & \lambda a_2 & \lambda a_3 \end{vmatrix}$

$$= \mathbf{i}(\lambda a_2 a_3 - \lambda a_2 a_3) - \mathbf{j}(\lambda a_1 a_3 - \lambda a_1 a_3) + \mathbf{k}(\lambda a_1 a_2 - \lambda a_1 a_2)$$
$$= 0\mathbf{i} + 0\mathbf{j} + 0\mathbf{k}$$

That is, $\mathbf{a} \times \mathbf{b} = \mathbf{0}$

For any vectors **a**, **b** and **c** and scalar t

$\mathbf{b} \times \mathbf{a} = -\mathbf{a} \times \mathbf{b}$

$\mathbf{a} \times (\mathbf{b} + \mathbf{c}) = \mathbf{a} \times \mathbf{b} + \mathbf{a} \times \mathbf{c}$

$t(\mathbf{a} \times \mathbf{b}) = (t\mathbf{a}) \times \mathbf{b} = \mathbf{a} \times (t\mathbf{b})$

$\mathbf{a} \times \mathbf{b} = \mathbf{0}$ precisely when either $\mathbf{a} = \mathbf{0}$, or $\mathbf{b} = \mathbf{0}$, or $\mathbf{a} = \lambda\mathbf{b}$, $\lambda \in \mathbb{R}, \lambda \neq 0$

As with matrices, vector multiplication is not commutative.

$\times$ is distributive over $+$.

FP3

Exercise 6.1

1 Expand a suitable determinant to find $\mathbf{a} \times \mathbf{b}$ for these pairs of vectors.

a $\mathbf{a} = 4\mathbf{i} + \mathbf{j} + 2\mathbf{k}$ and $\mathbf{b} = 6\mathbf{i} + 2\mathbf{j} + \mathbf{k}$

b $\mathbf{a} = 5\mathbf{i} - 2\mathbf{j} + \mathbf{k}$ and $\mathbf{b} = 3\mathbf{i} + 2\mathbf{j}$

c $\mathbf{a} = \mathbf{i} + \mathbf{j} + \mathbf{k}$ and $\mathbf{b} = \frac{1}{2}\mathbf{i} - \mathbf{j} + \frac{3}{2}\mathbf{k}$

d $\mathbf{a} = -2\mathbf{i} + \mathbf{k}$ and $\mathbf{b} = 4\mathbf{j} + 3\mathbf{k}$

2 Given that $\mathbf{a} = 2\mathbf{i} + 3\mathbf{j} + \mathbf{k}$, $\mathbf{b} = \mathbf{i} - 2\mathbf{j} + 2\mathbf{k}$ and $\mathbf{c} = 5\mathbf{i} + 2\mathbf{j} + 3\mathbf{k}$

a find $\mathbf{a} \times \mathbf{b}$ and $\mathbf{a} \times \mathbf{c}$

b find $\mathbf{a} \times (\mathbf{b} + \mathbf{c})$

c verify that $\mathbf{a} \times (\mathbf{b} + \mathbf{c}) = \mathbf{a} \times \mathbf{b} + \mathbf{a} \times \mathbf{c}$

3 The vectors $\mathbf{a} = 6\mathbf{i} - 2\mathbf{j} + 3\mathbf{k}$ and $\mathbf{b} = -2\mathbf{i} + \mathbf{j} + p\mathbf{k}$, where p is a constant, are such that the vector product $\mathbf{a} \times \mathbf{b} = -7\mathbf{i} + q\mathbf{j} + 2\mathbf{k}$, where q is a constant.

a Show that $p = 2$

b Find the value of q

c Find, in component form, the vector $\mathbf{b} \times \frac{1}{2}\mathbf{a}$

4 The vectors $\mathbf{a} = 3\mathbf{i} + p\mathbf{j} - 2\mathbf{k}$ and $\mathbf{b} = 4\mathbf{i} + q\mathbf{j} + 3\mathbf{k}$, where p and q are constants, are such that $\mathbf{a} \times \mathbf{b} = 11\mathbf{i} + r\mathbf{j} - 26\mathbf{k}$, for r a constant.

a Show that $r = -17$

b Find the value of p and the value of q.

5 Given that $\mathbf{c} = \mathbf{a} \times \mathbf{b}$, where $\mathbf{a}$ and $\mathbf{b}$ are any vectors, express these quantities in the form $\lambda\mathbf{c}$, where λ is an integer.

a $\mathbf{a} \times (\mathbf{a} + 2\mathbf{b})$

b $(\mathbf{b} + 2\mathbf{a}) \times (3\mathbf{b} - \mathbf{a})$

c $\mathbf{b} \times (\mathbf{a} + \mathbf{c}) + \mathbf{c} \times \mathbf{b}$

6 Simplify these expressions. Give each answer as the vector product of two vectors.

a $\mathbf{a} \times \mathbf{b} + \mathbf{a} \times \mathbf{c}$

b $\mathbf{a} \times \mathbf{c} + \mathbf{c} \times \mathbf{b}$

c $\mathbf{a} \times \mathbf{b} + \mathbf{a} \times \mathbf{c} + \mathbf{b} \times \mathbf{c}$

For part c use $\mathbf{c} \times \mathbf{c} = 0$

FP3

7 Vectors $\mathbf{a} = \mathbf{i} + 3\mathbf{j} - \mathbf{k}$, $\mathbf{b} = 2\mathbf{i} + 3\mathbf{j} + \mathbf{k}$ and $\mathbf{c} = p\mathbf{i} + q\mathbf{j} + r\mathbf{k}$, where $p, q, r \in \mathbb{R}$, are such that $\mathbf{a} \times \mathbf{c} = -3\mathbf{i} + 6\mathbf{j} + 15\mathbf{k}$ and $\mathbf{b} \times \mathbf{c}$ is parallel to the vector $\mathbf{i} - 2\mathbf{k}$

a Find the components of $\mathbf{c}$.

b Hence, or otherwise, find $\frac{1}{9}(\mathbf{a} - \mathbf{c}) \times (2\mathbf{b} + \mathbf{c})$.

8 Given that $\mathbf{a} = 4\mathbf{i} - 2\mathbf{j} + \mathbf{k}$ and $\mathbf{b} = p\mathbf{i} - 2q\mathbf{j} + q\mathbf{k}$, where $p, q \in \mathbb{R}$

a find an expression for $\mathbf{a} \times \mathbf{b}$ involving p and q

b hence state the value of $(\mathbf{a} \times \mathbf{b}) \times \mathbf{c}$, where $\mathbf{c} = \mathbf{j} + 2\mathbf{k}$.

9 $\mathbf{a}$ and $\mathbf{b}$ are any pair of non-zero, non-parallel vectors and $\mathbf{c}$ is any non-zero vector.

a Show that $\mathbf{a} \times \mathbf{c} = \mathbf{c} \times \mathbf{b}$ precisely when $\mathbf{c}$ is parallel to $(\mathbf{a} + \mathbf{b})$.

b Given that $\mathbf{a} = 2\mathbf{i} + \mathbf{j} + 5\mathbf{k}$ and $\mathbf{b} = 3\mathbf{i} - \mathbf{j} + \mathbf{k}$, give an example of a non-zero vector $\mathbf{c}$ such that $\mathbf{a} \times \mathbf{c} = \mathbf{c} \times \mathbf{b}$

10 The diagram shows a trapezium $ABCD$ in which sides AB and DC are parallel.

$\mathbf{p} = \overrightarrow{AB}$, $\mathbf{q} = \overrightarrow{DA}$ and $\mathbf{r} = \overrightarrow{CA}$

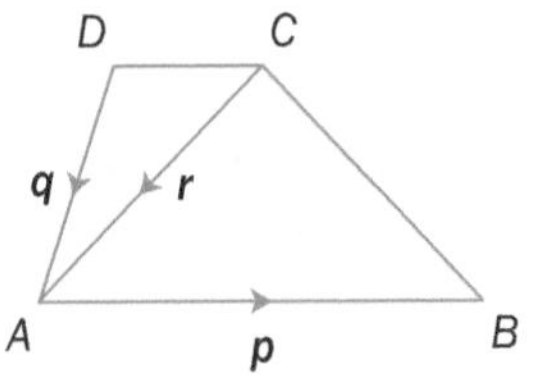

Prove that $\mathbf{p} \times \mathbf{q} = \mathbf{p} \times \mathbf{r}$

Use the result of question 9.

11 The diagram shows a triangle PQR.

$\mathbf{a} = \overrightarrow{PQ}$, $\mathbf{b} = \overrightarrow{QR}$ and $\mathbf{c} = \overrightarrow{QS}$,

where S is *any* point on the line RP.

Prove that $\mathbf{a} \times \mathbf{c} + \mathbf{b} \times \mathbf{a} + \mathbf{b} \times \mathbf{c} = \mathbf{0}$

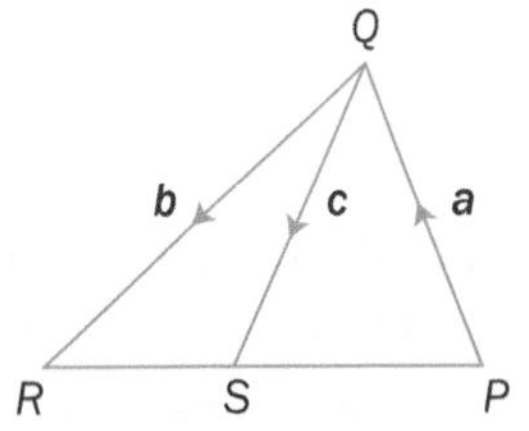

12 It is given that the area of a triangle, two of whose sides are represented by the vectors **a** and **b** is $\frac{1}{2}|\mathbf{a} \times \mathbf{b}|$

Let $\mathbf{a} = \overrightarrow{OA}$ etc

a Use this result to find the exact area of the triangle OAB, where O is the origin and the points A and B have coordinates $A(1, 2, 1)$ and $B(0, 1, 1)$.

b Find the acute angle, in degrees, between the vectors $\overrightarrow{OA}$ and $\overrightarrow{OB}$. Use this angle to verify your answer to part **a**.

c Use an appropriate vector product to calculate the area of the triangle with vertices $P(6, 4, 5)$, $Q(3, 6, 8)$ and $R(6, 3, 2)$. Give your answer in simplified surd form.

13 Let $\mathbf{a} = a_1\mathbf{i} + a_2\mathbf{j} + a_3\mathbf{k}$, $\mathbf{b} = b_1\mathbf{i} + b_2\mathbf{j} + b_3\mathbf{k}$ and $\mathbf{c} = c_1\mathbf{i} + c_2\mathbf{j} + c_3\mathbf{k}$

a Use appropriate determinants to prove that

$\mathbf{a} \times \mathbf{b} + \mathbf{a} \times \mathbf{c} = \mathbf{a} \times (\mathbf{b} + \mathbf{c})$

Given that $\mathbf{a} \times \mathbf{b} = \mathbf{a} \times \mathbf{c}$, with $\mathbf{a} \neq \mathbf{0}$

b show that $(\mathbf{b} - \mathbf{c}) = \lambda\mathbf{a}$, for some $\lambda \in \mathbb{R}$

Given further that $\mathbf{a}.\mathbf{b} = \mathbf{a}.\mathbf{c}$

c show that $\mathbf{b} = \mathbf{c}$

You may assume any standard results about scalar products.

6.2 Planes

A plane in three-dimensional space is a flat surface with zero thickness.

A plane is often denoted by the letter Π. The faces of this closed cuboid form six planes, three of which are visible (Π_1, Π_2 and Π_3).

Π is the uppercase letter Pi in the Greek alphabet.

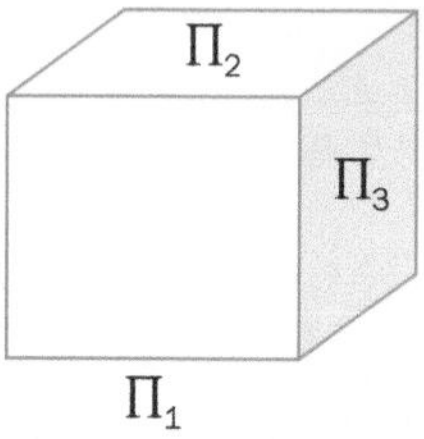

If three points A, B and C are not collinear then they lie on a unique plane Π.
You can find an equation for Π by using position vectors.

The diagram shows a plane Π containing the fixed points A, B and C.
Point R is *any* point on Π.

Collinear means 'lying on a common line'.

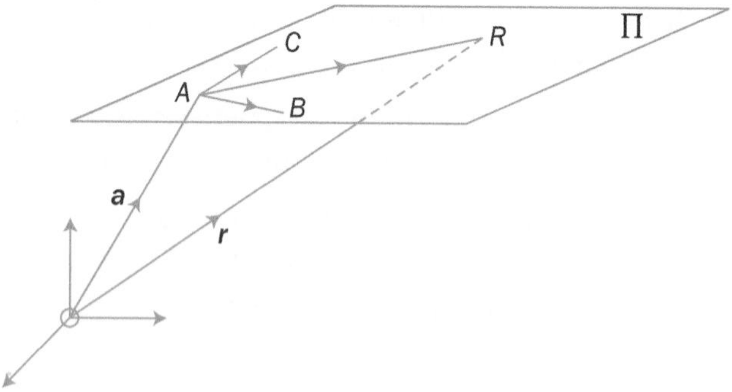

Relative to the origin O, the points A and R have position vector $\mathbf{a}$ and $\mathbf{r}$ respectively.

Using addition of vectors

$$\mathbf{r} = \mathbf{a} + \overrightarrow{AR}$$

where $\overrightarrow{AR}$ can be expressed as the sum of a multiple of $\overrightarrow{AB}$ and a multiple of $\overrightarrow{AC}$.

that is, $\overrightarrow{AR} = \lambda\overrightarrow{AB} + \mu\overrightarrow{AC}$, for real numbers λ and μ

λ and μ do not depend on each other.

Hence
$$\begin{aligned}\mathbf{r} &= \mathbf{a} + \overrightarrow{AR}\\ &= \mathbf{a} + \lambda\overrightarrow{AB} + \mu\overrightarrow{AC}\\ &= \mathbf{a} + \lambda(\mathbf{b} - \mathbf{a}) + \mu(\mathbf{c} - \mathbf{a})\end{aligned}$$

$\overrightarrow{AB} = \overrightarrow{OB} - \overrightarrow{OA} = \mathbf{b} - \mathbf{a}$
Refer to C4.

where $\mathbf{b} = \overrightarrow{OB}$ and $\mathbf{c} = \overrightarrow{OC}$ are the position vectors of B and C respectively.

A vector equation for a plane which passes through the non-collinear points A, B and C is given by

$$\mathbf{r} = \mathbf{a} + \lambda(\mathbf{b} - \mathbf{a}) + \mu(\mathbf{c} - \mathbf{a}), \quad \lambda, \mu \in \mathbb{R}$$

where **a**, **b** and **c** are the position vectors of A, B and C respectively.

This result is in the FP3 section of the formula booklet.

EXAMPLE 1

A plane Π passes through the points $A(2, 1, 3)$, $B(4, 2, 1)$ and $C(3, 3, 2)$.

a Find a vector equation for Π.

b Given that the point $P(6, 0, c)$ lies on Π, find the value of the constant c.

---

a Use the position vectors of A, B and C to calculate $(\mathbf{b} - \mathbf{a})$ and $(\mathbf{c} - \mathbf{a})$:

$$\mathbf{a} = 2\mathbf{i} + \mathbf{j} + 3\mathbf{k}, \mathbf{b} = 4\mathbf{i} + 2\mathbf{j} + \mathbf{k}, \mathbf{c} = 3\mathbf{i} + 3\mathbf{j} + 2\mathbf{k}$$

$$\mathbf{b} - \mathbf{a} = (4\mathbf{i} + 2\mathbf{j} + \mathbf{k}) - (2\mathbf{i} + \mathbf{j} + 3\mathbf{k})$$
$$= 2\mathbf{i} + \mathbf{j} - 2\mathbf{k}$$

$$\mathbf{c} - \mathbf{a} = (3\mathbf{i} + 3\mathbf{j} + 2\mathbf{k}) - (2\mathbf{i} + \mathbf{j} + 3\mathbf{k})$$
$$= \mathbf{i} + 2\mathbf{j} - \mathbf{k}$$

Use the general result $\mathbf{r} = \mathbf{a} + \lambda(\mathbf{b} - \mathbf{a}) + \mu(\mathbf{c} - \mathbf{a})$:

A vector equation for Π is

$$\mathbf{r} = (2\mathbf{i} + \mathbf{j} + 3\mathbf{k}) + \lambda(2\mathbf{i} + \mathbf{j} - 2\mathbf{k}) + \mu(\mathbf{i} + 2\mathbf{j} - \mathbf{k}), \lambda, \mu \in \mathbb{R}$$

You could also find the answer by using one of the other points (e.g. B) in place of A.

b Use the equation found in part a:

If **p** is the position vector of $P(6, 0, c)$ then $\mathbf{p} = 6\mathbf{i} + c\mathbf{k}$

The **j** component of **p** is zero.

Since P lies on Π, there exist values for λ and μ such that

$$\mathbf{p} = \mathbf{a} + \lambda(\mathbf{b} - \mathbf{a}) + \mu(\mathbf{c} - \mathbf{a})$$

Collect together the **i**, **j** and **k** components.

that is, $6\mathbf{i} + c\mathbf{k} = (2\mathbf{i} + \mathbf{j} + 3\mathbf{k}) + \lambda(2\mathbf{i} + \mathbf{j} - 2\mathbf{k}) + \mu(\mathbf{i} + 2\mathbf{j} - \mathbf{k})$

$$= (2 + 2\lambda + \mu)\mathbf{i} + (1 + \lambda + 2\mu)\mathbf{j} + (3 - 2\lambda - \mu)\mathbf{k}$$

Compare **i** components in this vector equation:

$6 = 2 + 2\lambda + \mu$ so $2\lambda + \mu = 4$ ... (1)

Compare **j** components in this vector equation:

$0 = 1 + \lambda + 2\mu$ so $\lambda + 2\mu = -1$ ... (2)

Solve equations (1) and (2) simultaneously:

$2 \times$ eqn(2) – eqn(1)

$\lambda = 3, \mu = -2$

Compare **k** components using these values of λ and μ:

$$c = 3 - 2\lambda - \mu$$
$$= 3 - 2(3) - (-2)$$

so $c = -1$

FP3

Exercise 6.2

1 Use the result $\mathbf{r} = \mathbf{a} + \lambda(\mathbf{b} - \mathbf{a}) + \mu(\mathbf{c} - \mathbf{a})$ to find a vector equation for the planes which pass through these points. Give components as integers where appropriate.

a $A(2,2,1)$, $B(3,1,7)$, $C(4,3,2)$

b $A(7,-2,3)$, $B(5,2,-1)$, $C(6,-6,4)$

c $A\left(\frac{1}{2},\frac{5}{2},1\right)$, $B\left(\frac{5}{2},\frac{3}{2},4\right)$, $C(0,1,1)$

2 A plane Π has vector equation

$$\mathbf{r} = (3\mathbf{i} - \mathbf{j} + 4\mathbf{k}) + \lambda(\mathbf{i} + 2\mathbf{j} - 2\mathbf{k}) + \mu(4\mathbf{i} + \mathbf{j} - 2\mathbf{k}),\ \lambda, \mu \in \mathbb{R}$$

a Find the coordinates of the point P on this plane corresponding to the values $\lambda = 2$ and $\mu = 3$.

Point $Q(s, 1, -2)$ lies on Π, where s is a constant.

b Find the value of s.

3 A plane Π has vector equation

$$\mathbf{r} = (7\mathbf{i} + \mathbf{j} + 3\mathbf{k}) + \lambda(\mathbf{i} + \mathbf{j} + \mathbf{k}) + \mu(\mathbf{i} + 2\mathbf{j} + 3\mathbf{k}),\ \lambda, \mu \in \mathbb{R}$$

a Show that the point $P(8,-1,2)$ does not lie on Π.

b Given that the point $Q(a, 2, a)$, where $a \in \mathbb{R}$, lies on Π, find the value of a.

c Find a vector equation for the plane which passes through the origin O and the points P and Q.

4 The plane Π passes through the points $A(1, 2, 4)$, $B(3, 1, 5)$ and $C(2, 0, 4)$.

a Find a vector equation for Π.

b Show that Π intersects the x-axis at the point $P(-4, 0, 0)$ and find the coordinates of the points Q and R, where Π intersects the y-axis and z-axis, respectively.

c Find a vector equation for the plane which passes through the points P, Q and R and give a geometrical reason why this plane cannot contain the origin.

5 Show that the points $A(2, 5, -1)$, $B(7, 7, 2)$ $C(2, 4, 5)$ and $D(-3, 2, 2)$ are coplanar (that is, show that all four points lie on a common plane).

6 Line l_1 passes through the point $A(2, -1, 1)$ and is parallel to the vector $\mathbf{d} = \mathbf{i} + 4\mathbf{j} - \mathbf{k}$
Line l_2 passes through the point $B(3, 3, 2)$ and is parallel to the vector $\mathbf{e} = \mathbf{i} + 4\mathbf{j} - 3\mathbf{k}$
l_1 and l_2 intersect at point C.

a Find the coordinates of point C.

Refer to C4.

b Hence find a vector equation of the plane containing the points A, B and C.

7 The line l has vector equation

$$\mathbf{r} = 4\mathbf{i} - \mathbf{j} + s(\mathbf{i} + \mathbf{j} + \mathbf{k}),\ s \in \mathbb{R}$$

a Show that the point $A(4, 3, 2)$ does not lie on l.

b Find a vector equation of the plane Π which contains the line l and the point A.

A plane contains a line if every point on the line is on the plane.

Point $A'(8, p, q)$, for p and q constants, is the reflection of point A in the line l.

c Find the value of p and the value of q.

Use the fact that A' lies on Π.

FP3

6.3 Normal vectors

A normal vector to a plane is a vector which is perpendicular to the plane. You can specify the orientation of a plane by using a normal vector.

The diagram shows three vectors, each of which is normal to the given plane Π.

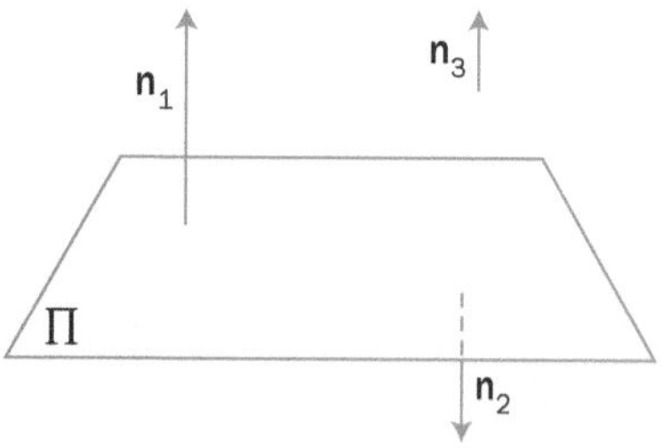

n_1 and n_2 point in opposite directions but are both normal vectors to Π.

The tail of a normal vector need not be on the plane itself, as in n_3

Any plane has exactly two normal vectors of unit length with opposing directions. The symbol $\hat{n}$ indicates a unit normal vector to a plane.

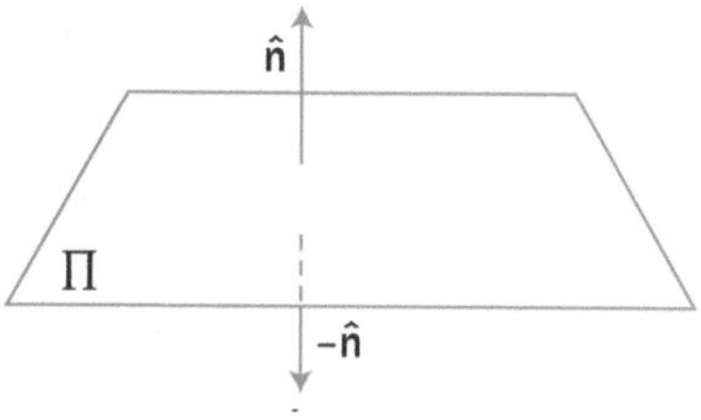

$|\hat{n}| = 1$
A vector of unit length is called a unit vector. Refer to C4.

If **v** is perpendicular to the non-parallel, non-zero vectors **a** and **b** then **v** is a normal vector to the plane containing **a** and **b**.

EXAMPLE 1

A plane Π has vector equation
$\mathbf{r} = (2\mathbf{i} - 3\mathbf{j} + 8\mathbf{k}) + \lambda(\mathbf{i} - 4\mathbf{k}) + \mu(-\mathbf{i} + \mathbf{j}),\ \lambda, \mu \in \mathbb{R}$
Show that $\mathbf{n} = 4\mathbf{i} + 4\mathbf{j} + \mathbf{k}$ is a normal vector to Π.

Use the plane equation to identify two vectors each parallel to Π:
The vectors $\mathbf{a} = \mathbf{i} - 4\mathbf{k}$ and $\mathbf{b} = -\mathbf{i} + \mathbf{j}$ are each parallel to Π.

Calculate appropriate scalar products:

$$\mathbf{n.a} = (4\mathbf{i} + 4\mathbf{j} + \mathbf{k}) . (\mathbf{i} - 4\mathbf{k}) = 4 \times 1 + 4 \times 0 + 1 \times (-4) = 0$$

$$\mathbf{n.b} = (4\mathbf{i} + 4\mathbf{j} + \mathbf{k}) . (-\mathbf{i} + \mathbf{j}) = 4 \times (-1) + 4 \times 1 + 1 \times 0 = 0$$

$\mathbf{p.q} = 0$ for $\mathbf{p}, \mathbf{q} \neq 0$ means **p** and **q** are perpendicular. Refer to C4.

So **n** is perpendicular to both **a** and **b** and hence is perpendicular to Π, that is,
$\mathbf{n} = 4\mathbf{i} + 4\mathbf{j} + \mathbf{k}$ is a normal vector to Π, as required.

Exercise 6.3

1 By calculating appropriate scalar products, show that $\mathbf{n} = 2\mathbf{i} - 3\mathbf{j} + \mathbf{k}$ is a normal vector to the plane with vector equation
$\mathbf{r} = (3\mathbf{i} + 2\mathbf{j} + \mathbf{k}) + \lambda(\mathbf{i} - \mathbf{j} - 5\mathbf{k}) + \mu(\mathbf{i} - 2\mathbf{k}),\ \lambda, \mu \in \mathbb{R}$

2 a Show that $\mathbf{n} = 4\mathbf{i} + 3\mathbf{k}$ is a normal vector to the plane Π with vector equation
$\mathbf{r} = (\mathbf{i} + 3\mathbf{j} + \mathbf{k}) + \lambda(9\mathbf{i} - 2\mathbf{j} - 12\mathbf{k}) + \mu(3\mathbf{i} - \mathbf{j} - 4\mathbf{k}),\ \lambda, \mu \in \mathbb{R}$

b Hence find a unit vector which is normal to this plane.

3 The plane Π passes through the points $A(2, 3, 1)$, $B(4, 0, -3)$ and $C(-2, 3, 3)$.
$\mathbf{n} = \mathbf{i} + p\mathbf{j} + 2\mathbf{k}$, where p is a constant, is a normal vector to Π.

a Show that $p = -2$

Point D is such that the vector $\overrightarrow{AD}$ is perpendicular to Π.

b Given that $|\overrightarrow{AD}| = 6$, find the possible coordinates of point D.

Use the fact that $\overrightarrow{AD}$ is parallel to $\mathbf{n}$.

4 The vector $\mathbf{n} = p\mathbf{i} + 3\mathbf{j} + q\mathbf{k}$, where p and q are constants, is a normal vector to the plane with equation

$$\mathbf{r} = (\mathbf{i} + \mathbf{j} + \mathbf{k}) + \lambda(2\mathbf{i} + \mathbf{k}) + \mu(\mathbf{i} + 2\mathbf{j} + 2\mathbf{k}),\ \lambda, \mu \in \mathbb{R}$$

a Find the values of p and q.

b Hence find two unit vectors which are normal to this plane.

5 The diagram shows a cube of side length 1 unit.

By inspection of the diagram, find a normal vector to each of these planes.

a The plane passing through the points A, B and C.

b The plane passing through the points C, D and E.

c The plane passing through the points G, F and B.

d The plane containing the points G, E and B.

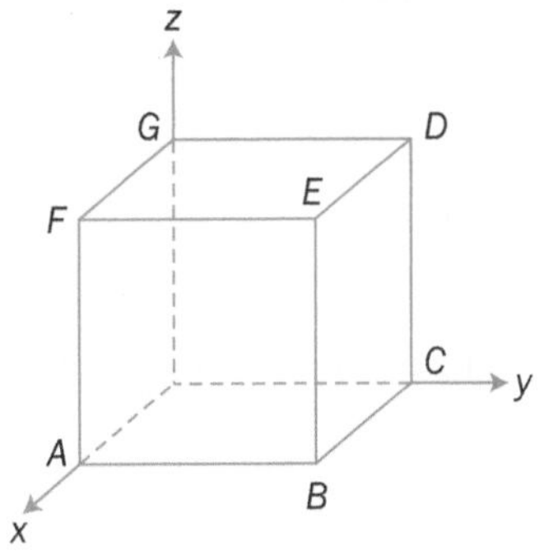

6 The plane Π has vector equation

$$\mathbf{r} = (\mathbf{i} + \mathbf{k}) + \lambda(-\mathbf{i} + \mathbf{j}) + \mu(\mathbf{i} + 2\mathbf{j} - 2\mathbf{k}),\ \lambda, \mu \in \mathbb{R}$$

The plane Π contains the point $A(a, 3, -a)$, where a is a constant.
It is given that $\mathbf{n} = 2\mathbf{i} + 2\mathbf{j} + 3\mathbf{k}$ is a normal vector to Π.

a Find the value of a.

b Show that $\overrightarrow{AP}$ is perpendicular to Π, where P has coordinates $P(5, 7, 5)$.

c Find the coordinates of the point P' which is the reflection of point P in Π.

FP3

6.4 A geometrical approach to vector products

You can interpret the vector product $\mathbf{a} \times \mathbf{b}$ geometrically. The diagram shows two non-zero, non-parallel vectors **a** and **b**, drawn tail-to-tail.

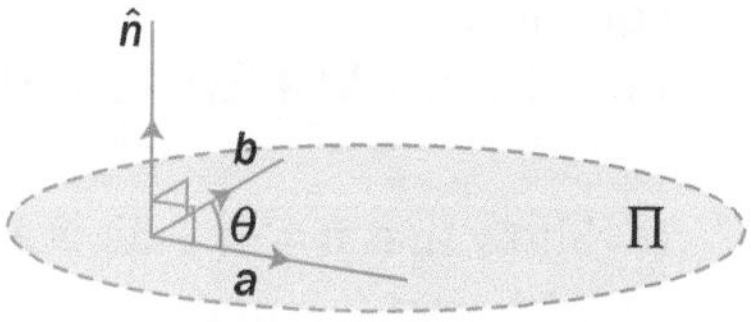

Also shown is the (unique) plane Π which contains these two vectors.

The angle between **a** and **b** is θ, where $0° < \theta < 180°$.

By definition Π has two unit normal vectors, in opposite directions.

$\hat{\mathbf{n}}$ is a unit vector which is normal to this plane.

For non-parallel, non-zero vectors **a** and **b**
$$\mathbf{a} \times \mathbf{b} = |\mathbf{a}|\,|\mathbf{b}| \sin\theta\,\hat{\mathbf{n}}$$

This result is in the FP3 section of the formula booklet.

The correct choice for $\hat{\mathbf{n}}$ is determined by the right-hand rule:

- Make a 'thumbs up' sign with your right hand.
- Orient the curl of your fingers with the direction of rotation *from* **a** *to* **b**.
- Your thumb will then be pointing in the direction of $\mathbf{a} \times \mathbf{b}$.

FP3

EXAMPLE 1

Show geometrically that $\mathbf{i} \times \mathbf{j} = \mathbf{k}$

Apply the result $\mathbf{a} \times \mathbf{b} = |\mathbf{a}|\,|\mathbf{b}| \sin\theta\,\hat{\mathbf{n}}$, using the right-hand rule:

$0° < \theta < 180°$

The appropriate angle θ between the unit vectors **i** and **j** is 90°.

The plane which contains the vectors **i** and **j** is the $x-y$ plane. The two unit vectors which are normal to this plane are **k** and **-k**.

The right-hand rule selects **k** as the correct normal vector.

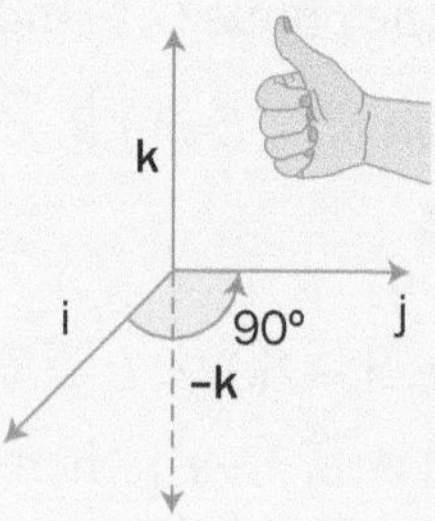

Curl the fingers so that they turn from i to j.

Hence $\mathbf{i} \times \mathbf{j} = |\mathbf{i}|\,|\mathbf{j}| \sin\theta\,\hat{\mathbf{n}}$
$$= 1 \times 1 \times \sin 90° \times \mathbf{k}$$
$$= \mathbf{k}$$
that is, $\mathbf{i} \times \mathbf{j} = \mathbf{k}$, as required.

For non-parallel, non-zero vectors **a** and **b**
a × **b** is a non-zero vector, normal to the plane containing **a** and **b**

$|\mathbf{a} \times \mathbf{b}| = ab\sin\theta$, where $a = |\mathbf{a}|$, $b = |\mathbf{b}|$

When either **a** = **0**, or **b** = **0**, or **a** and **b** are parallel vectors, then **a** × **b** is defined to be the zero vector, that is, **a** × **b** = **0**

In these cases, there is not a unique plane containing **a** and **b**.

EXAMPLE 2

Points *P* and *Q* have coordinates (2, 1, 2) and (4, 3, 2) respectively.
Find the area of triangle *POQ*, where *O* is the origin.

Use the vector product **p** × **q**:

The area of this triangle is

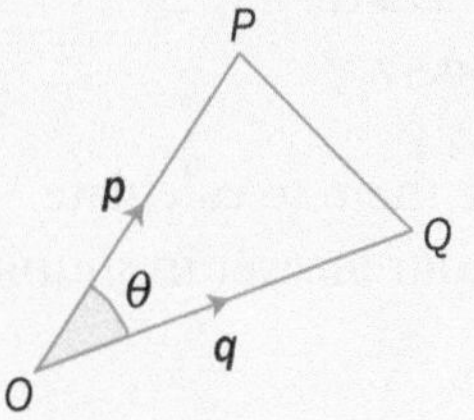

In the sketch, you can ignore magnitudes and directions.

$$A = \frac{1}{2}pq\sin\theta$$

$$= \frac{1}{2}|\mathbf{p} \times \mathbf{q}|$$

$|\mathbf{p} \times \mathbf{q}| = pq\sin\theta$

where $\mathbf{p} \times \mathbf{q} = \begin{vmatrix} \mathbf{i} & \mathbf{j} & \mathbf{k} \\ 2 & 1 & 2 \\ 4 & 3 & 2 \end{vmatrix} = -4\mathbf{i} + 4\mathbf{j} + 2\mathbf{k}$

Hence $A = \frac{1}{2}|\mathbf{p} \times \mathbf{q}| = \frac{1}{2}\sqrt{(-4)^2 + 4^2 + 2^2}$

$$= \frac{1}{2} \times \sqrt{36}$$

$$= 3$$

Triangle *POQ* has area 3 square units.

The area of the triangle *ABD* is $\frac{1}{2}|\overrightarrow{AB} \times \overrightarrow{AD}|$

The area of the parallelogram *ABCD* is $|\overrightarrow{AB} \times \overrightarrow{AD}|$

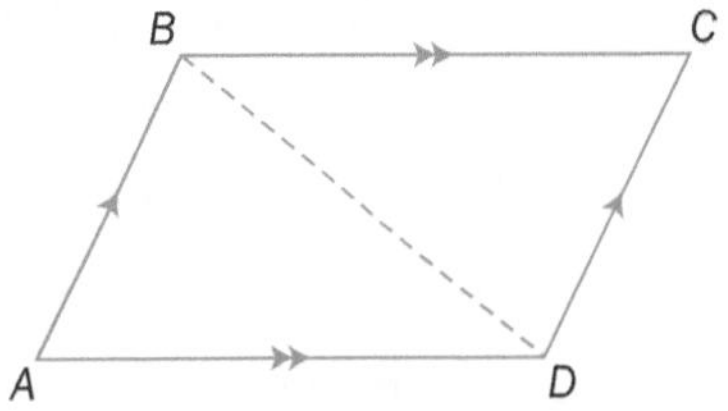

Exercise 6.4

1 Use the geometrical definition of a vector product to show that

a $\mathbf{j} \times \mathbf{k} = \mathbf{i}$ **b** $\mathbf{j} \times \mathbf{i} = -\mathbf{k}$

Verify each of your answers by expanding an appropriate determinant.

2 Find the area of the triangle AOB with these vertices. Give answers in simplified surd form where appropriate

a $A(2,3,0), B(0,-3,1)$

b $A(0,2,-1), B(2,1,2)$

c $A(1,2,3), B(3,2,1)$

3 Points $A(2, 2, 3)$, $B(5,2,6)$ and $C(3,1,5)$ define a triangle.

a Find $\overrightarrow{AB}$ and $\overrightarrow{AC}$.

b Hence show that the area of this triangle is $\frac{3}{2}\sqrt{3}$ square units.

4 The diagram shows the parallelogram $ABCD$.

The coordinates of the vertices A, B and D are $(3, 1, 4)$, $(-2, 4, 1)$ and $(1, -1, 3)$ respectively.

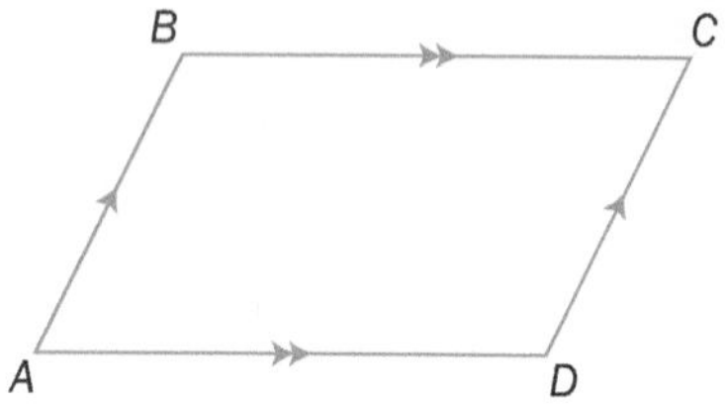

a Find the vectors $\overrightarrow{AB}$ and $\overrightarrow{AD}$, and use them to calculate the area of the parallelogram. Give your answer in simplified surd form.

b Without further calculation, show that this area is also given by $|\overrightarrow{AB} \times \overrightarrow{AC}|$

5 For the points A (2, 3, 1), B (5, 0, 7) and C (4, 1, p), where p is a real number, $p \leqslant 5$

a Show that $|\overrightarrow{AB} \times \overrightarrow{AC}| = 3\sqrt{2}(5 - p)$

b Hence, or otherwise, find the exact area of triangle ABC when $p = 4$

c State a geometrical relationship between A, B and C when $p = 5$

6 Use vector products to find a unit vector which is normal to these planes.

a The plane passing through the origin and the points $A(2, 4, -3)$ and $B(-1\ -4, 3)$.

b The plane passing through the origin O and the points $A(0, 2, 1)$ and $B(4, 3, 2)$.

c The plane with vector equation

$\mathbf{r} = (3\mathbf{i} + 4\mathbf{j} + 2\mathbf{k}) + \lambda(2\mathbf{i} + \mathbf{j} + 2\mathbf{k}) + \mu(\mathbf{i} + 2\mathbf{k}),\ \lambda, \mu \in \mathbb{R}$

d The plane passing through the points A (4, 2, 3), B (2, 3, 2) and $C(7, 1, 5)$.

FP3

7 The diagram shows a trapezium $OABC$, where O is the origin. Vertices A and C have position vectors $\mathbf{a}$ and $\mathbf{c}$ respectively.

Consider the vector $\overrightarrow{AC}$.

It is given that $\overrightarrow{AB} = \lambda\mathbf{c}$, where $\lambda > 0$

Prove that the area of the trapezium is

$\frac{1}{2}(1 + \lambda)|\mathbf{a} \times \mathbf{c}|$

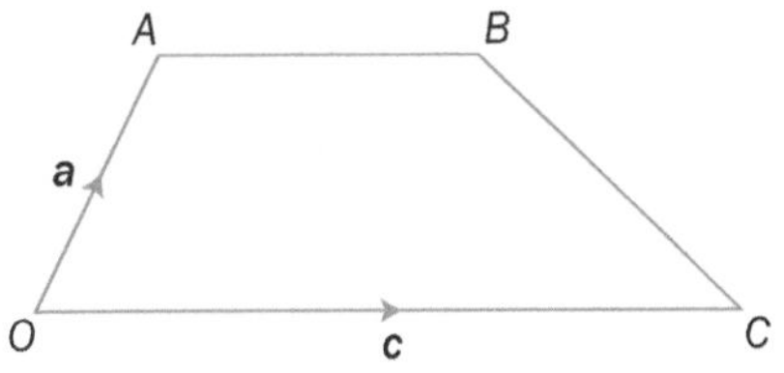

8 The diagram shows a parallelogram $PQRS$, where $\overrightarrow{PQ} = \mathbf{a}$ and $\overrightarrow{QR} = \mathbf{b}$

M is the midpoint of the side PS.
Find the proportion of this parallelogram occupied by triangle QMS.

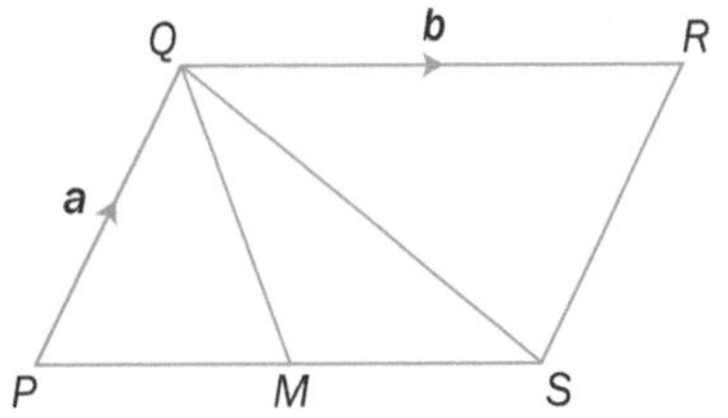

9 The diagram shows a parallelogram-based pyramid.

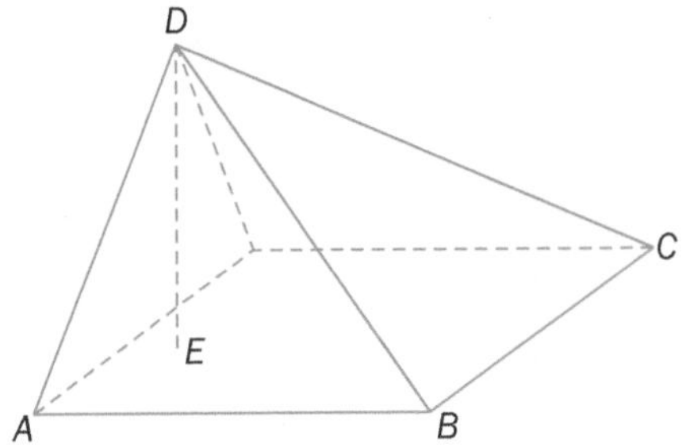

The vertices A, B and C have coordinates $A(3, 1, -2)$, $B(4, 3, -2)$ and $C(5, 3, -3)$. Point $E(4, 2, -\frac{5}{2})$ is the foot of the perpendicular from the apex D of this pyramid to its base.

a Calculate $\overrightarrow{AB}$ and $\overrightarrow{AC}$.

b Find a vector equation for the plane Π containing the points A, B and C.

c Calculate $\overrightarrow{AB} \times \overrightarrow{AC}$ and hence find a vector equation of the line passing through points D and E.

The line passing through points A and D has vector equation

$\mathbf{r} = (3\mathbf{i} + \mathbf{j} - 2\mathbf{k}) + s(10\mathbf{i} - 2\mathbf{j} + 7\mathbf{k}), s \in \mathbb{R}$

d Show that point D has coordinates $(8, 0, \frac{3}{2})$.

e Calculate the volume V of this pyramid.

$V = \frac{1}{3}bh$, where b is the base area and h is the perpendicular height of a pyramid.

FP3

6.5 Scalar triple products

A scalar triple product is a calculation involving both a vector product and a scalar product.

For example, the expression $\mathbf{a}.(\mathbf{b}\times\mathbf{c})$ is the scalar product of the vector **a**, with the vector product of **b** and **c**.

$\mathbf{a}.(\mathbf{b}\times\mathbf{c})$ is usually written without brackets: $\mathbf{a}.\mathbf{b}\times\mathbf{c}$

A scalar triple product is always a real number.

EXAMPLE 1

Given that $\mathbf{a} = 2\mathbf{i} + 3\mathbf{j} + \mathbf{k}$, $\mathbf{b} = \mathbf{i} + \mathbf{j} - \mathbf{k}$ and $\mathbf{c} = 3\mathbf{i} - \mathbf{j} + 2\mathbf{k}$

a evaluate the scalar triple product $\mathbf{a}.\mathbf{b}\times\mathbf{c}$

b verify that $\mathbf{a}.\mathbf{b}\times\mathbf{c} = \begin{vmatrix} 2 & 3 & 1 \\ 1 & 1 & -1 \\ 3 & -1 & 2 \end{vmatrix}$

The rows of this matrix are the components of **a**, **b** and **c**, *in that order.*

a First find the vector product $\mathbf{b}\times\mathbf{c}$:

$$\mathbf{b}\times\mathbf{c} = \begin{vmatrix} \mathbf{i} & \mathbf{j} & \mathbf{k} \\ 1 & 1 & -1 \\ 3 & -1 & 2 \end{vmatrix}$$

$$= \mathbf{i} - 5\mathbf{j} - 4\mathbf{k}$$

Find the scalar product of **a** with $\mathbf{b}\times\mathbf{c}$:

See C4 for the scalar product.

$$\mathbf{a}.\mathbf{b}\times\mathbf{c} = (2\mathbf{i} + 3\mathbf{j} + \mathbf{k}).(\mathbf{i} - 5\mathbf{j} - 4\mathbf{k})$$

$$= (2\times 1) + (3\times -5) + (1\times -4)$$

$$= -17$$

A scalar triple product can be negative.

b Expand the given determinant along the first row:

$$\begin{vmatrix} 2 & 3 & 1 \\ 1 & 1 & -1 \\ 3 & -1 & 2 \end{vmatrix} = 2\begin{vmatrix} 1 & -1 \\ -1 & 2 \end{vmatrix} - 3\begin{vmatrix} 1 & -1 \\ 3 & 2 \end{vmatrix} + 1\begin{vmatrix} 1 & 1 \\ 3 & -1 \end{vmatrix}$$

$$= (2\times 1) - (3\times 5) + (1\times -4)$$

$$= -17$$

Notice the similarity between the bracketed terms here and those shown in part **a**.

so $\quad \mathbf{a}.\mathbf{b}\times\mathbf{c} = \begin{vmatrix} 2 & 3 & 1 \\ 1 & 1 & -1 \\ 3 & -1 & 2 \end{vmatrix}$, as required.

If $\mathbf{a} = a_1\mathbf{i} + a_2\mathbf{j} + a_3\mathbf{k}$, $\mathbf{b} = b_1\mathbf{i} + b_2\mathbf{j} + b_3\mathbf{k}$ and $\mathbf{c} = c_1\mathbf{i} + c_2\mathbf{j} + c_3\mathbf{k}$ then

$$\mathbf{a}.\mathbf{b}\times\mathbf{c} = \begin{vmatrix} a_1 & a_2 & a_3 \\ b_1 & b_2 & b_3 \\ c_1 & c_2 & c_3 \end{vmatrix}$$

This result is in the FP3 section of the formula booklet.

Exercise 6.5

1 Use a suitable determinant to evaluate these scalar triple products.

a $\mathbf{a}.\mathbf{b}\times\mathbf{c}$ given that $\mathbf{a} = 3\mathbf{i} + 2\mathbf{j} - \mathbf{k}$, $\mathbf{b} = 2\mathbf{i} + 4\mathbf{j} - \mathbf{k}$ and $\mathbf{c} = \mathbf{i} - 2\mathbf{j} + \mathbf{k}$

b $\mathbf{b}.\mathbf{a}\times\mathbf{c}$ given that $\mathbf{a} = 4\mathbf{i} - \mathbf{j}$, $\mathbf{b} = -3\mathbf{j} - \mathbf{k}$ and $\mathbf{c} = 5\mathbf{i} + 2\mathbf{j} + 3\mathbf{k}$

c $\mathbf{b}\times\mathbf{a}.\mathbf{c}$ given that $\mathbf{a} = 3\mathbf{i} - 2\mathbf{k}$, $\mathbf{b} = 2\mathbf{i} + 2\mathbf{j} + \mathbf{k}$ and $\mathbf{c} = -5\mathbf{i} + 3\mathbf{j} - \mathbf{k}$

Scalar products are commutative.

2 Relative to the origin, the points A, B, C and D have coordinates $A(5,1,7)$, $B(-4,2,1)$, $C(3, 5, -2)$ and $D(-2, 1, 0)$.
Evaluate the scalar triple product $\overrightarrow{AD}.\overrightarrow{BC}\times\overrightarrow{CA}$

3 Vectors $\mathbf{a} = 2\mathbf{i} - \mathbf{j} + 2\mathbf{k}$, $\mathbf{b} = 4\mathbf{i} + 2\mathbf{j}$ and $\mathbf{c} = p\mathbf{i} - p\mathbf{j} + \mathbf{k}$, where p is a constant, are such that $\mathbf{a}.\mathbf{b}\times\mathbf{c} = -28$

a Show that $p = 3$

b Find the value of $\mathbf{b}.\mathbf{a}\times\mathbf{c}$

4 For vectors $\mathbf{a} = \mathbf{i} + \mathbf{j} + 2\mathbf{k}$, $\mathbf{b} = 4\mathbf{i} + 2\mathbf{k}$ and $\mathbf{c} = 3\mathbf{i} + \mathbf{j} + 2\mathbf{k}$, the acute angle between $\mathbf{c}$ and $\mathbf{a}\times\mathbf{b}$ is θ

a Show that $\cos\theta = \frac{1}{7}$ and find the exact value of $\sin\theta$

b Hence, or otherwise, find the value of

$$|\mathbf{c}\times(\mathbf{a}\times\mathbf{b})|$$

Give your answer in simplified surd form.

5 Given that $\mathbf{a} = a_1\mathbf{i} + a_2\mathbf{j} + a_3\mathbf{k}$, $\mathbf{b} = b_1\mathbf{i} + b_2\mathbf{j} + b_3\mathbf{k}$ and $\mathbf{c} = c_1\mathbf{i} + c_2\mathbf{j} + c_3\mathbf{k}$ prove that

$$\mathbf{a}.\mathbf{b}\times\mathbf{c} = \begin{vmatrix} a_1 & a_2 & a_3 \\ b_1 & b_2 & b_3 \\ c_1 & c_2 & c_3 \end{vmatrix}$$

Show that
$\mathbf{a}\times(\mathbf{b}\times\mathbf{c}) = (\mathbf{a}\times\mathbf{c})\mathbf{b} - (\mathbf{a}\times\mathbf{b})\mathbf{c}$

FP3

6.6 Calculating volumes

You can find the volumes of certain types of solid shapes by calculating a scalar triple product.

In the following, **a**, **b** and **c** are any three mutually adjacent edges of the given shape.

- The volume V of a parallelepiped is given by $V = |\mathbf{a}.\mathbf{b} \times \mathbf{c}|$

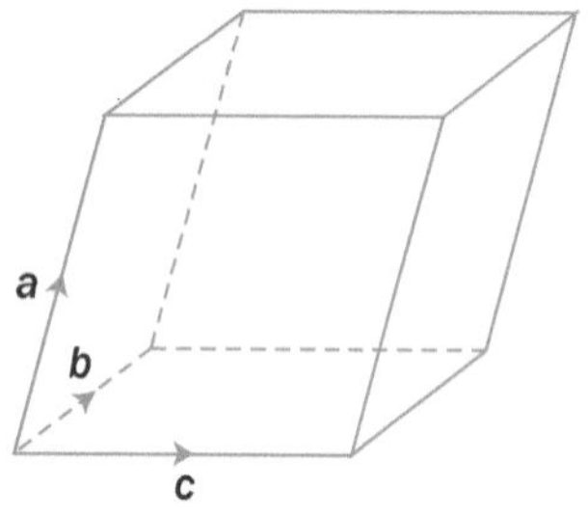

A parallelepiped is a six-sided shape, in which each pair of opposing faces are parallelograms.

The modulus sign avoids a negative answer.

The point where the triangular faces meet is the **apex** of the pyramid.

- The volume V of a pyramid whose base is a parallelogram is given by
$V = \frac{1}{3}|\mathbf{a}.\mathbf{b} \times \mathbf{c}|$

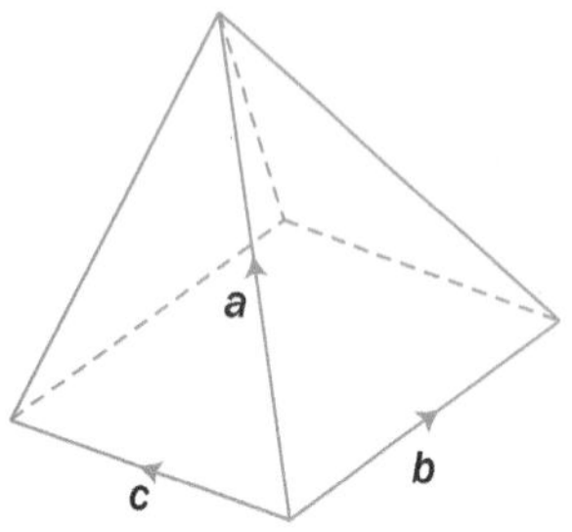

Remember these formulae for the exam. They are **not** given in the formula booklet.

- The volume V of a tetrahedron (a triangular based pyramid) is given by

$V = \frac{1}{6}|\mathbf{a}.\mathbf{b} \times \mathbf{c}|$

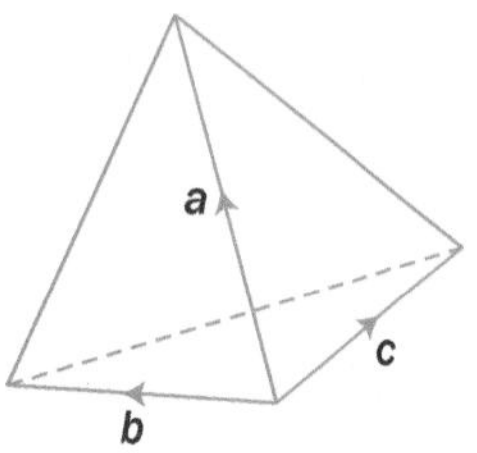

EXAMPLE 1

The vertices of the tetrahedron *PQRS* have coordinates $P(1,2,1)$, $Q(3,7,2)$ $R(4,0,2)$, and $S(3,-1,3)$.

Find the volume of this tetrahedron.

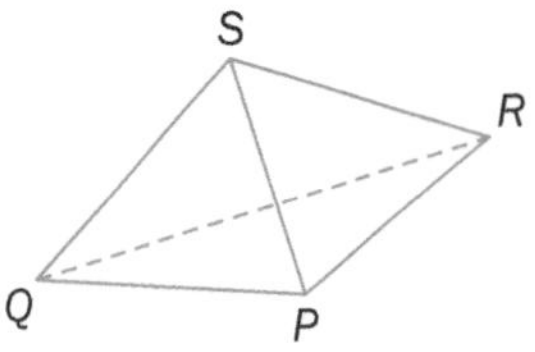

Find vectors representing any three adjacent edges of this shape:

Let $\mathbf{a} = \overrightarrow{PQ}$, $\mathbf{b} = \overrightarrow{PR}$ and $\mathbf{c} = \overrightarrow{PS}$

$$\mathbf{a} = \overrightarrow{PQ} = \overrightarrow{OQ} - \overrightarrow{OP}$$
$$= (3\mathbf{i} + 7\mathbf{j} + 2\mathbf{k}) - (\mathbf{i} + 2\mathbf{j} + \mathbf{k})$$
$$= 2\mathbf{i} + 5\mathbf{j} + \mathbf{k}$$

$$\mathbf{b} = \overrightarrow{PR} = \overrightarrow{OR} - \overrightarrow{OP}$$
$$= (4\mathbf{i} + 2\mathbf{k}) - (\mathbf{i} + 2\mathbf{j} + \mathbf{k})$$
$$= 3\mathbf{i} - 2\mathbf{j} + \mathbf{k}$$
$$\mathbf{c} = \overrightarrow{PS} = \overrightarrow{OS} - \overrightarrow{OP}$$
$$= (3\mathbf{i} - \mathbf{j} + 3\mathbf{k}) - (\mathbf{i} + 2\mathbf{j} + \mathbf{k})$$
$$= 2\mathbf{i} - 3\mathbf{j} + 2\mathbf{k}$$

Use the appropriate formula $V = \frac{1}{6}|\mathbf{a}.\mathbf{b} \times \mathbf{c}|$:

Use a determinant to find the scalar triple product.

$$\mathbf{a}.\mathbf{b} \times \mathbf{c} = \begin{vmatrix} 2 & 5 & 1 \\ 3 & -2 & 1 \\ 2 & -3 & 2 \end{vmatrix}$$

$$= 2\begin{vmatrix} -2 & 1 \\ -3 & 2 \end{vmatrix} - 5\begin{vmatrix} 3 & 1 \\ 2 & 2 \end{vmatrix} + 1\begin{vmatrix} 3 & -2 \\ 2 & -3 \end{vmatrix}$$
$$= (2 \times -1) - (5 \times 4) + (1 \times -5)$$
$$= -27$$

$$\text{Volume of tetrahedron} = \frac{1}{6} \times |-27|$$
$$= 4.5 \text{ cubic units}$$

FP3

Three non-zero vectors are coplanar if they are all parallel to a common plane. You can use a scalar triple product to determine whether or not three vectors are coplanar.

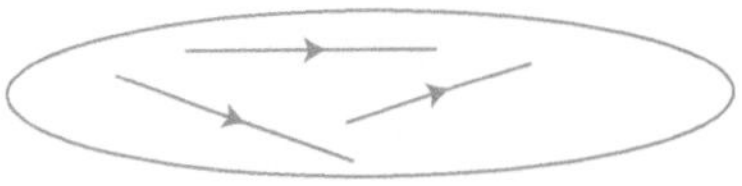

Three non-zero vectors **a**, **b** and **c** are coplanar precisely when $\mathbf{a}.\mathbf{b} \times \mathbf{c} = 0$, that is, precisely when

$$\begin{vmatrix} a_1 & a_2 & a_3 \\ b_1 & b_2 & b_3 \\ c_1 & c_2 & c_3 \end{vmatrix} = 0$$

where $\mathbf{a} = a_1\mathbf{i} + a_2\mathbf{j} + a_3\mathbf{k}$, $\mathbf{b} = b_1\mathbf{i} + b_2\mathbf{j} + b_3\mathbf{k}$ and $\mathbf{c} = c_1\mathbf{i} + c_2\mathbf{j} + c_3\mathbf{k}$

EXAMPLE 2

Show that $\mathbf{a} = 3\mathbf{i} - 2\mathbf{j}$, $\mathbf{b} = \mathbf{i} + \mathbf{j} + 5\mathbf{k}$ and $\mathbf{c} = 4\mathbf{i} - \mathbf{j} + 5\mathbf{k}$ are coplanar.

Evaluate $\mathbf{a}.\mathbf{b} \times \mathbf{c}$:

$$\mathbf{a}.\mathbf{b} \times \mathbf{c} = \begin{vmatrix} 3 & -2 & 0 \\ 1 & 1 & 5 \\ 4 & -1 & 5 \end{vmatrix} = 3\begin{vmatrix} 1 & 5 \\ -1 & 5 \end{vmatrix} - (-2)\begin{vmatrix} 1 & 5 \\ 4 & 5 \end{vmatrix} + 0\begin{vmatrix} 1 & 1 \\ 4 & -1 \end{vmatrix}$$

$$= (3 \times 10) + (2 \times -15)$$

$\mathbf{a}.\mathbf{b} \times \mathbf{c} = 0$ and so $\mathbf{a}$, $\mathbf{b}$ and $\mathbf{c}$ are coplanar.

$\mathbf{a}.\mathbf{b} \times \mathbf{c} = 0$ means that the parallelepiped with mutually adjacent edges **a**, **b** and **c** has zero volume (that is, it is flat). Thus **c** must lie on the plane containing **a** and **b**.

Exercise 6.6

1 The position vectors of points $A(2,-3,0)$, $C(-3,1,2)$ and $G(4, 0, 5)$ are **a**, **c** and **g**, respectively. These vectors form three mutually adjacent edges of a parallelepiped. Calculate the volume of this parallelepiped.

Position vectors start from the origin O.

2 The diagram shows a pyramid with base $OABC$ and apex D. Points $A(3,4,5)$, $C(-1,2,-1)$ and $D(4,0,1)$ have position vectors **a**, **c** and **d**, respectively.

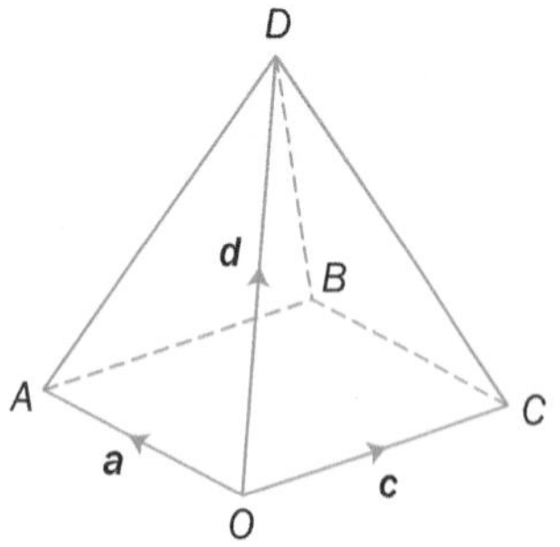

a Given that B has coordinates $B(2,6,4)$, show that the base of this pyramid is a rectangle.

b Find the volume of this pyramid.

3 The diagram shows the tetrahedron $ABCD$. The coordinates of A, B, C and D are $A(2,5,1)$, $B(4,2,3)$, $C(4,-1,1)$ and $D(6,8,5)$.

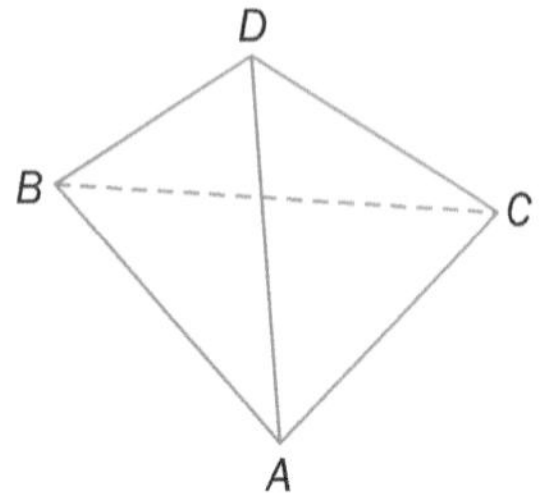

a Find the vectors $\overrightarrow{AB}$, $\overrightarrow{AC}$ and $\overrightarrow{AD}$.

b Hence calculate the volume of the tetrahedron.

4 Find the volumes of these solids:

a the parallelepiped with three mutually adjacent sides AB, AC and AD, where the coordinates of A, B, C, D are $(2,1,4)$, $(-1,2,0)$, $(-3,3,2)$ and $(5,1,-2)$, respectively.

b the pyramid with three mutually adjacent sides AB, AC and AD, where A, B, C, D are the points $(5,2,-1)$, $(1,-2,3)$, $(3,4,0)$ and $(-3,1,2)$, respectively.

5 The diagram shows the tetrahedron $OABC$, where the vertices A, B and C have coordinates $(2,1,3)$, $(-3,-2,4)$ and $(p,2,0)$ respectively, for p a real number.

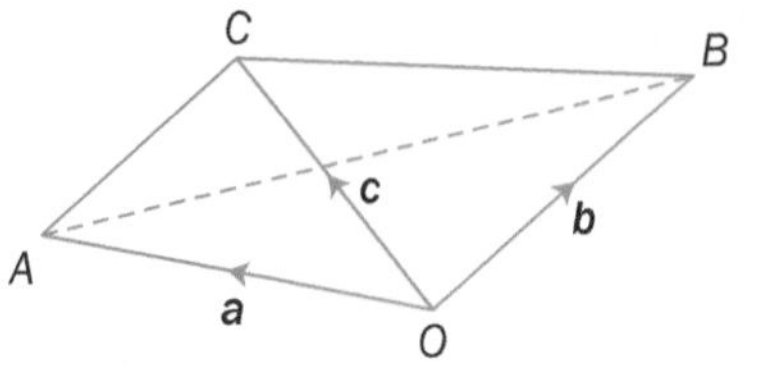

The position vectors of A, B and C are **a**, **b** and **c** respectively. The volume of this tetrahedron is 6 cubic units.

a Find the possible values of p.

b Hence find the possible areas of the triangular face OAC. Give each answer in simplified surd form.

6 Determine which of these sets of vectors are coplanar.

a $\mathbf{a} = 4\mathbf{i} - 3\mathbf{j} + 2\mathbf{k}$, $\mathbf{b} = -\mathbf{i} + \mathbf{j} + 4\mathbf{k}$ and $\mathbf{c} = 2\mathbf{i} - 2\mathbf{j} - \mathbf{k}$

b $\mathbf{a} = 3\mathbf{i} - \mathbf{j} + 4\mathbf{k}$, $\mathbf{b} = 2\mathbf{i} + 3\mathbf{j} + \mathbf{k}$ and $\mathbf{c} = \mathbf{i} - 4\mathbf{j} + 3\mathbf{k}$

c $\mathbf{a} = \mathbf{i} + \mathbf{j}$, $\mathbf{b} = p\mathbf{i} + p\mathbf{j} + \mathbf{k}$ and $\mathbf{c} = \mathbf{i} + \mathbf{j} + p\mathbf{k}$, where p is any constant.

d $\mathbf{a} = \mathbf{i} - \mathbf{j} + q\mathbf{k}$, $\mathbf{b} = q\mathbf{i} + q\mathbf{j} + \mathbf{k}$ and $\mathbf{c} = -4\mathbf{i} - \mathbf{j} + q\mathbf{k}$, where q is some constant.

7 The plane Π contains the non-zero, non-parallel vectors **a** and **b**, and has normal vector **n**.
If **c** is any vector which is perpendicular to **n**, show that **a**, **b** and **c** are coplanar.

6.7 Cartesian equations of a line

You can express the equation of a line using cartesian equations.

EXAMPLE 1

The line l has vector equation $\mathbf{r} = (2\mathbf{i} + 3\mathbf{j} + 4\mathbf{k}) + \lambda(4\mathbf{i} + 5\mathbf{j} + 2\mathbf{k})$, $\lambda \in \mathbb{R}$

a Find cartesian equations for l.

b Hence show that the point $P(10, 13, 8)$ lies on l.

---

a Use the vector equation $\mathbf{r} = \mathbf{a} + \lambda\mathbf{d}$, where $\mathbf{a} = 2\mathbf{i} + 3\mathbf{j} + 4\mathbf{k}$ is the position vector of a fixed point on l and $\mathbf{d} = 4\mathbf{i} + 5\mathbf{j} + 2\mathbf{k}$ is a direction vector of l:

For any point $R(x, y, z)$ on l, there exists a value λ_0 such that

$$x\mathbf{i} + y\mathbf{j} + z\mathbf{k} = \mathbf{r} = (2\mathbf{i} + 3\mathbf{j} + 4\mathbf{k}) + \lambda_0(4\mathbf{i} + 5\mathbf{j} + 2\mathbf{k})$$
$$= (2 + 4\lambda_0)\mathbf{i} + (3 + 5\lambda_0)\mathbf{j} + (4 + 2\lambda_0)\mathbf{k}$$

Collect together the **i**, **j** and **k** components.

Hence $x = 2 + 4\lambda_0$, $y = 3 + 5\lambda_0$, $z = 4 + 2\lambda_0$

Compare components.

So $\lambda_0 = \frac{x-2}{4}$, $\lambda_0 = \frac{y-3}{5}$, $\lambda_0 = \frac{z-4}{2}$

Make λ_0 the subject of each equation.

The line l has cartesian equations $\frac{x-2}{4} = \frac{y-3}{5} = \frac{z-4}{2}$

b Substitute the x-, y- and z-coordinates of the given point into the appropriate expression:

At the point $P(10, 13, 8)$, $x = 10$, $y = 13$ and $z = 8$

So $\frac{x-2}{4} = \frac{10-2}{4} = 2$, $\frac{y-3}{5} = \frac{13-3}{5} = 2$ and

$\frac{z-4}{2} = \frac{8-4}{2} = 2$

The common value 2 of these ratios is the value λ_0 of the parameter corresponding to the point P.

The three ratios are equal at point P and hence P lies on l, as required.

A line l passing through the point A, with position vector $\mathbf{a} = a_1\mathbf{i} + a_2\mathbf{j} + a_3\mathbf{k}$ and with direction $\mathbf{d} = d_1\mathbf{i} + d_2\mathbf{j} + d_3\mathbf{k}$ has cartesian equations

$$\frac{x-a_1}{d_1} = \frac{y-a_2}{d_2} = \frac{z-a_3}{d_3}$$

This result is in the FP3 section of the formula booklet.

The components of **a** and **d** appear in these equations.

EXAMPLE 2

A line l passes through the point $A(0, 2, 4)$ and is parallel to the vector $\mathbf{i} + 3\mathbf{j}$.
Find cartesian equations for l.

Use the components of the vectors $\mathbf{a} = 0\mathbf{i} + 2\mathbf{j} + 4\mathbf{k}$, $\mathbf{d} = \mathbf{i} + 3\mathbf{j}$:

Cartesian equations for l are: $\frac{x-0}{1} = \frac{y-2}{3} = \frac{z-4}{0}$

l has cartesian equations $\quad x = \frac{y-2}{3},\ z = 4$

The equation $z = 4$ makes sense since l passes through $A(0, 2, 4)$ and the $\mathbf{k}$ component of $\mathbf{d}$ is zero, and so every point on l has z-coordinate 4.

The ratio $\frac{z-4}{0}$ is interpreted as the equation $z = 4$.

Exercise 6.7

1 Find cartesian equations for the lines with these vector equations.

a $\mathbf{r} = (3\mathbf{i} + 2\mathbf{j} + \mathbf{k}) + \lambda(4\mathbf{i} - 2\mathbf{j} + 3\mathbf{k}), \lambda \in \mathbb{R}$

b $\mathbf{r} = (\mathbf{i} - 2\mathbf{j} - \mathbf{k}) + \lambda(2\mathbf{i} + 5\mathbf{j}), \lambda \in \mathbb{R}$

c $\mathbf{r} = (\mathbf{j} + 2\mathbf{k}) + \lambda(4\mathbf{i} - 2\mathbf{k}), \lambda \in \mathbb{R}$

2 Find vector equations for the lines with these cartesian equations.

a $\frac{x-5}{2} = \frac{y-3}{2} = \frac{z-1}{3}$ b $\frac{x+3}{4} = y = \frac{z+1}{-2}$ c $x = 2, y + 2 = \frac{z+4}{5}$

3 The line l_1 has vector equation $\mathbf{r} = (\mathbf{i} + 2\mathbf{j} - \mathbf{k}) + \lambda(3\mathbf{i} + \mathbf{j} + \mathbf{k}), \lambda \in \mathbb{R}$

The line l_2 has cartesian equations $\frac{x-5}{-2} = \frac{y-1}{-3} = \frac{z-3}{2}$

Find the coordinates of the point P, where these lines intersect.

Find the vector equation of l_2

4 A line l has cartesian equations $\frac{x-p}{2} = \frac{y+1}{3} = \frac{z-2}{q}$, where p and q are non-zero constants. It is given that l passes through the point $P(2, -7, -8)$.

a Find the value of p and the value of q.

b Show that l is perpendicular to the line with cartesian equations

$$\frac{x}{-4} = y - 2 = z + 3$$

5 Find a vector equation for the line with cartesian equations

$$\frac{2x-1}{4} = \frac{3-y}{2} = \frac{1-3z}{2}$$

Express the equations in the form $\frac{x-a_1}{d_1} = \frac{y-a_2}{d_2} = \frac{z-a_3}{d_3}$

FP3

6.8 The vector product equation of a line

You can express the equation of a line using a vector product.

In the diagram, the line l is parallel to the vector **d**, and passes through the point A with position vector **a**. Point R, with position vector **r**, is any point on l.

$\overrightarrow{AR}$ is parallel to **d** for those, and only those, points **R** on l.

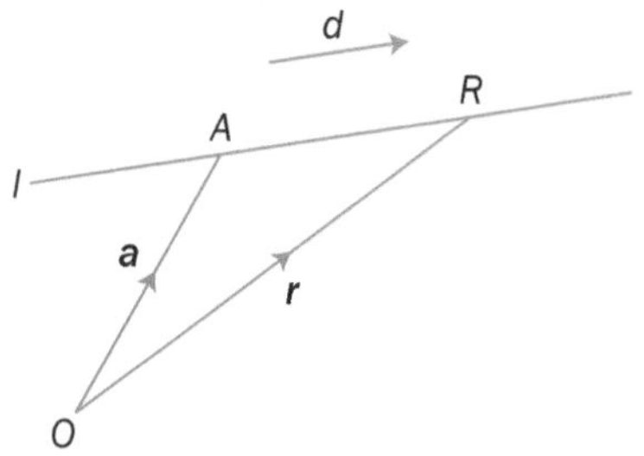

Since R is on l, $\overrightarrow{AR}$ is parallel to **d**.
Hence $\overrightarrow{AR} \times \mathbf{d} = \mathbf{0}$ where $\overrightarrow{AR} = \overrightarrow{OR} - \overrightarrow{OA} = \mathbf{r} - \mathbf{a}$
so $(\mathbf{r} - \mathbf{a}) \times \mathbf{d} = \mathbf{0}$

The vector product of parallel vectors is the zero vector.

$(\mathbf{r} - \mathbf{a}) \times \mathbf{d} = \mathbf{0}$ is the equation of l in vector product form.

A line l which passes through a point with position vector **a**, and which is parallel to the vector **d**, has equation

$$(\mathbf{r} - \mathbf{a}) \times \mathbf{d} = \mathbf{0}$$

where **r** is the position vector of any point on l.

Learn this result - it is **not** in the formula booklet.

EXAMPLE 1

A line l has vector equation

$$\mathbf{r} = (\mathbf{i} + 2\mathbf{j} - \mathbf{k}) + \lambda(3\mathbf{i} - 4\mathbf{j} + 2\mathbf{k}), \lambda \in \mathbb{R}$$

Find the equation of l in the form $(\mathbf{r} - \mathbf{a}) \times \mathbf{d} = \mathbf{0}$

Identify appropriate vectors **a** and **d**:

$$\mathbf{r} = (\mathbf{i} + 2\mathbf{j} - \mathbf{k}) + \lambda(3\mathbf{i} - 4\mathbf{j} + 2\mathbf{k}), \lambda \in \mathbb{R}$$

So $\mathbf{a} = \mathbf{i} + 2\mathbf{j} - \mathbf{k}$, $\mathbf{d} = 3\mathbf{i} - 4\mathbf{j} + 2\mathbf{k}$

Hence an equation of l is

$$(\mathbf{r} - \mathbf{i} - 2\mathbf{j} + \mathbf{k}) \times (3\mathbf{i} - 4\mathbf{j} + 2\mathbf{k}) = \mathbf{0}$$

$(\mathbf{r} - \mathbf{a}) = \mathbf{r} - (\mathbf{i} + 2\mathbf{j} - \mathbf{k})$
$= \mathbf{r} - \mathbf{i} - 2\mathbf{j} + \mathbf{k}$

EXAMPLE 2

A line l has equation $(\mathbf{r} - 3\mathbf{i} + 2\mathbf{j} + s\mathbf{k}) \times (4\mathbf{i} + t\mathbf{j}) = \mathbf{0}$, where s and t are constants. l passes through the point $P(7, -5, 2)$. Find the value of s and the value of t.

Substitute the position vector of point P into the given equation:

$$(\mathbf{p} - 3\mathbf{i} + 2\mathbf{j} + s\mathbf{k}) \times (4\mathbf{i} + t\mathbf{j}) = \mathbf{0}$$

so $((7\mathbf{i} - 5\mathbf{j} + 2\mathbf{k}) - 3\mathbf{i} + 2\mathbf{j} + s\mathbf{k}) \times (4\mathbf{i} + t\mathbf{j}) = \mathbf{0}$

$$(4\mathbf{i} - 3\mathbf{j} + (2 + s)\mathbf{k}) \times (4\mathbf{i} + t\mathbf{j}) = \mathbf{0}$$

P lies on *l*.

position vector of *p* is $p = 7\mathbf{i} - 5\mathbf{j} + 2\mathbf{k}$

Express this equation as a determinant:

$$\begin{vmatrix} \mathbf{i} & \mathbf{j} & \mathbf{k} \\ 4 & -3 & (2+s) \\ 4 & t & 0 \end{vmatrix} = \mathbf{0}$$

so $-t(2 + s)\mathbf{i} + 4(2 + s)\mathbf{j} + (4t + 12)\mathbf{k} = 0\mathbf{i} + 0\mathbf{j} + 0\mathbf{k}$

Compare $\mathbf{j}$ components
$4(2 + s) = 0$

Compare $\mathbf{k}$ components
$4t + 12 = 0$

Hence $s = -2$ and $t = -3$

You could also find s and *t* by first finding the vector equation of *l*.

Exercise 6.8

1 Express the equation of these lines in the form $(\mathbf{r} - \mathbf{a}) \times \mathbf{d} = \mathbf{0}$

  a the line passing through the point $A(2, 3, 1)$ and which is parallel to $3\mathbf{i} - \mathbf{j} + \mathbf{k}$

  b the line parallel to $2\mathbf{i} - 5\mathbf{j} - 3\mathbf{k}$ and which passes through the point $A(4, 0, -2)$

  c the line with vector equation $\mathbf{r} = 3\mathbf{j} + \mathbf{k} + \lambda(2\mathbf{i} - \mathbf{j})$, $\lambda \in \mathbb{R}$

2 A line l has equation $(\mathbf{r} - 7\mathbf{i} + 2\mathbf{j} - \mathbf{k}) \times (4\mathbf{i} - 3\mathbf{j}) = \mathbf{0}$

  a Find a unit vector which is parallel to l.

  b Show that point $A(3, 1, 1)$ lies on l.

  Given that point $B(-3, 5, 3)$ does not lie on l

  c find the equation of the line which passes through B and which is parallel to l. Give your answer in the form $(\mathbf{r} - \mathbf{p}) \times \mathbf{q} = \mathbf{0}$

3 Express the equation of the line with cartesian equations

$$\frac{x+3}{2} = y - 2 = \frac{z-1}{4} \text{ in the form } (\mathbf{r} - \mathbf{a}) \times \mathbf{d} = \mathbf{0}$$

4 The variable point R has position vector $\mathbf{r}$. Points A and B are fixed, with position vectors $\mathbf{a}$ and $\mathbf{b}$, respectively, where $\mathbf{b} \neq \mathbf{0}$.

Given that, for all points R, $\mathbf{r} \times \mathbf{b} = \mathbf{a} \times \mathbf{b}$ describe the locus of R.

A locus is the path traced out by a moving point.

FP3

6.9 The equation of a plane using scalar products

You can express the equation of a plane using scalar products.

In the diagram, the plane Π passes through the point A, which has position vector **a**. The vector **n** is normal to Π. Point R, with position vector **r**, is *any* point on Π.

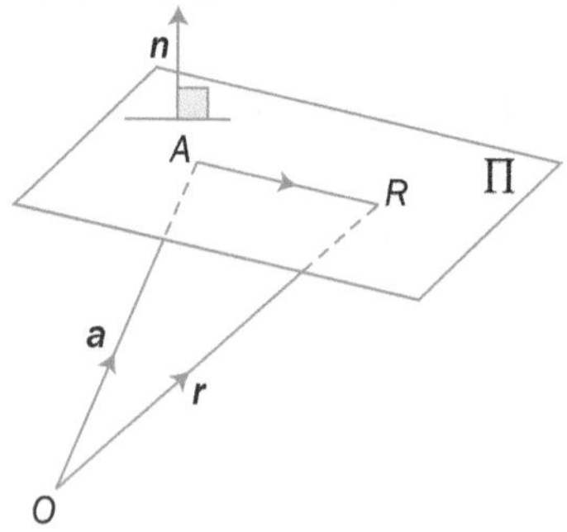

Since R is on Π, $\overrightarrow{AR}$ is perpendicular to **n**.

Hence $\overrightarrow{AR}.\mathbf{n} = 0$ where $\overrightarrow{AR} = \overrightarrow{OR} - \overrightarrow{OA} = \mathbf{r} - \mathbf{a}$

so $(\mathbf{r} - \mathbf{a}).\mathbf{n} = 0$

The scalar product of perpendicular vectors is zero. Refer to C4.

Expand the brackets:

$$\mathbf{r}.\mathbf{n} - \mathbf{a}.\mathbf{n} = 0$$

$$\mathbf{r}.\mathbf{n} = \mathbf{a}.\mathbf{n}$$

For a given plane with normal vector **n**, the RHS of this equation is a constant.

The scalar product equation of a plane Π through A with normal vector **n** is

$$\mathbf{r}.\mathbf{n} = \mathbf{a}.\mathbf{n}$$

where **a** is the position vector of A and **r** is the position vector of any point on Π.

EXAMPLE 1

A plane Π passes through the point $A(2, 1, 4)$. The vector $\mathbf{n} = 3\mathbf{i} + 2\mathbf{j} - \mathbf{k}$ is normal to this plane. Find the equation of Π in scalar product form.

Use the result $\mathbf{r}.\mathbf{n} = \mathbf{a}.\mathbf{n}$ to find the equation of Π:

$\mathbf{a} = 2\mathbf{i} + \mathbf{j} + 4\mathbf{k}$, $\mathbf{n} = 3\mathbf{i} + 2\mathbf{j} - \mathbf{k}$ so an equation for Π is

$$\mathbf{r}.\mathbf{n} = \mathbf{a}.\mathbf{n}$$

$$\mathbf{r}.(3\mathbf{i} + 2\mathbf{j} - \mathbf{k}) = (2\mathbf{i} + \mathbf{j} + 4\mathbf{k}).(3\mathbf{i} + 2\mathbf{j} - \mathbf{k})$$
$$= (2 \times 3) + (1 \times 2) + (4 \times -1)$$
$$= 4$$

so the plane Π has equation $\mathbf{r}.(3\mathbf{i} + 2\mathbf{j} - \mathbf{k}) = 4$

You can find a *cartesian* equation of a plane by calculating scalar products.
The plane Π through A with normal vector $\mathbf{n} = n_1\mathbf{i} + n_2\mathbf{j} + n_3\mathbf{k}$ has a *cartesian* equation

$$n_1x + n_2y + n_3z = \mathbf{a}.\mathbf{n}$$

where **a** is the position vector of A.

In the formula booklet, this result is given as

$n_1x + n_2y + n_3z + d = 0$,
$d = -\mathbf{a}.\mathbf{n}$

This equation is found by substituting $\mathbf{r} = x\mathbf{i} + y\mathbf{j} + z\mathbf{k}$ into the scalar product equation $\mathbf{r}.\mathbf{n} = \mathbf{a}.\mathbf{n}$, where $\mathbf{r}$ is the position vector of any point $R(x, y, z)$ on the plane.

If a plane Π has cartesian equation

$$ax + by + cz = d, \text{ where } a, b, c, d \in \mathbb{R}$$

then $\mathbf{n} = a\mathbf{i} + b\mathbf{j} + c\mathbf{k}$ is a normal vector to Π.

The coefficients of x, y and z are the components of a normal vector to Π. See Example 2.

EXAMPLE 2

A plane Π has cartesian equation $x + 3y - 2z = -8$

a Show that point $B(6, 3, 1)$ does not lie on Π.

b Find a cartesian equation for the plane Π_1 which is parallel to Π and which passes through point B.

---

a Substitute the x, y and z coordinates of point B into the LHS of the cartesian equation:

At B (6, 3, 1), $x = 6, y = 3$ and $z = 1$

So $x + 3y - 2z = 6 + 3(3) - 2(1)$

$= 13 \neq -8$

Hence B does not lie on Π.

A point $R(x, y, z)$ lies on Π precisely when $x + 3y - 2z = -8$

b Use an appropriate normal vector to Π_1 and the position vector of a point on Π_1:

The vector $\mathbf{n} = \mathbf{i} + 3\mathbf{j} - 2\mathbf{k}$ is a normal vector to Π.

Use the coefficients of x, y and z in the equation for Π.

Π_1 is parallel to Π so $\mathbf{n} = \mathbf{i} + 3\mathbf{j} - 2\mathbf{k}$ is also a normal vector to Π_1.

The point $B(6, 3, 1)$, with position vector $\mathbf{b}$, lies on Π_1.

Hence a cartesian equation for Π_1 is

$x + 3y - 2z = 13$

$\mathbf{b}.\mathbf{n} = 13$, see calculation in part a

FP3

Exercise 6.9

1 Find, in scalar product form, an equation for the plane which passes through the point A and which has normal vector $\mathbf{n}$, as given.

a $A(6, -1, 3)$, $\mathbf{n} = 5\mathbf{i} - 3\mathbf{j} + \mathbf{k}$

b $A(-3, 4, -2)$, $\mathbf{n} = 4\mathbf{i} - \mathbf{j} - 3\mathbf{k}$

2 A plane Π has equation $\mathbf{r}.(4\mathbf{i} - 3\mathbf{k}) = 7$

a Find a unit normal vector which is normal to this plane.

b Given that the point $B(-2, -5, k)$ lies on Π, find the value of the constant k.

Point P is such that $\overrightarrow{BP}$ is perpendicular to Π.

c Given that $|\overrightarrow{BP}| = 15$, find the possible coordinates of point P.

3 Find a cartesian equation for these planes.

a The plane passing through $A(5, 2, 3)$ and which has normal vector $\mathbf{n} = 2\mathbf{i} + \mathbf{j} + \mathbf{k}$

b The plane passing through $A(2, -3, 1)$ and which has normal vector $\mathbf{n} = 3\mathbf{i} - 2\mathbf{j} - \mathbf{k}$

c The plane with scalar product equation $\mathbf{r}.(5\mathbf{i} + 2\mathbf{j} - 3\mathbf{k}) = 7$

4 Find a unit vector which is normal to the planes with these equations.

a $2x + 3y + 6z = 4$

b $5x - 4y - 20z = 3$

FP3

5 A plane Π passes through the origin O and the points $A(2, -2, 1)$ and $B(3, 2, 4)$.

a Show that $\mathbf{n} = 2\mathbf{i} + \mathbf{j} - 2\mathbf{k}$ is a normal vector to Π.

Calculate $\overrightarrow{OA} \times \overrightarrow{OB}$

b Hence find a cartesian equation of Π.

Given that Π passes through the point $P(-2, t, -1)$, where t is a constant

c find the value of t.

6 Find a cartesian equation of the plane passing through these points.

a $A(1, 1, 1), B(1, 0, -1), C(3, -1, 0)$

Calculate $\overrightarrow{AB} \times \overrightarrow{AC}$

b $A(3, 1, 3), B(4, -1, -6), C(-2, -3, -1)$

7 A plane Π has vector equation

$$\mathbf{r} = (3\mathbf{i} + 2\mathbf{j}) + \lambda(4\mathbf{i} + 8\mathbf{j} - \mathbf{k}) + \mu(5\mathbf{i} + 4\mathbf{j} - 2\mathbf{k}),\ \lambda,\ \mu \in \mathbb{R}$$

a Show that $\mathbf{n} = 4\mathbf{i} - \mathbf{j} + 8\mathbf{k}$ is a normal vector to Π.

b Hence, or otherwise, find a cartesian equation of Π.

The line l with equation $\mathbf{r} = (p\mathbf{i} + 2\mathbf{j} + 2\mathbf{k}) + s(q\mathbf{i} + 2\mathbf{k}), s \in \mathbb{R}$, where p and q are constants, lies on Π.

c Find the value of p and the value of q.

8 The diagram shows a plane Π which passes through the point $A(-1, -1, -3)$. The equation of Π is $3x + y - 2z = d$, where d is a constant. Also shown is the line AB, where B has coordinates $B(5, 1, -7)$.

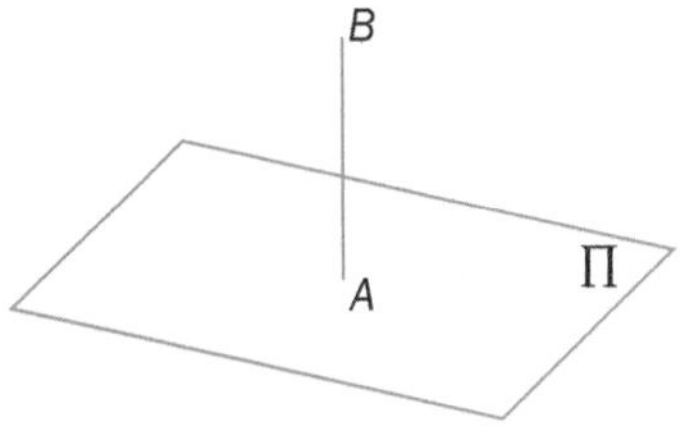

a Find the value of d.

b Show that $\overrightarrow{BA}$ is a normal vector to Π.

c Find the coordinates of the point C, which is the reflection in Π of the point B.

d Hence find a cartesian equation of the plane Π_1 which is parallel to Π and which passes through point C.

9 The line l with equation

$$r = (2\mathbf{i} + 3\mathbf{k}) + \lambda(2\mathbf{i} - \mathbf{j} + 4\mathbf{k}), \lambda \in \mathbb{R}$$

is perpendicular to a plane Π. The point $P(0, m, n)$ lies on l and Π.

a Find the value of the constants m and n.

b Hence find the equation of Π, giving your answer in the form

$$ax + by + cz + d = 0$$

for constants a, b, c and d.

10 The line l_1 has vector equation

$$r = (7\mathbf{i} + 10\mathbf{j} + 6\mathbf{k}) + \lambda(\mathbf{i} + 2\mathbf{j} + \mathbf{k}), \lambda \in \mathbb{R}$$

The line l_2 is parallel to the vector $5\mathbf{j} + \mathbf{k}$. The plane Π contains both of these lines.

a Find a normal vector to Π.

b Hence, or otherwise, show that a cartesian equation for Π is

$$3x + y - 5z = 1$$

l_2 passes through the point $P(4, -1, k)$, where k is a constant.

c Find the value of k and hence express the equation of l_2 in cartesian form.

6.10 The intersection of a line and a plane

You can find the coordinates of the point where a line and plane intersect.

EXAMPLE 1

The diagram shows the plane Π with equation

$$\mathbf{r}.(\mathbf{i}-\mathbf{j}+\mathbf{k})=5$$

and the line l with equation

$$\mathbf{r}=(2\mathbf{i}+\mathbf{j})+t(3\mathbf{i}+3\mathbf{j}+2\mathbf{k}),\quad t\in\mathbb{R}.$$

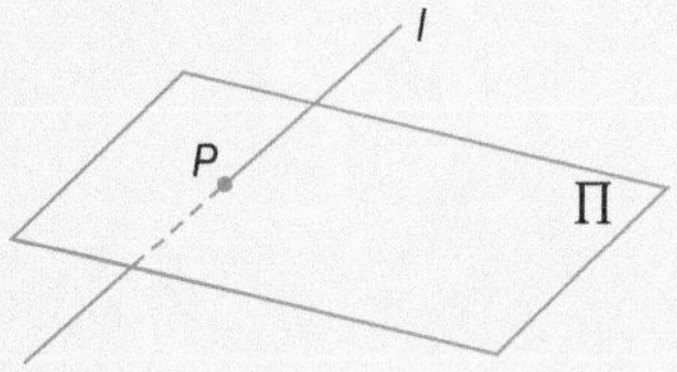

P is the point where l and Π intersect.
Find the coordinates of point P.

Use the two defining properties of the position vector **p** of P:

i P lies on l so $\mathbf{p}=(2\mathbf{i}+\mathbf{j})+t(3\mathbf{i}+3\mathbf{j}+2\mathbf{k})$ for some value of t,

ii P lies on Π so

$$\mathbf{p}.(\mathbf{i}-\mathbf{j}+\mathbf{k})=5$$
$$[(2\mathbf{i}+\mathbf{j})+t(3\mathbf{i}+3\mathbf{j}+2\mathbf{k})].(\mathbf{i}-\mathbf{j}+\mathbf{k})=5$$

So $[(2+3t)\mathbf{i}+(1+3t)\mathbf{j}+2t\mathbf{k}].(\mathbf{i}-\mathbf{j}+\mathbf{k})=5$

Hence $(2+3t)-(1+3t)+2t=5$

$$1+2t=5$$

that is, $t=2$

so $\mathbf{p}=(2\mathbf{i}+\mathbf{j})+2(3\mathbf{i}+3\mathbf{j}+2\mathbf{k})$
$=8\mathbf{i}+7\mathbf{j}+4\mathbf{k}$

The coordinates of P are $P(8, 7, 4)$.

The aim is to find t so that **p**, and therefore the coordinates of P, can be found.

Collect together the **i**, **j** and **k** components.

Use the components to calculate the scalar product.

EXAMPLE 2

The diagram shows the plane Π with cartesian equation

$$2x + y + 3z = 6$$

Also shown is the point P on Π and the point $Q(5, 3, 7)$. The line through PQ is perpendicular to Π.

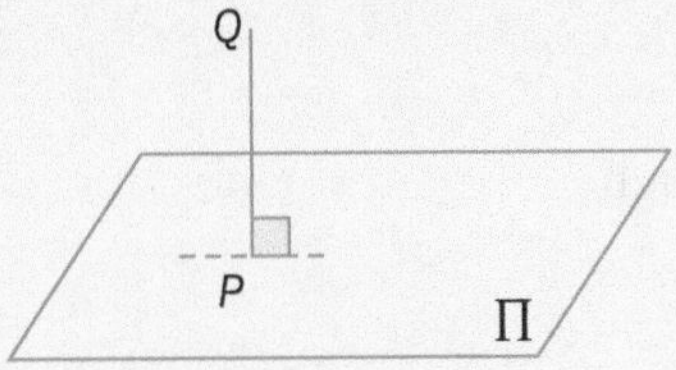

Find the coordinates of P.

P is the foot of the perpendicular from Q to the plane.

Find a vector equation for the line l through P and Q:

$$\mathbf{r} = (5\mathbf{i} + 3\mathbf{j} + 7\mathbf{k}) + t\,(2\mathbf{i} + \mathbf{j} + 3\mathbf{k}),\ t \in \mathbb{R}$$
$$= (5 + 2t)\mathbf{i} + (3 + t)\mathbf{j} + (7 + 3t)\mathbf{k}$$

The vector $\mathbf{n} = 2\mathbf{i} + \mathbf{j} + 3\mathbf{k}$ is normal to Π.
l is perpendicular to Π and so its direction is parallel to $\mathbf{n} = 2\mathbf{i} + \mathbf{j} + 3\mathbf{k}$

Use the two defining properties of point P:

i Since $P(x_0, y_0, z_0)$ lies on l
$x_0 = 5 + 2t$, $y_0 = 3 + t$ and
$z_0 = 7 + 3t$ for some value of t.

ii Since $P(x_0, y_0, z_0)$ lies on Π
$2x_0 + y_0 + 3z_0 = 6$

The aim is to calculate t so that the value of x_0, y_0 and z_0 can then be found.

Substitute the expressions in i into the equation in ii:

$$2(5 + 2t) + (3 + t) + 3(7 + 3t) = 6$$
$$34 + 14t = 6$$
$$t = -2$$

$14t + 34 = 6$ so $t = -\frac{28}{14} = -2$

Use the equations in i to find the coordinates of P:

$$x_0 = 5 + 2\,(-2) = 1$$
$$y_0 = 3 + (-2) = 1$$
$$z_0 = 7 + 3\,(-2) = 1$$

The coordinates of P are (1, 1, 1).

Check that $P(1, 1, 1)$ lies on Π:
$2x + y + 3z = 2 \times 1 + 1 + 3 \times 1$
$= 6$ Correct!

Exercise 6.10

1 Find the coordinates of the point P where the lines and planes with these equations intersect.

a l: $\mathbf{r} = (7\mathbf{i} + 3\mathbf{j} + 2\mathbf{k}) + t\,(3\mathbf{i} + \mathbf{j} + 2\mathbf{k}),\ t \in \mathbb{R}$ Π: $\mathbf{r}.\,(2\mathbf{i} + 3\mathbf{j} - \mathbf{k}) = 7$

b l: $\mathbf{r} = (4\mathbf{i} - 4\mathbf{j} - 5\mathbf{k}) + t\,(-\mathbf{i} + 2\mathbf{j} + 4\mathbf{k}),\ t \in \mathbb{R}$ Π: $\mathbf{r}.\,(5\mathbf{i} - 3\mathbf{k}) = 8$

c l: $\mathbf{r} = (2\mathbf{i} + 3\mathbf{k}) + t\,(2\mathbf{i} - 3\mathbf{j}),\ t \in \mathbb{R}$ Π: $2x + 3y + 3z = 8$

FP3

2 A line l passes through the point $A(0, 11, 4)$ and is parallel to $\mathbf{d} = -2\mathbf{i} + 2\mathbf{j} + \mathbf{k}$.
The plane Π has cartesian equation $6x - 3y + 2z = -17$

Find the coordinates of

a the point P where l and Π intersect

b the other point, B, on l, such that $|\overrightarrow{BP}| = |\overrightarrow{AP}|$

3 The plane Π has equation $2x - 3y + z = 7$. The line l passes through the point $A(7, -5, 6)$ and is perpendicular to Π.

a Find a vector equation for l.

b Find the coordinates of the point P where l and Π intersect.

4 The plane Π contains the point $A(5, 11, 0)$. The line l with vector equation

$$\mathbf{r} = (\mathbf{i} + 2\mathbf{j} + \mathbf{k}) + s(-\mathbf{i} + 3\mathbf{j} + \mathbf{k}), s \in \mathbb{R}$$

is perpendicular to Π.

a Find a cartesian equation for Π.

b Find the coordinates of the point P where l intersects Π.

5 A plane Π has equation $2x + y - 2z = 7$. The point Q has coordinates $(4, 2, -3)$.

Refer to Example 2.

a Find the coordinates of P, the foot of the perpendicular from Q to Π.

b Find the length PQ.

Point $T(4, p, q)$ on Π is such that triangle TPQ is isosceles.

c Find the possible coordinates of T.

6 A plane Π has equation $\mathbf{r}.(4\mathbf{i} + 3\mathbf{j} + 5\mathbf{k}) = 22$. The line l passes through the point $Q\left(\frac{9}{5}, \frac{8}{5}, 4\right)$ and is parallel to the vector $\mathbf{d} = 3\mathbf{i} - 4\mathbf{j} - 5\mathbf{k}$

a Find the coordinates of the point P where l intersects Π.

b Find the coordinates of R, the foot of the perpendicular from Q to Π.

c Calculate, in radians, the acute angle QPR. Give your answer in terms of π.

7 The plane Π has equation $x + 3y + z = 8$. The line l passes through the point $A(0, 6, 2)$ and is parallel to the vector $\mathbf{i} - 2\mathbf{j} - \mathbf{k}$.

a Verify that the point $P(2, 2, 0)$ lies on l and Π.

The line l' passes through A and has cartesian equations

$$\frac{x}{3} = \frac{y-6}{2} = \frac{z-2}{-1}$$

b Show that l' is perpendicular to l.

c Find the coordinates of the point Q where l' intersects Π.

d Hence, or otherwise, show that the area of triangle PAQ is $3\sqrt{21}$ square units.

8 A plane Π passes through the points $A(4, -3\ -6)$, $B(-1, 1, -8)$ and $C(5, 1, 4)$.

The line l has equation $\mathbf{r} = (-\mathbf{i} + 5\mathbf{j} - 2\mathbf{k}) + t\,(\mathbf{i} - 2\mathbf{j} - \mathbf{k}), t \in \mathbb{R}$.

a Find the area of triangle ABC.

b Find a cartesian equation of Π.

The line l intersects the plane Π at point P.

c Show that the coordinates of P are $P(1, 1, -4)$.

d Show that B, P and C are collinear and hence find the area of triangle APC.

As an extra challenge, avoid using a calculator for any part of this question.

9 The diagram shows the plane Π with equation $3x - y + 2z = 7$. Also shown are the lines l_1 and l_2, which intersect Π at points A and B, respectively, and each other at point $C(10, 1, -1)$.

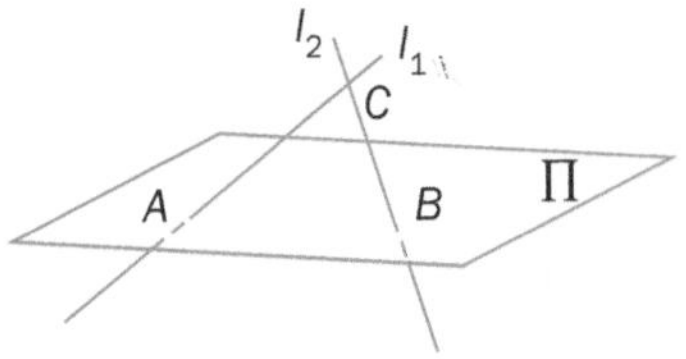

The equation of l_1 is $\mathbf{r} = (6\mathbf{i} + \mathbf{j}) + t(4\mathbf{i} - \mathbf{k}), t \in \mathbb{R}$

a Find the coordinates of point A.

b Given that l_2 is parallel to $3\mathbf{i} + \mathbf{j} + \mathbf{k}$

i find the coordinates of point B

ii show that a cartesian equation of the plane containing the points A, B and C is

$$x - 7y + 4z + 1 = 0$$

FP3

6.11 Shortest distances

You can find the shortest, that is the perpendicular, distance of a point from a plane.

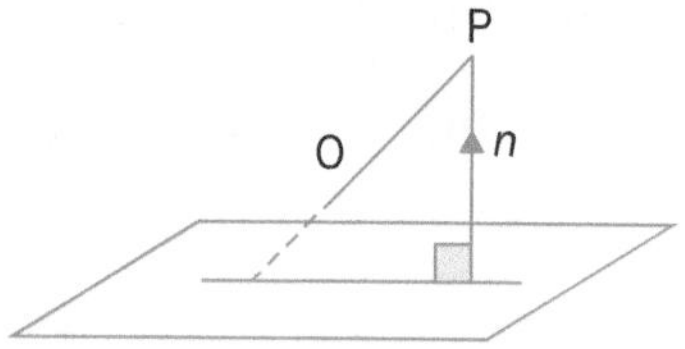

The perpendicular distance of a point P(α, β, γ) from a plane with equation $n_1x + n_2y + n_3z + d = 0$ is

$$\frac{|n_1\alpha + n_2\beta + n_3\gamma + d|}{\sqrt{n_1^2 + n_2^2 + n_3^2}}$$

This result is in the FP3 section of the formula booklet.

You can also find the shortest distance between two non-parallel lines.

If the non-parallel lines l_1 and l_2 have equations l_1: $\mathbf{r} = \mathbf{a} + s\mathbf{c}$, l_2: $\mathbf{r} = \mathbf{b} + t\mathbf{d}$, $s, t \in \mathbb{R}$ then the shortest distance between l_1 and l_2 is given by

$$\frac{|(\mathbf{a} - \mathbf{b}).\mathbf{c} \times \mathbf{d}|}{|\mathbf{c} \times \mathbf{d}|}$$

This result is **not** in the formula

This is the length of the line PQ, where P is on l_1, Q is on l_2 and the line PQ is perpendicular to l_1 and l_2.

EXAMPLE 1

Find the shortest distance of the point $A(1, 2, 2)$ from the plane with equation $5x + 3y + 4z + 1 = 0$

Identify a vector normal to this plane:

$\mathbf{n} = 5\mathbf{i} + 3\mathbf{j} + 4\mathbf{k}$ is normal to the plane.

Use the coefficients of x, y and z in the equation for Π.

Use the coordinates $A(1, 2, 2)$ to find the required distance:

$$\text{shortest distance} = \frac{|n_1\alpha + n_2\beta + n_3\gamma + d|}{\sqrt{n_1^2 + n_2^2 + n_3^2}}$$

$$= \frac{|5\times1 + 3\times2 + 4\times2 + 1|}{\sqrt{5^2 + 3^2 + 4^2}}$$

$$= \frac{20}{\sqrt{50}}$$

$$= \frac{4}{\sqrt{2}}$$

$$= 2\sqrt{2}$$

The shortest distance of A from this plane is $2\sqrt{2}$ units.

EXAMPLE 2

Find the shortest distance between the lines l_1 and l_2 with equations
l_1: $\mathbf{r} = (3\mathbf{i} + 2\mathbf{j}) + s(4\mathbf{i} + 2\mathbf{j} + 3\mathbf{k}), s \in \mathbb{R}$ and
l_2: $\mathbf{r} = (-\mathbf{i} + \mathbf{j} + 2\mathbf{k}) + t(3\mathbf{i} + \mathbf{j} + 2\mathbf{k}), t \in \mathbb{R}$

Identify the appropriate position and direction vectors for each line:

For l_1, $\mathbf{a} = 3\mathbf{i} + 2\mathbf{j}$, $\mathbf{c} = 4\mathbf{i} + 2\mathbf{j} + 3\mathbf{k}$
For l_2, $\mathbf{b} = -\mathbf{i} + \mathbf{j} + 2\mathbf{k}$, $\mathbf{d} = 3\mathbf{i} + \mathbf{j} + 2\mathbf{k}$

a is the position vector of a particular point on l_1. **c** is a direction vector of l_1.

Calculate **a** – **b**:

$$\mathbf{a} - \mathbf{b} = (3\mathbf{i} + 2\mathbf{j}) - (-\mathbf{i} + \mathbf{j} + 2\mathbf{k})$$
$$= 4\mathbf{i} + \mathbf{j} - 2\mathbf{k}$$

Calculate the vector product **c** × **d**:

$$\mathbf{c}\times\mathbf{d} = \begin{vmatrix} \mathbf{i} & \mathbf{j} & \mathbf{k} \\ 4 & 2 & 3 \\ 3 & 1 & 2 \end{vmatrix}$$
$$= \mathbf{i}(4-3) - \mathbf{j}(8-9) + \mathbf{k}(4-6)$$
$$= \mathbf{i} + \mathbf{j} - 2\mathbf{k}$$

Use the appropriate formula to find the required distance:

$$\text{shortest distance} = \frac{|(\mathbf{a}-\mathbf{b}).\mathbf{c}\times\mathbf{d}|}{|\mathbf{c}\times\mathbf{d}|}$$
$$= \frac{|(4\mathbf{i}+\mathbf{j}-2\mathbf{k}).(\mathbf{i}+\mathbf{j}-2\mathbf{k})|}{|\mathbf{i}+\mathbf{j}-2\mathbf{k}|}$$
$$= \frac{9}{\sqrt{6}}$$

$(\mathbf{a} - \mathbf{b}).\,\mathbf{c} \times \mathbf{d}$ means $[(\mathbf{a} - \mathbf{b})].[\mathbf{c} \times \mathbf{d}]$

$(4\mathbf{i} + \mathbf{j} - 2\mathbf{k}).(\mathbf{i} + \mathbf{j} - 2\mathbf{k})$
$= (4 \times 1) + (1 \times 1) + (-2 \times -2)$
$= 9$

The shortest distance between l_1 and l_2 is $\frac{3}{2}\sqrt{6}$ units.

$\frac{9}{\sqrt{6}} = \frac{9\sqrt{6}}{6} = \frac{3}{2}\sqrt{6}$

FP3

Exercise 6.11

1 Find the shortest distance of these points from the planes with these equations. Where appropriate, give answers in simplified surd form.

a $A(2, 1, 3)$, Π: $3x - y + 2z + 3 = 0$
b $A(-2, 3, -3)$, Π: $4x + 2y - z - 4 = 0$
c $A(5, -2, 1)$, Π: $6x - 3y - 2z = 6$
d $A(5, 0, 3)$, Π: $\mathbf{r}.(3\mathbf{i} + \mathbf{j} - 4\mathbf{k}) = -10$

2 A line l passes through the points $A(3, 7, 6)$ and $B(0, -8, -3)$.
The plane Π has equation $5x + 2y - 5z + 2 = 0$

a Find the shortest distance of each of the points A and B from the plane Π.

b Hence state whether or not l is parallel to Π. You may assume A and B lie on the same side of this plane.

3 A tetrahedron $ABCD$ is such that the vertices A, B and C lie on a plane Π with equation $2x - y + 2z = 5$. The area of triangle ABC is 5 square units. Point D has coordinates $D(6, 3, 1)$.

a Show that the shortest distance of D from the plane Π is 2 units.

b Hence find the volume of this tetrahedron.

4 A plane Π has equation $x - 2y + 2z = 9$

a Find the shortest distance from Π to the origin.

P is the point on Π which is nearest the origin. Q is any point on Π such that $|\overrightarrow{OQ}| = 6$

b Find, $|\overrightarrow{PQ}|$ giving your answer in simplified surd form.

5 A plane Π passes through the points $A(3, -1, -1)$, $B(2, 1, 1)$ and $C(-1, 2, 4)$.

a Find a cartesian equation for Π.

A plane Π_1, which does not contain the origin, is parallel to Π.
A point D on Π_1 is such that the shortest distance from D to Π is $\sqrt{2}$ units.

b Find a cartesian equation for Π_1.

c Calculate the volume of the tetrahedron $ABCD$.

6 A line l passes through the point $A(8, 3, -1)$ and is parallel to $\mathbf{d} = 4\mathbf{i} + 2\mathbf{j} + 5\mathbf{k}$. A plane Π has equation $x - y + 2z + 9 = 0$

a Find the coordinates of the point P where l intersects Π.

b Show that the shortest distance from point A to the plane Π is $2\sqrt{6}$ units.

c Hence, or otherwise, find the exact distance PQ, where Q is the foot of the perpendicular from A to Π.

7 Find the shortest distance between the pairs of non-parallel lines with these equations. Give answers in simplified surd form.

a l_1: $\mathbf{r} = (2\mathbf{i} + \mathbf{j} - \mathbf{k}) + s(2\mathbf{i} - 2\mathbf{j} + \mathbf{k}), s \in \mathbb{R}$

l_2: $\mathbf{r} = (4\mathbf{i} + 5\mathbf{j}) + t(\mathbf{i} + 2\mathbf{j} + 2\mathbf{k}), t \in \mathbb{R}$

b l_1: $\mathbf{r} = (3\mathbf{i} + \mathbf{j}) + s(3\mathbf{i} + 4\mathbf{j} + \mathbf{k}), s \in \mathbb{R}$

l_2: $\mathbf{r} = (2\mathbf{i} - 5\mathbf{j} + \mathbf{k}) + t(\mathbf{i} + 2\mathbf{j} + \mathbf{k}), t \in \mathbb{R}$

c l_1: $\mathbf{r} = (\mathbf{i} + 2\mathbf{j} - 3\mathbf{k}) + s(2\mathbf{i} - 3\mathbf{j} + \mathbf{k}), s \in \mathbb{R}$

l_2: $\mathbf{r} = (\mathbf{i} - 4\mathbf{j} + 2\mathbf{k}) + t(4\mathbf{i} + 2\mathbf{j} - 3\mathbf{k}), t \in \mathbb{R}$

8 Non-parallel lines l_1 and l_2 have equations

l_1: $\mathbf{r} = (3\mathbf{i} + \mathbf{j} + 2\mathbf{k}) + s(\mathbf{i} + \mathbf{j} + 2\mathbf{k}), s \in \mathbb{R}$ and
l_2: $\mathbf{r} = (\mathbf{i} + 9\mathbf{j} + 8\mathbf{k}) + t(-2\mathbf{i} + 3\mathbf{j} + \mathbf{k}), t \in \mathbb{R}$

By calculating the shortest distance between l_1 and l_2, show that these lines intersect.

9 The non-parallel lines l_1 and l_2 have equations l_1: $\mathbf{r} = (2\mathbf{i} + \mathbf{k}) + s\,(2\mathbf{i} - \mathbf{j} + 3\mathbf{k}),\ s \in \mathbb{R}$ and l_2: $\mathbf{r} = (p\mathbf{i} + 3\mathbf{j} - \mathbf{k}) + t(4\mathbf{i} - 2\mathbf{j} + \mathbf{k}),\ t \in \mathbb{R}$, where $p < 0$

a Show that an expression for the shortest distance between l_1 and l_2 is $\frac{|4 + p|}{\sqrt{5}}$

b Find the value of p in the case when

i this shortest distance is $2\sqrt{5}$ units

ii the two lines lie on a common plane. Give a cartesian equation for this plane.

10 The plane Π passes through the points $A(1,0,2)$, $B(4,1,1)$ and $C(3,-2,2)$.

a Calculate $\overrightarrow{AB} \times \overrightarrow{AC}$ and hence find a cartesian equation for Π

The line l is parallel to the vector $\mathbf{i} + \mathbf{j}$ and passes through point $P(3,2,k)$, where $k > 0$. The shortest distance of P from Π is $2\sqrt{2}$ units.

b Find the value of k

c Calculate the shortest distance between l and the line which passes through the points A and B. Give your answer in simplified surd form.

11 The diagram shows a plane Π with cartesian equation $\mathbf{n.a} + d = 0$, where $d \in \mathbb{R}$, $\mathbf{n}$ is a normal vector to Π and $\mathbf{a}$ is the position vector of a fixed point A on Π.

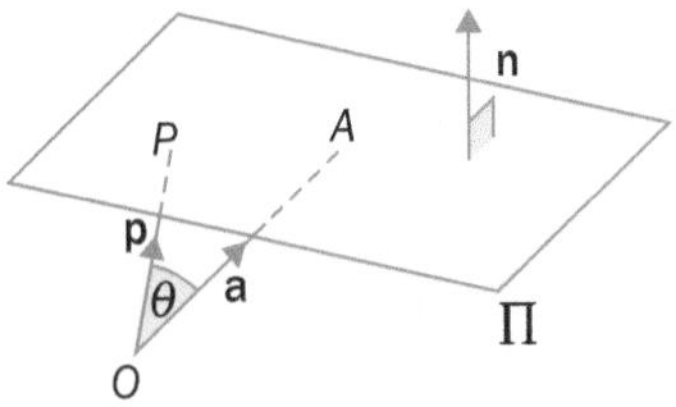

Point P, with position vector $\mathbf{p}$, is the foot of the perpendicular from the origin O to Π. Angle θ is the acute angle between the vectors $\mathbf{a}$ and $\mathbf{p}$.

a Use trigonometry to show that $|\mathbf{p}| = |\mathbf{a}|\cos\theta$

b Deduce that the shortest distance from O to Π is $\frac{\mathbf{n.a}}{|\mathbf{n}|}$ (You may assume that vectors $\mathbf{p}$ and $\mathbf{n}$ are pointing in the same direction.)

c Hence show that the shortest distance from any point $B(\alpha, \beta, \gamma)$ to Π is given by

$$\frac{|n_1\alpha + n_2\beta + n_3\gamma + d|}{\sqrt{n_1^2 + n_2^2 + n_3^2}}$$

where $\mathbf{n} = n_1\mathbf{i} + n_2\mathbf{j} + n_3\mathbf{k}$

(For simplicity, you may assume B and Π lie on the same side of the origin.)

Consider the plane parallel to Π and which contains point B.

FP3

6.12 The equation of the line of intersection of two planes

Two non-parallel planes intersect in a unique line. You can find the equation of this common line of intersection by using a vector product.

If the non-parallel planes Π_1 and Π_2 have a line of intersection l, then a direction vector of l is $\mathbf{n}_1 \times \mathbf{n}_2$, where $\mathbf{n}_1$ and $\mathbf{n}_2$ are vectors normal to Π_1 and Π_2, respectively.

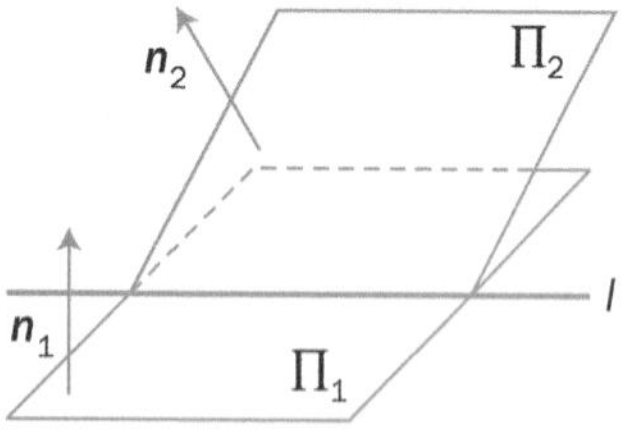

Any line on Π_1 is perpendicular to $\mathbf{n}_1$. Any line on Π_2 is perpendicular to $\mathbf{n}_2$. Since l lies on **both** planes, l is perpendicular to $\mathbf{n}_1$ and $\mathbf{n}_2$, and hence is parallel to the vector $\mathbf{n}_1 \times \mathbf{n}_2$. See Section 6.4.

EXAMPLE 1

Find an equation for the line l of intersection of the planes Π_1 and Π_2 with equations $x - y - z = 1$ and $2x + 4y - 5z = 5$ respectively.

Identify vectors normal to each plane:

$\mathbf{n}_1 = \mathbf{i} - \mathbf{j} - \mathbf{k}$ is a normal vector to Π_1

$\mathbf{n}_2 = 2\mathbf{i} + 4\mathbf{j} - 5\mathbf{k}$ is a normal vector to Π_2

Π_1: $x - y - z = 1$ so $\mathbf{n}_1 = \mathbf{i} - \mathbf{j} - \mathbf{k}$ is normal Π_1

Find the vector product $\mathbf{n}_1 \times \mathbf{n}_2$:

$$\mathbf{n}_1 \times \mathbf{n}_2 = \begin{vmatrix} \mathbf{i} & \mathbf{j} & \mathbf{k} \\ 1 & -1 & -1 \\ 2 & 4 & -5 \end{vmatrix} = \mathbf{i}\,(5 + 4) - \mathbf{j}(-5 + 2) + \mathbf{k}\,(4 + 2)$$

$$= 9\mathbf{i} + 3\mathbf{j} + 6\mathbf{k}$$

Hence $\mathbf{d} = 3\mathbf{i} + \mathbf{j} + 2\mathbf{k}$ is a direction vector of l.

$3\mathbf{i} + \mathbf{j} + 2\mathbf{k}$ is parallel to $9\mathbf{i} + 3\mathbf{j} + 6\mathbf{k}$

Find the coordinates of a point on l by substituting $y = 0$ into both plane equations:

For Π_1, when $y = 0$, $x - z = 1$ (1)

For Π_2, when $y = 0$, $2x - 5z = 5$ (2)

Solve (1) and (2) simultaneously: $z = -1$, $x = 0$

So the point $A(0, 0, -1)$ is a point on l.

Hence a vector equation for l is $\mathbf{r} = -\mathbf{k} + t\,(3\mathbf{i} + \mathbf{j} + 2\mathbf{k})$, $t \in \mathbb{R}$

When finding a point on l, you can set any of x, y or z to zero, provided the corresponding component in a direction vector **d** of l is non-zero.

For example, if $\mathbf{d} = 3\mathbf{i} + 2\mathbf{k}$ is a direction vector of l, a line of intersection of two planes, then, since its **j**-component is zero, setting $y = 0$ in the plane equations may fail to find a point on l. In this case, you should set either $x = 0$ or $z = 0$ to find a point on l.

Exercise 6.12

1 Find a vector equation for the line of intersection of the planes with these equations.

a $\Pi_1: x - y - 2z = 1$ $\Pi_2: 2x - 3y - 2z = -5$

b $\Pi_1: 3x + y - 3z = -1$ $\Pi_2: 3x + 2y = 10$

c $\Pi_1: 4x + 2y - z = 7$ $\Pi_2: 3x + 4y - 2z = 4$

2 The plane Π_1 has equation $px - 4y - z = 1$, where p is a constant. The point $A(2, 1, 1)$ lies on this plane.

a Show that $p = 3$

The plane Π_2 has equation $x + 2y - 2z = 2$. The line l is the line of intersection of these two planes.

b Find a vector equation of l.

Point B on Π_1 and Π_2 is such that $AB = 9$ units.

c Find the possible coordinates of point B.

3 The plane Π_1 with equation $3x + 2y - z = d$, where d is a constant, passes through the point $A(1, 1, 3)$. The plane Π_2 has equation $x - 2y + z = 6$

a Find the value of d

b Hence show that the line l of intersection of these two planes has vector equation

$$\mathbf{r} = 2\mathbf{i} + 4\mathbf{k} + t(\mathbf{j} + 2\mathbf{k}), t \in \mathbb{R}$$

Point $B(p, -4, 3)$, where p is a constant, lies on Π_2

c Find the value of p

d Show that the shortest distance between the line l and the line passing through the points A and B is $\frac{1}{5}\sqrt{70}$ units.

4 The planes Π_1 and Π_2 have equations $\Pi_1: x - y = 2$ and $\Pi_2: x - 2y + 2z = 5$

The line l is the line of intersection of these two planes.

a Find a vector which is parallel to the direction of l.

Line p on Π_1 is parallel to the vector $\mathbf{i} + \mathbf{j} - 4\mathbf{k}$. Line q on Π_2 is perpendicular to l.

b Find a direction vector for q and hence find the acute angle θ between the lines p and q. Give your answer in radians, in terms of π.

FP3

1 The points $A(2, 1, 0)$, $B(2, 2, 1)$ and $C(-1, 3, -7)$ lie on the plane Π.

a Find $\overrightarrow{AB} \times \overrightarrow{AC}$

b Hence, or otherwise, show that a cartesian equation for Π is $3x + y - z = 7$

The perpendicular distance from the point $D(1, 2, k)$, where $k \in \mathbb{R}$, to the plane Π is $\frac{1}{2}\sqrt{11}$ units.

c Find the possible values of k.

2 The plane Π contains the non-zero, non-parallel vectors **a** and **b**. The vector **p** is perpendicular to Π.

a Explain why $\mathbf{p} \times (\mathbf{a} \times \mathbf{b}) = \mathbf{0}$, where $\mathbf{0}$ is the zero vector.

b State, with a reason, the value of $\mathbf{p}.(\mathbf{p} \times \mathbf{b})$

3 The plane Π has cartesian equation $x - 2y + 7z = 7$. The line l with vector equation

$$\mathbf{r} = (2\mathbf{i} + 2\mathbf{j} + 3\mathbf{k}) + t(-\mathbf{i} + 2\mathbf{j} + \mathbf{k}),\ t \in \mathbb{R}$$

intersects Π at point A.

a Find the coordinates of the point A.

Point A is the foot of the perpendicular from the point $P(a, b, 11)$, where a and b are constants, to Π.

b Find the value of a and the value of b.

c Hence find the coordinates of the point P' which is the reflection of point P in Π.

4 With respect to the origin O, the points A, B and C have position vectors

$$\mathbf{a} = -\mathbf{i} + 3\mathbf{k},\ \mathbf{b} = 2\mathbf{i} + 2\mathbf{j} - 3\mathbf{k} \text{ and } \mathbf{c} = \mathbf{i} + \mathbf{j} + 2\mathbf{k}$$

a Find $\mathbf{a} \times \mathbf{b}$

b Hence find the volume of the tetrahedron $OABC$.

The plane Π containing the points A, B and C has cartesian equation $px + qy - z + 7 = 0$, where p and q are constants.

c Find the value of p and the value of q.

d Hence, or otherwise, find the shortest distance of O from the plane Π. Give your answer in simplified surd form.

5 The line l_1 has vector equation $\mathbf{r} = (\mathbf{i} + 2\mathbf{j} - \mathbf{k}) + t\,(3\mathbf{i} - \mathbf{j} + \mathbf{k}), t \in \mathbb{R}$

The line l_2 has cartesian equation

$$\frac{x-4}{2} = \frac{y}{2} = \frac{z-1}{-1}$$

a Show that the shortest distance between l_1 and l_2 is $\frac{1}{\sqrt{10}}$ units.

The plane Π with cartesian equation $ax + by - 5z = 2$, where a and b are constants, contains the line l_1.

b Find the value of a and the value of b.

c Find the coordinates of the point P where l_2 intersects Π.

6 The plane Π_1 has equation $\mathbf{r}.(4\mathbf{i} + 3\mathbf{j} - \mathbf{k}) = d$, where d is a constant.

The plane Π_2 has equation $\mathbf{r}.\,(2\mathbf{i} + 2\mathbf{j} + \mathbf{k}) = 4$

Point $A(-1, 2, 1)$ lies on Π_1.

a Find the value of d.

b Find a vector equation for the line l of intersection of these two planes.

Point $B(p, 2, q)$, where p and q are constants lies on Π_2. The line l', which passes through A and B, is perpendicular to l.

c Find the value of p and the value of q.

d Calculate the shortest distance between l and l'. Give your answer to 1 d.p.

7 Points A, B and C have coordinates $(2, -2, 0)$, $(0, 1, -1)$ and $(3, 1, 2)$ respectively.

a Find $\overrightarrow{AB}$ and $\overrightarrow{AC}$.

b Hence calculate the area of triangle ABC. Give your answer in simplified surd form.

The line l passes through the points B and C.

c Find a vector equation for l.

D is any point on l.

d Show that $\overrightarrow{AB} \times \overrightarrow{AD}$ is parallel to the vector $3\mathbf{i} + \mathbf{j} - 3\mathbf{k}$

e Find the possible coordinates of the point D on l such that the area of triangle ABD is $3\sqrt{19}$ square units.

8 The diagram shows the pyramid $OABCD$, where O is the origin.
The base $OABC$ is a parallelogram and point D is the apex of the pyramid.

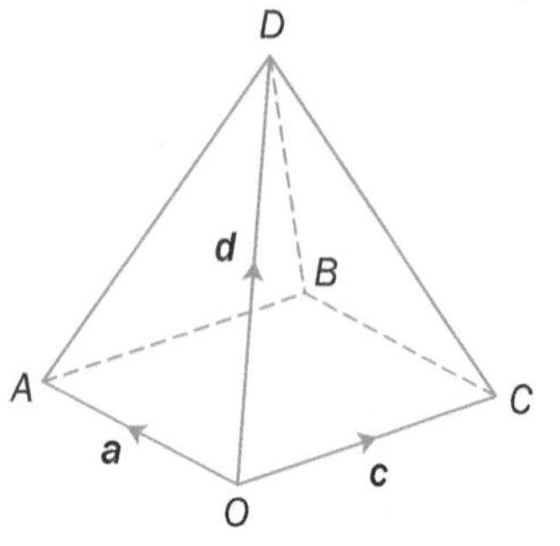

The triangular planes OAD and OCD have cartesian equations

$3x + 5y + 3z = 0$ and $9x + 7y + z = 0$ respectively.

a Show that the line of intersection of these two triangular planes has cartesian equations

$$\frac{x}{2} = \frac{y}{-3} = \frac{z}{3}$$

The position vectors of A, C and D are

$\mathbf{a} = \mathbf{i} - \mathbf{k}$, $\mathbf{c} = 3\mathbf{i} - 4\mathbf{j} + \mathbf{k}$

and $\mathbf{d} = p\mathbf{i} + q\mathbf{j} - 3\mathbf{k}$

for $p, q \in \mathbb{R}$, respectively.

b Find the value of p and the value of q.

c Hence show that the volume of this pyramid is $\frac{8}{3}$ cubic units.

d Find the coordinates of the point P, which is the foot of the perpendicular from D to the base of the pyramid.

9 The plane Π_1 passes through the point $P(-1, 2, -3)$. The line l_1 with equation

$(\mathbf{r} + 6\mathbf{i} - 5\mathbf{j} - 2\mathbf{k}) \times (3\mathbf{i} - \mathbf{j} - 2\mathbf{k}) = \mathbf{0}$

is perpendicular to Π_1

a Show that a cartesian equation for Π_1 is $3x - y - 2z = 1$

b Hence find the coordinates of the point Q where l_1 intersects Π_1.

The plane Π_2 has equation

$\mathbf{r}.(-2\mathbf{i} + 3\mathbf{j} + \mathbf{k}) = 1$

Π_1 and Π_2 intersect in the common line l_2.

c Find a vector equation for l_2.

d Show that the shortest distance between l_1 and l_2 is $\frac{2}{5}\sqrt{42}$ units.

FP3

10 The lines l_1 and l_2 have equations

$$l_1: \mathbf{r} = (2\mathbf{i} + \alpha\mathbf{j} + \mathbf{k}) + s\,(4\mathbf{i} - \mathbf{j} + 3\mathbf{k}),\ s \in \mathbb{R}$$

and $l_2: \mathbf{r} = (\mathbf{i} + \alpha\mathbf{k}) + t\,(3\mathbf{i} + 2\mathbf{j} - \mathbf{k}),\ t \in \mathbb{R}$

where α is a constant.
It is given that l_1 and l_2 intersect at point P.

a Show that $\alpha = -3$

b Hence find the coordinates of point P.

The plane Π_1 has equation $\mathbf{r}.(2\mathbf{i} - \mathbf{j} - 3\mathbf{k}) = 6$

c Show that l_1 does not intersect Π_1

The plane Π_2 is parallel to Π_1 and contains the line l_1.

d Find a cartesian equation for Π_2

e Show that the shortest distance between these two planes is $\frac{1}{7}\sqrt{14}$ units.

11 The line l_1 passes through the points $A(1, 2, 1)$ and $B(3, 3, 2)$.
The line l_2 is parallel to the vector $\mathbf{d} = 3\mathbf{i} - 2\mathbf{j} - \mathbf{k}$ and passes through the point $C\,(5, -3, c)$, where c is a constant. The plane Π contains the lines l_1 and l_2.

a Find a vector equation for the plane Π

b Hence, or otherwise, show that $c = -2$

c Find the area of triangle ABC. Give your answer in simplified surd form.

12 $\mathbf{a} = 2\mathbf{i} + 2\mathbf{j} - \mathbf{k}$, $\mathbf{b} = 4\mathbf{i} + 2p\mathbf{j} + \mathbf{k}$, $\mathbf{c} = -4\mathbf{i} + p\mathbf{j} - 2\mathbf{k}$, where p is a constant.

Find the value of p in the case when

a $\mathbf{a} \times \mathbf{b}$ is parallel to $\mathbf{c}$

b $\mathbf{a}$, $\mathbf{b}$ and $\mathbf{c}$ are coplanar.

13 The point P has coordinates $(-2, 5, 9)$. The reflection of point P in the plane Π is the point $P'(6, -7, -11)$.

a Show that a cartesian equation of Π is $2x - 3y - 5z = 12$

The line L has cartesian equations

$$\frac{x-2}{d} = \frac{y+2}{e} = \frac{z+8}{3}$$

where d and e are non-zero constants. L passes through point P.

b Find the value of d and the value of e.

c Find the coordinates of the point Q where L intersects Π.

6 Exit

- $\mathbf{a}\times\mathbf{b}=\begin{vmatrix}\mathbf{i} & \mathbf{j} & \mathbf{k}\\ a_1 & a_2 & a_3\\ b_1 & b_2 & b_3\end{vmatrix}$ where $\mathbf{a}=a_1\mathbf{i}+a_2\mathbf{j}+a_3\mathbf{k}$ and $\mathbf{b}=b_1\mathbf{i}+b_2\mathbf{j}+b_3\mathbf{k}$ 6.1
- For any vectors **a**, **b** and **c**, $\mathbf{b}\times\mathbf{a}=-\mathbf{a}\times\mathbf{b}$
  $\mathbf{a}\times\mathbf{b}=0$ precisely when either $\mathbf{a}=0$, or $\mathbf{b}=0$ or $\mathbf{a}=\lambda\mathbf{b}$, $\lambda\in\mathbb{R}$, $\lambda\neq 0$
- A plane Π can be given in vector equation form, $\mathbf{r}=\mathbf{a}+\lambda(\mathbf{b}-\mathbf{a})+\mu(\mathbf{c}-\mathbf{a})\ \lambda,\ \mu\in\mathbb{R}$, 6.2, 6.9
  or scalar product form $\mathbf{r.n}=\mathbf{a.n}$, or cartesian equation form $ax+by+cz=d$
- For non-parallel, non-zero vectors **a** and **b**, $\mathbf{a}\times\mathbf{b}=|\mathbf{a}||\mathbf{b}|\sin\theta\,\hat{\mathbf{n}}$, where $\hat{\mathbf{n}}$ 6.2
  is a unit vector which is normal to the unique plane containing **a** and **b**. 6.3
- The area of the triangle ABC is $\frac{1}{2}|\overrightarrow{AB}\times\overrightarrow{AC}|$ 6.4
- The scalar triple product $\mathbf{a.b}\times\mathbf{c}=\begin{vmatrix}a_1 & a_2 & a_3\\ b_1 & b_2 & b_3\\ c_1 & c_2 & c_3\end{vmatrix}$, where $\mathbf{a}=a_1\mathbf{i}+a_2\mathbf{j}+a_3\mathbf{k}$ etc. 6.5
- You can use vectors to find the volumes of parallelepipeds,
  parallelogram-based pyramids and tetrahedrons. 6.6
- A line l can be given in
  cartesian form: $\frac{x-a_1}{d_1}=\frac{y-a_2}{d_2}=\frac{z-a_3}{d_3}$ or vector product form: $(\mathbf{r}-\mathbf{a})\times\mathbf{d}=\mathbf{0}$
- The shortest distance 6.7, 6.8
  - of a point $P(\alpha, \beta, \gamma)$ from a plane with equation $n_1x+n_2y+n_3z+d=0$ is
    $\frac{|n_1\alpha+n_2\beta+n_3\gamma+d|}{\sqrt{n_1^2+n_2^2+n_3^2}}$
  - between the non-parallel lines l_1 and l_2, with equations
    $l_1:\mathbf{r}=\mathbf{a}+s\mathbf{c}$, $s\in\mathbb{R}$ and $l_2:\mathbf{r}=\mathbf{b}+t\mathbf{d}$, $t\in\mathbb{R}$, is $\frac{|(\mathbf{a}-\mathbf{b}).\mathbf{c}\times\mathbf{d}|}{|\mathbf{c}\times\mathbf{d}|}$ 6.11
- If the non-parallel planes Π_1 and Π_2 have a line of intersection l, then l has
  direction vector $\mathbf{n}_1\times\mathbf{n}_2$, for $\mathbf{n}_1$, $\mathbf{n}_2$ normal vectors to Π_1 and Π_2 respectively. 6.12

Links

Vectors, which combine both magnitude and direction, provide a natural language for describing forces, velocities and accelerations. As a consequence the laws of physics are often written as vector equations.

When architects and engineers work together to design a new building they must ensure that all the forces acting on an element of the building are balanced. To do this they need to be able to calculate with vectors.

Revision 2

1 The transformation T is represented by the matrix $\mathbf{A} = \begin{pmatrix} 3 & 1 \\ 2 & 2 \end{pmatrix}$

a Find the image, under T, of the line with equation $y = 2 - 4x$

b Find the eigenvalues of $\mathbf{A}$

c Hence find cartesian equations for the two lines passing through the origin which are invariant under T.

2 The diagram shows a pyramid, with a rectangular base $OABC$ and apex D. With respect to the origin, the points $A(1, 1, 2)$, $C(-1, 1, 0)$ and $D(2, 3, -1)$ have position vectors **a**, **c** and **d**, respectively.

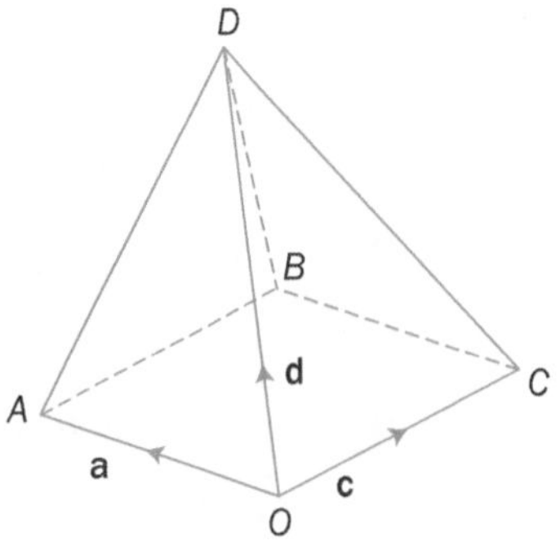

a Find $\mathbf{a} \times \mathbf{c}$

b Find the area of the base $OABC$. Give your answer in simplified surd form.

c dShow that the volume of this pyramid is 4 cubic units.

3 The hyperbola C has equation $\frac{x^2}{a^2} - \frac{y^2}{b^2} = 1$

a Show that an equation of the normal to C at the point $P(a\sec t, b\tan t)$ is

$$ax\sin t + by = (a^2 + b^2)\tan t$$

The normal to C at P cuts the x-axis at the point A and S is a focus of C. Given that the eccentricity of C is $\frac{3}{2}$, and that $OA = 3OS$, where O is the origin

b determine the possible values of t, for $0 \leqslant t < 2\pi$.

4 A plane Π passes through the point $A(4, 1, 0)$.

Point $B(3, p, q)$, for constants p and q, lies on the line l_1 with cartesian equations $\frac{x+5}{2} = y = \frac{z-3}{-3}$.

l_1 is perpendicular to Π.

a Find the value of p and the value of q.

b Show that a cartesian equation for Π is $2x + y - 3z = 9$

c Find the coordinates of the point C where l_1 intersects Π.

The line l_2 is parallel to Π and passes through point B.

Point $D(8, a, b)$ on l_2, where a and b are constants, is such that $BD = \sqrt{35}$

d Find the value of a and the value of b.

5 The ellipse E has equation $\frac{x^2}{a^2} + \frac{y^2}{8} = 1$, where $a > 2\sqrt{2}$

The eccentricity of E is $\frac{1}{\sqrt{2}}$

a Calculate the value of a.

The ellipse E cuts the y-axis at the points D and D'. The foci of E are S and S'.

b Calculate the area of the quadrilateral $SDS'D'$.

6 $\mathbf{M} = \begin{pmatrix} 1 & p & 2 \\ 0 & 3 & q \\ 2 & p & 1 \end{pmatrix}$, where p and q are constants.

Given that $\begin{pmatrix} 1 \\ 2 \\ 1 \end{pmatrix}$ is an eigenvector of $\mathbf{M}$

a show that $q = 4p$

Given also that $\lambda = 5$ is an eigenvalue of $\mathbf{M}$, and $p < 0$ and $q < 0$, find

b the values of p and q

c an eigenvector corresponding to the eigenvalue $\lambda = 5$

7 The plane Π passes through the points $P(-1, 3, -2)$, $Q(4, -1, -1)$ and $R(3, 0, c)$, where c is a constant.

a Find, in terms of c, $\overrightarrow{RP} \times \overrightarrow{RQ}$

Given that $\overrightarrow{RP} \times \overrightarrow{RQ} = 3\mathbf{i} + d\mathbf{j} + \mathbf{k}$, where d is a constant

b find the value of c and show that $d = 4$

c find an equation of Π in the form $\mathbf{r.n} = p$, where p is a constant

The point S has position vector $\mathbf{i} + 5\mathbf{j} + 10\mathbf{k}$. The point S' is the image of S under reflection in Π.

d Find the position vector of S'.

8 $\mathbf{A} = \begin{pmatrix} 3 & 2 & 4 \\ 2 & 0 & 2 \\ 4 & 2 & k \end{pmatrix}$

a Show that det $\mathbf{A} = 20 - 4k$

b Find $\mathbf{A}^{-1}$

Given that $k = 3$ and that $\begin{pmatrix} 0 \\ 2 \\ -1 \end{pmatrix}$ is an eigenvector of $\mathbf{A}$

c find the corresponding eigenvalue.

Given that the only other distinct eigenvalue of $\mathbf{A}$ is 8

d find a corresponding eigenvector.

9 The ellipse E has equation $\frac{x^2}{9}+\frac{y^2}{2}=1$. The line l with equation $6y = x + k$, where $k \in \mathbb{R}$, is a tangent to E.

a Find the possible values of k

b Show that an equation for the normal N to E at the point $P\left(3\cos\theta, \sqrt{2}\sin\theta\right)$ is $\sqrt{2}y = (3\tan\theta)x - 7\sin\theta$

The points Q and R are where this normal intersects the x-axis and y-axis, respectively. Point M is the midpoint of QR.

c Show that, as θ varies, the locus of M is an ellipse E'. Give the equation of this ellipse in the form $px^2 + qy^2 = 49$ for integers p and q to be stated.

d Show that E and E' have equal eccentricities, and state this common value.

10 The plane Π_1 passes through the point P, with position vector $\mathbf{i} + 2\mathbf{j} - \mathbf{k}$, and is perpendicular to the line L with equation

$\mathbf{r} = 3\mathbf{i} - 2\mathbf{k} + \lambda(-\mathbf{i} + 5\mathbf{j} + 3\mathbf{k})$

a Show that the cartesian equation of Π_1 is $x - 5y - 3z = -6$

The plane Π_2 contains the line L and passes through the point Q with position vector $\mathbf{i} + 2\mathbf{j} + 2\mathbf{k}$

b Find the perpendicular distance of Q from Π_1

c Find the equation of Π_2 in the form $\mathbf{r} = \mathbf{a} + s\mathbf{b} + t\mathbf{c}$

11 The line l_1 with vector equation $\mathbf{r} = (2\mathbf{i} - 5\mathbf{j}) + \lambda(\mathbf{i} - 3\mathbf{j}),\ \lambda \in \mathbb{R}$ lies on the plane Π with equation $3x + y - 5z = d$, where d is a constant.

a Find the value of d

The line l_2 passes through the point $A(9, 4, -8)$ and intersects Π at point P. Given that l_2 is perpendicular to Π

b show that the length $AP = 2\sqrt{35}$ units.

Point Q on l_1 is such that $\overrightarrow{PQ}$ is perpendicular to l_1

c Find, in exact form, the distance PQ.

d Hence, or otherwise, find the exact length AQ.

12 The matrix $\mathbf{M}$ is given by $\mathbf{M} = \begin{pmatrix} 1 & 4 & -1 \\ 3 & 0 & p \\ a & b & c \end{pmatrix}$, where p, a, b and c are constants and $a > 0$.

Given that $\mathbf{MM}^\mathrm{T} = k\mathbf{I}$, for some constant k, find

a the value of p

b the value of k

c the values of a, b and c

d $|\det \mathbf{M}|$

FP3 June 2004 Q5

13 The points A, B and C lie on the plane Π_1 and, relative to a fixed origin O, they have position vectors $\mathbf{a} = \mathbf{i} + 3\mathbf{j} - \mathbf{k}$, $\mathbf{b} = 3\mathbf{i} + 3\mathbf{j} - 4\mathbf{k}$ and $\mathbf{c} = 5\mathbf{i} - 2\mathbf{j} - 2\mathbf{k}$, respectively.

a Find $(\mathbf{b} - \mathbf{a}) \times (\mathbf{c} - \mathbf{a})$

b Find an equation for Π_1, giving your answer in the form $\mathbf{r}.\mathbf{n} = p$

The plane Π_2 has cartesian equation $x + z = 3$ and Π_1 and Π_2 intersect in the line l.

c Find an equation for l, giving your answer in the form $(\mathbf{r} - \mathbf{p}) \times \mathbf{q} = 0$

The point P is the point on l that is the nearest to the origin O.

FP3 June 2006 Q7

d Find the coordinates of P.

14 $\mathbf{A} = \begin{pmatrix} 4 & -1 & 3 \\ -1 & p & 0 \\ 3 & 0 & p \end{pmatrix}$, where $p \in \mathbb{R}$.

$\begin{pmatrix} 2 \\ 1 \\ -3 \end{pmatrix}$ is an eigenvector of $\mathbf{A}$ corresponding to the eigenvalue λ_1

a Find the value of λ_1

b Show that $p = 1$

c Find

i the other two eigenvalues of $\mathbf{A}$

ii an eigenvector of $\mathbf{A}$ corresponding to each of these eigenvalues.

d Hence find an orthogonal matrix $\mathbf{P}$ and a diagonal matrix $\mathbf{D}$ such that $\mathbf{P}^\mathrm{T}\mathbf{AP} = \mathbf{D}$

e For these matrices $\mathbf{P}$ and $\mathbf{D}$, find the matrix $\mathbf{P}^\mathrm{T}\mathbf{A}^2\mathbf{P}$

Answers

Chapter 1

Before you start

1 **a** $x = \ln 2$ **b** $x = -\ln 4$ **c** $x = \ln 4$
d $x = \ln 3, \ln 5$ **e** $x = \ln 9$

2 **a**

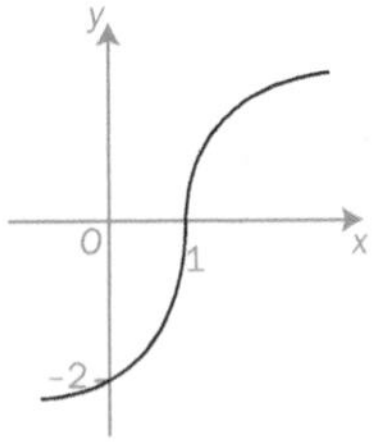

b

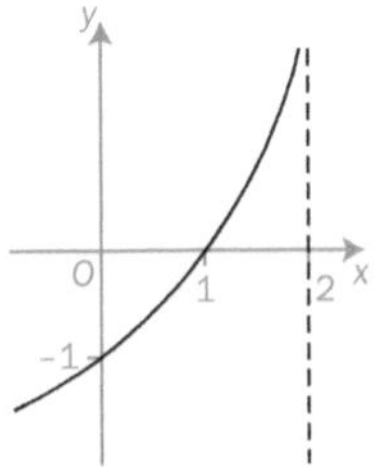

Exercise 1.1

1 **a** 10.07 **b** – 1.18 **c** 0.32 **d** 37.69

2 **a** $\frac{4}{3}$ **b** $\frac{3}{5}$ **c** $\frac{3\sqrt{2}}{2}$
d 1 **e** $3\sqrt{3}+1$ **f** $\frac{3-2\sqrt{3}}{3}$

3 **a** 3 **b** $-\sqrt{3}$ **c** $-3+2\sqrt{3}$

5 **a**

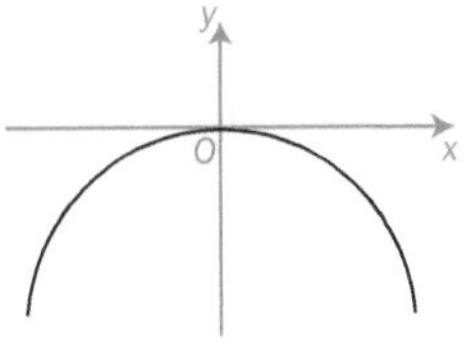

b

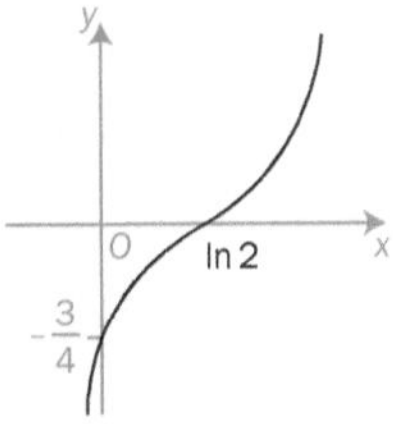

c

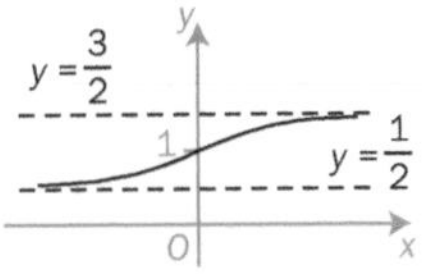

6 **a**

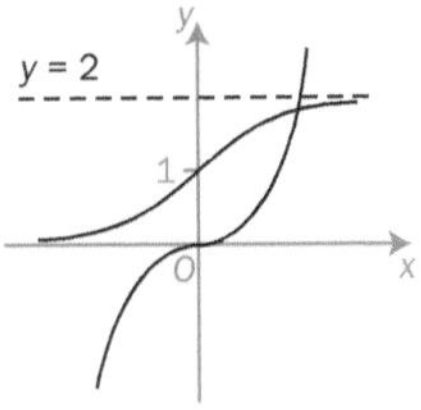

b Exactly one real root
c **i** No real roots
ii Exactly two real roots

7 **a** $a = -\ln 3, b = 2$ **b** $\frac{25}{12}$

Exercise 1.2

1 **a** 0.17 **b** 0.89 **c** 1.00

2 **a** $\frac{13}{12}$ **b** $\frac{\sqrt{5}}{3}$ **c** $2\sqrt{3}$

4 **a** $\frac{20}{29}$ **b** $\frac{20}{21}$ **c** $\frac{29}{21}$

5 **a** $\frac{5}{4}$ **b** $\frac{9}{41}$ **c** $\frac{3}{4}$

6 **a** $\tanh a = \frac{3}{5}$ **b** $a = \ln 2$

7 **a**

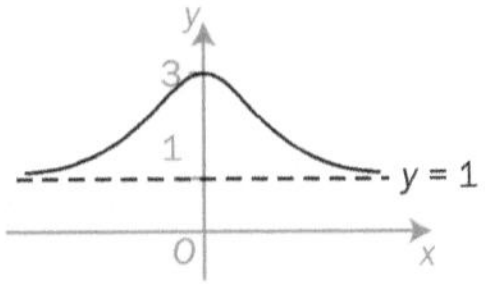

b

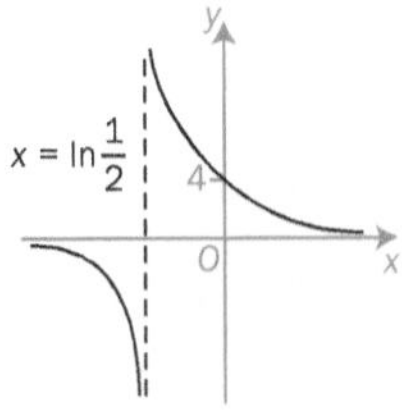

c

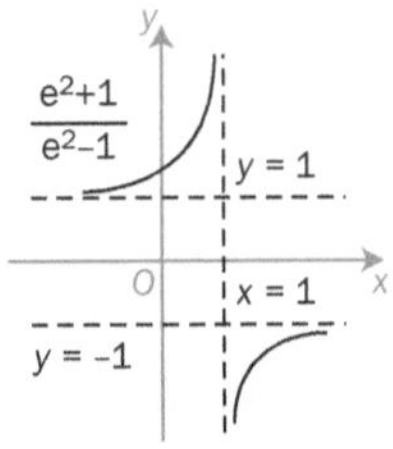

Exercise 1.3

1 **a** $x = \ln 3, x = \ln\left(\frac{1}{2}\right)$ **b** $x = \ln 3, x = \ln\left(\frac{1}{5}\right)$
c $x = \ln\left(\frac{1}{2}\right)$

2 **a** $x = -1.48, x = -0.46$ **b** $x = 0.82, x = 1.75$

3 $x = -\ln 3$

4 $x = 0, x = \ln 5$

5 $x = \ln(5-2\sqrt{6}),\ a = 5,\ b = -2$

6 **a** $k = -5$ **b** $x = \ln 3$

7 **a** $x = \ln 2$ **b** $x = \ln\left(\frac{1}{4}\right)$

8 **a** $x = \ln 3,\ x = \ln\left(\frac{1}{11}\right)$ **b** $x = \ln\left(\frac{1}{3}\right)$

9 $x = \text{In}\left(\frac{a-b}{a+b}\right)$

Exercise 1.4

3 **a** $\sqrt{5}$ **b** $4\sqrt{5}$ **c** 9

4 **a** $\pm\frac{1}{2}\sqrt{5}$ **b** $\pm\frac{1}{3}\sqrt{5}$ **c** $\pm\frac{3}{7}\sqrt{5}$

5 **a** **i** $\cosh(x+y) \equiv \cosh x \cosh y + \sinh x \sinh y$
ii $\cosh 3x \equiv 4\cosh^3 x - 3\cosh x$
iii $\tanh 2x \equiv \frac{2\tanh x}{1+\tanh^2 x}$ **iv** $\coth^2 x - 1 \equiv \text{cosech}^2 x$

6 **b** $\frac{\sqrt{3}}{12}$

8 **b** $x = \ln 2$

9 **b** $\tanh 2x = \frac{2\sin\theta}{1+\sin^2\theta}$

11 **b**

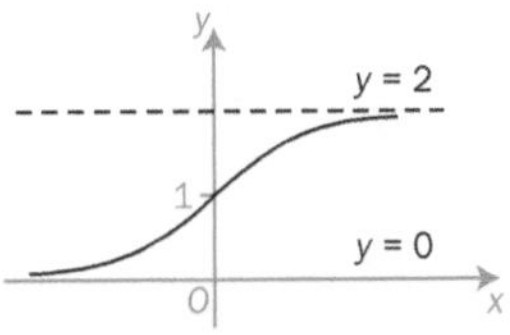

FP3

12 b Using Osborne's rule suggests $(\cosh x + \sinh x)^2 \equiv 1 + \sinh 2x$
This is false for (any) non-zero value of x.
For example, $x = \ln 2$, LHS = 4 but RHS = $\frac{25}{8}$

13 a $a = \pm 1$ c $x = \ln(\sqrt{2} \pm 1)$

Exercise 1.5

1 a $\ln(3+\sqrt{10})$ b $\ln(\sqrt{2}+1)$ c $\ln 2$

d $\ln 3$ e $\ln\left(\frac{\sqrt{5}+1}{2}\right)$ f $\ln(1+\sqrt{2})$

2 a

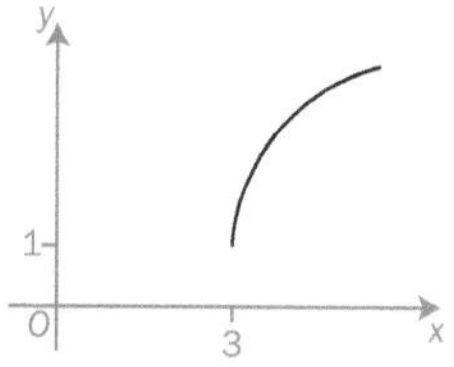

b

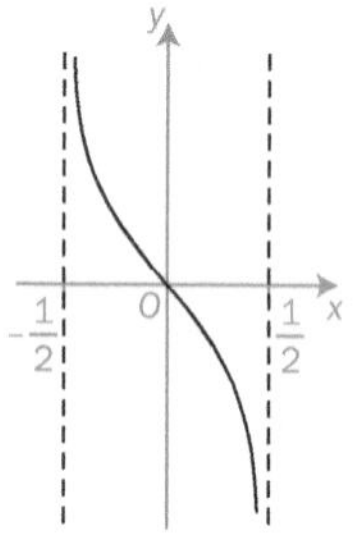

c

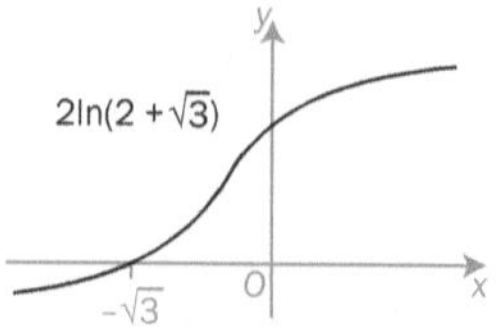

3 a $\ln(4+\sqrt{17})$ b $\ln(3\pm 2\sqrt{2})$ c $\ln(9+4\sqrt{5})$

d $\ln(2+\sqrt{3})$ e $\ln(2-\sqrt{3})$ f $\ln(\sqrt{2}\pm 1)$

4 c $f(x) = \ln(2x-1)$, $a = 2$, $b = -1$

6 a $\ln(\sqrt{3}\pm\sqrt{2})$ b $\ln\left(\frac{3\pm\sqrt{5}}{2}\right)$

c $\ln 3$ d $x = 2\ln(\sqrt{2}\pm 1)$

9 a $\ln\left(\frac{\sqrt{3}}{2}\right)$

10 a $b = \ln(\sqrt{8}+3)$ b $\frac{2}{3}\sqrt{2}$

11 a $\ln\left(1+\sqrt{1+x^2}\right)$ b $\sqrt{e(e-2)}$

Exercise 1.6

1 a $x = \ln(-2+\sqrt{5})$, $\ln(3+\sqrt{10})$

b $x = \ln(-1+\sqrt{2})$, $\ln\left(\frac{-3+\sqrt{13}}{2}\right)$

c $x = 0$, $\ln\left(\frac{3\pm\sqrt{5}}{2}\right)$ d $x = \ln\left(\frac{7\pm 2\sqrt{10}}{3}\right)$

2 a $x = 0$, $\frac{1}{2}\ln 7$ b $x = -\frac{1}{2}\ln 5$

c $x = \ln(1+\sqrt{2})$, $-\frac{1}{2}\ln 3$

3 a $x = \frac{1}{2}\ln 2$ b $x = \frac{1}{2}\ln 2$

4 a $x = \frac{1}{2}\ln(3+\sqrt{10})$ b $x = \frac{1}{3}\ln(\sqrt{2}\pm 1)$

c $x = \frac{1}{4}\ln(2\sqrt{2}+3)$

5 b $x = 0$, $\frac{1}{2}\ln 5$

6 a $x = 0$, $\ln\left(\frac{5\pm\sqrt{21}}{2}\right)$ b $x = \ln(2+\sqrt{5})$, $\ln\left(\frac{1+\sqrt{5}}{2}\right)$

c $x = \frac{1}{4}\ln 7$ d $x = 0$, $\frac{1}{2}\ln 3$

7 a $x = 0$, $\frac{1}{2}\ln 3$ b $x = \ln(2\pm\sqrt{3})$

c $x = 0$, $\ln(4\pm\sqrt{15})$ d $x = \ln(\sqrt{2}\pm 1)$

8 a $\frac{1}{1-\tanh x} + \frac{1}{1+\tanh x} \equiv 2\cosh^2 x$ b $x = \ln(\sqrt{2} \pm 1)$

9 a $\sinh 3x \equiv 4\sinh^3 x + 3\sinh x$ b $x = -\frac{1}{6}\ln 3$, $a = -6$

10 b $a = 6$

11 a $k = \frac{3}{4}$ b $x = \frac{1}{4}\ln 7$

12 a

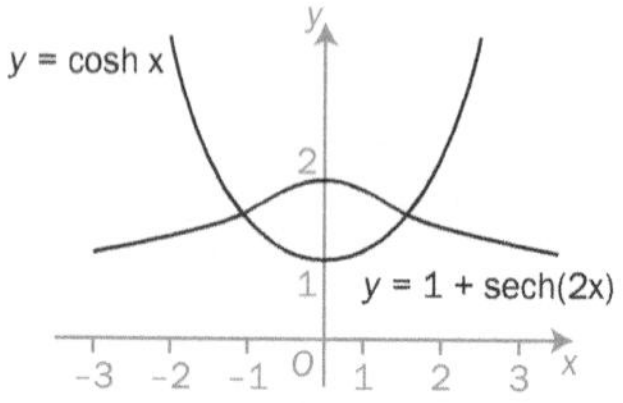

b 2

c P(−0.831, 1.366) Q(+0.831, 1.366)
PQ = 1.66

13 $x = 0$, $\ln(1+\sqrt{2})$

14 a $\cosh^4 x - \sinh^4 x \equiv \cosh 2x$ b $x = \frac{1}{2}\ln(2+\sqrt{5})$

15 a $x = \ln(-1+\sqrt{2})$, $\ln(2+\sqrt{5})$

b $x = \ln(1+\sqrt{2})$, $\ln(-1+\sqrt{2})$ c $x = \frac{1}{2}\ln 3$

Review 1

1 $x = \ln\frac{1}{2}$, $\ln 5$

2 a $a = 2$

4 c $x = \pm\frac{1}{2}\ln 2$, $q = \pm\frac{1}{2}$

5 $x = \ln\left(\frac{1+\sqrt{5}}{2}\right)$, $\ln(-1+\sqrt{2})$

6 b $P(\sqrt{3}, \ln\sqrt{3})$

7 a

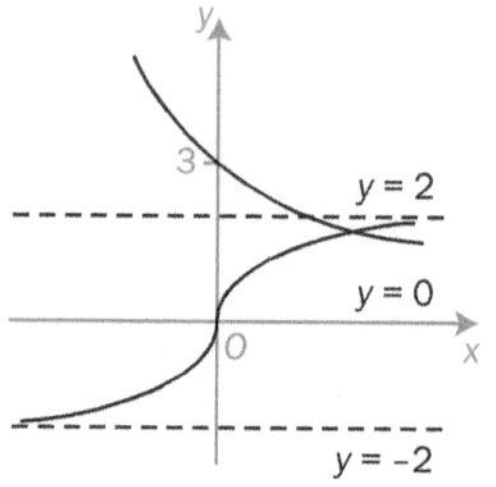

b $(\ln 3, 1)$

8 $\ln(2\pm\sqrt{3})$, $\ln(3\pm\sqrt{8})$

10 $x = \ln\frac{2}{3}$, $q = \frac{2}{3}$

11 a $x = \ln(-2+\sqrt{5})$, $\ln\left(\frac{3+\sqrt{13}}{2}\right)$ b $x = \frac{1}{2}\ln 7$

12 b $x = \pm\ln(\sqrt{2}+\sqrt{3})$

Chapter 2

Before you start

1 a $\frac{2x}{x^2+1}$ b $xe^{-3x}(2-3x)$

c $\frac{1}{\cos x+1}$ d $e^{\tan x}(1-\sin 2x)$

2 a $y=2x-1$ b $-\frac{1}{\pi}$ c $(0,0), \left(\frac{1}{4}\pi, 1-\ln 4\right)$

3 a $\frac{1}{3}(x+1)^{-\frac{2}{3}}$ b $\frac{1}{2x\sqrt{\ln x}}$ c $\frac{1}{2\sqrt{x-1}}$

Exercise 2.1

1 a $2\cosh 2x$ b $2x\sinh(x^2)$ c $2\tanh x\,\text{sech}^2 x$

d $\frac{\cosh(\sqrt{x})}{\sqrt{x}}$ e $\frac{3\,\text{sech}^2 x}{2\sqrt{\tanh x}}$ f $12\sinh 3x\cosh^3 3x$

2 a $x(x\cosh x+2\sinh x)$ b $3x^2(x\sinh 3x+\cosh 3x)$

c $e^{2x}(\text{sech}^2 x+2\tanh x)$

d $2(2\sinh 2x\sinh 4x+\cosh 4x\cosh 2x)$

e $\sinh x(\sinh^2 x+2\cosh^2 x)$ f $\sinh x(1+\text{sech}^2 x)$

g $\frac{2\sinh 2x}{\sqrt{1+x}}-\frac{\cosh 2x}{2(1+x)^{\frac{3}{2}}}$ h $\frac{x}{\sqrt{1+x^2}}\sinh x+\sqrt{1+x^2}\cosh x$

4 a $\sinh 2x$

6 a $x(1-\tanh^2 x)+\tanh x$ b $y(1-y)$

7 b $\left(\ln\left(\frac{1}{2}\right), \ln\left(\frac{2}{5}\right)\right)$

8 a $\frac{1}{1+\cosh x}$ b $\frac{1}{3}$

9 a $4\sinh 4x$, $a=b=4$ b $2\sinh 4x$, $a=2$, $b=4$

c $2\sinh 2x$, $a=b=2$

10 b Yes, the result holds for all $n\leqslant -1$

11 a $U=e^x$ b $\frac{dV}{dx}=-V$, $V=e^{-x}$

Exercise 2.2

1 a $3y-4=5(x-\ln 3)$ b $8y-17=30(x-\ln 2)$

c $y=2(x-1)$ d $16y-9=-30(x+\ln 2)$

2 a $y=-2x+\ln 2$ b $15y+20=9(x-\ln 3)$

3 $\left(\ln 2, \frac{15}{16}\right), \left(-\ln 2, -\frac{15}{16}\right)$

4 a $x=\ln 3$ b $x=\frac{1}{2}\ln 5$

c $x=\ln(\sqrt{5}\pm 2)$ d $x=\ln 3$

5 a $c=20+12\ln 2$ b $P\left(\ln 3, \frac{3}{5}\right)$

6 b $(-\ln 2, \ln 16)$

7 b $\left(\ln(1+\sqrt{2}), \ln(1+\sqrt{2})+\sqrt{2}\right)$

This is a stationary point of inflection.

8 $\left(\ln(2+\sqrt{3}), 3\sqrt{3}\right), \left(\ln(2-\sqrt{3}), -3\sqrt{3}\right)$

9 b $y=-e^{2x}$

10 b $ey=(1-e^2)x+2$ c $R\left(0, \frac{2}{e}\right)$

11 a $\frac{dy}{dx}=m\sinh x\cosh x(8\sinh^{m-2}x-\cosh^{m-2}x)$

c The stationary point is a minimum.

Exercise 2.3

1 a $\frac{3}{\sqrt{1+9x^2}}$ b $\frac{8}{\sqrt{4x^2-1}}$ c $\frac{2x}{1-x^4}$

d $\frac{-1}{x\sqrt{x^2+1}}$ e $\frac{1}{\sqrt{4x^2-x}}$ f $\frac{-1}{x(x+2)}$

2 b $y-\ln(2+\sqrt{3})=\frac{1}{4}(x-2\sqrt{3})$

4 a $y=\frac{1}{2}\ln 2$ c $y-\frac{1}{2}\ln 2=\frac{4}{9}\left(x-\frac{1}{3}\right)$

d $PQ=\frac{\sqrt{97}}{8}\ln 2$, $p=97$

5 a $\frac{x^2}{\sqrt{1+x^2}}+2x\,\text{arsinh}\,x$ b $1+\frac{x\,\text{arcosh}\,x}{\sqrt{x^2-1}}$

c $\frac{-(1+2x\,\text{artanh}\,x)}{(x^2-1)^2}$ d $\frac{1}{\sqrt{(1+4x^2)}\,\text{arsinh}\,2x}$

6 a $\left(\frac{1}{2}, \frac{3}{2}\ln 3-2\right)$, minimum

$\left(-\frac{1}{2}, 2-\frac{3}{2}\ln 3\right)$, maximum

b $\left(\frac{2}{3}, 5\ln 3-4\right)$, maximum

$\left(-\frac{2}{3}, 4-5\ln 3\right)$, minimum

c $\left(\frac{9}{5}, \ln 5-3\right)$, maximum

7 a $\frac{x}{\sqrt{x^2-1}}$

8 b $\left(\frac{1}{4}, \frac{3}{2}\ln 3-2\right)$, minimum

$\left(-\frac{1}{4}, 2-\frac{3}{2}\ln 3\right)$, maximum

9 b $y-\ln 3=-\frac{4}{3}(x-\ln 2)$ c $a=\frac{1}{4}\ln 432$, $q=432$

11 a $x=\sqrt{2}$ c $2y-x=0$, $a=2$, $b=-1$, $c=0$

Exercise 2.4

1 a $\frac{2}{\sqrt{1-4x^2}}$ b $\frac{1}{\sqrt{x(2-x)}}$ c $\frac{2}{4+x^2}$

d $\frac{-2\arccos x}{\sqrt{1-x^2}}$ e $\frac{1}{x(1+(\ln x)^2)}$ f $\frac{-1}{x\sqrt{x^2-1}}$

4 a $\left(\frac{1}{2}\sqrt{3}, \frac{\pi}{3}-\sqrt{3}\right), \left(-\frac{1}{2}\sqrt{3}, \sqrt{3}-\frac{\pi}{3}\right)$

b $\left(\sqrt{3}, 2\pi-\sqrt{3}\ln 4\right)$ c $\left(\frac{1}{\sqrt{2}}, \frac{1}{2}+\frac{1}{4}\pi\right)$

5 a $2x\arccos x+\sqrt{1-x^2}$ b $\frac{1}{1+x}+\frac{\arctan\sqrt{x}}{\sqrt{x}}$

c $-\frac{1}{x^2}\left(\frac{2x}{\sqrt{2-x^2}}+\arcsin(1-x^2)\right)$

7 a $y+x=\frac{1}{4}\pi+\frac{1}{2}$

8 a $\frac{1}{\sqrt{x-4x^2}}$ b $\frac{1}{6}\pi$

9 $\frac{1}{3}\pi$

10 c $\left(\frac{1}{\sqrt{2}}, \frac{\pi^2}{16}\right)$, maximum

Review 2

1 b $P\left(\ln(1+\sqrt{2}), \sqrt{2}\right)$ c maximum

2 a $3\tanh^2 x(1-\tanh^2 x)$ b $x=\ln\sqrt{3}$, $\ln(2+\sqrt{3})$

3 b $-(\coth x+1)$ c $2y=3\ln 3-6x$

4 $3-4\ln 2$, $a=3$, $b=-4$

5 a $a=2$, $b=-1$ b $Q(\ln 3, 1-2\ln 3)$

c $(0,-1)$, maximum $(\ln 3, 1-2\ln 3)$, minimum

6 a $\frac{2\sqrt{2}x}{\sqrt{1+2x^4}}$

7 b $\sqrt{e}\ln(2+\sqrt{3})$

8 c $x=\frac{1}{4}\sqrt{3}$

9 b The tangent does not intersect the curve again.

10 a $k=2$

11 b $\text{sech}\,x$

Chapter 3

Before you start (+c is assumed in all answers where appropriate)

1 a $\frac{1}{10}(x^2+1)^5$ b $\frac{1}{4}\ln|6x^2+8x+1|$

c $\frac{2}{15}(x+1)^{\frac{3}{2}}(3x-2)$ d $\frac{1}{40}(x^2+1)^2(4x^2-1)$

2 a $\frac{1}{2}(1-\ln 2)$ b $\frac{1}{4}\ln 2-\frac{15}{256}$ c 2π

3 a $\frac{1}{3}\cos x(\cos^2 x-3)$ b $x+\frac{1}{2}\cos 2x$ c $2\tan\frac{1}{2}x$

Exercise 3.1

1 a $\frac{1}{18}(3x^2-1)^3$ b $\frac{1}{6}(x^4+5)^{\frac{3}{2}}$ c $\frac{2}{3}\ln|x^3-1|$

d $\frac{1}{6}\ln|3x^2-6x+1|$ e $\frac{3}{2}e^{2x^2}$ f $-\frac{3}{4}\cos^4 x$

2 a 1 b $2e(e-1)$ c $\frac{3}{2}\ln 5$

3 a $\ln|\sin x|$ b $\ln|\ln x|$ c $\ln|\tan x|$

4 a $\frac{1}{3}(x^2-1)^{\frac{3}{2}}$ b $\frac{1}{4}x^4+\frac{2}{3}x^3+\frac{1}{2}x^2$ c $\ln|x|-\frac{2}{x}$

d $\frac{5}{2}\sin(x^2+1)$ e $\frac{1}{2}\ln|2x+1|$ f $\frac{1}{2}\ln|x^2-2x-3|$

5 a $\frac{1}{2}\sin^4 x$ b $3\cos x-2\cos^3 x$

c $-\ln|1-\tan x|$

Exercise 3.2

1 a $\frac{1}{2}\sinh 2x$ b $\frac{2}{3}\cosh 3x$ c $12\ln\left(\cosh\frac{1}{3}x\right)$

2 a $\frac{49}{24}$ b $3\ln\left(\frac{17}{8}\right)$ c $\frac{3}{4}\left(\frac{e^2-1}{e}\right)$

3 a $x\cosh x-\sinh x$

b $\frac{1}{3}x\sinh 3x-\frac{1}{9}\cosh 3x$

c $\frac{1}{2}x^2\sinh 2x-\frac{1}{2}x\cosh 2x+\frac{1}{4}\sinh 2x$

4 b $\frac{40}{9}-\ln 9$

5 a $\frac{1}{4}\sinh^4 x$ b $\frac{2}{3}(\cosh x)^{\frac{3}{2}}$ c $\frac{1}{3}\ln(\cosh 3x)$

d $\frac{1}{4}\tanh^4 x$ e $2\ln\left(\sinh\frac{1}{2}x\right)$ f $-\text{sech}\,x$

6 a $5\ln 4-6$ b $\frac{3}{5}\ln 2-\ln\left(\frac{5}{4}\right)$

7 a $\frac{1}{4}e^{2x}+\frac{1}{2}x$ b $\frac{1}{3}e^{3x}-e^{-x}-2e^x$

8 a $\frac{1}{4}\sinh 4x$ b $x-\tanh x$ c $\frac{1}{2}\cosh^4 x$

d $\sinh x+\frac{1}{3}\sinh^3 x$ e $\frac{1}{2}\tanh x$ f $\sinh x+x$

9 b $\ln\left(\frac{9}{8}\right)$, $q=\frac{9}{8}$

10 a $\frac{1}{4}\sinh 2x+\frac{1}{2}x$ b $\frac{1}{4}\sinh 4x-x$

c $\tanh x-\frac{1}{3}\tanh^3 x$ d $x-2\tanh x$

11 b $\pi(20-9\ln 3)$, $a=20$, $b=9$

Exercise 3.3

1 a $\frac{1}{2}\arctan\left(\frac{x}{2}\right)$ b $\text{arsinh}\left(\frac{x}{3}\right)$ c $\frac{5}{2}\text{artanh}\left(\frac{x}{2}\right)$

d $2\sqrt{2}\,\text{arcosh}\left(\frac{x}{4}\right)$ e $\frac{1}{3}\arcsin(3x)$ f $\frac{1}{2}\arctan\left(\frac{2x}{3}\right)$

2 b $\frac{1}{12}\pi$

3 a $\ln(\sqrt{3}+2)$ b $\frac{\sqrt{3}}{54}\pi$ c $\frac{1}{2}\ln\left(\frac{3}{2}\right)$

4 b $\ln\left(\frac{3}{2}\right)$, $p=\frac{3}{2}$

5 b $\frac{\sqrt{3}}{12}\pi^2$

6 a $-\frac{1}{x}\sqrt{1-x^2}-\arcsin x$ b $-\frac{1}{x}\ln(4+x^2)+\arctan\left(\frac{x}{2}\right)$

c $\frac{\ln(3+x)}{3-x}-\frac{1}{3}\text{artanh}\left(\frac{x}{3}\right)$

7 b i $(x^2-9)^{\frac{1}{2}}-\text{arcosh}\left(\frac{x}{3}\right)$ ii $\frac{1}{4}\ln(1+4x^2)-\frac{1}{2}\arctan 2x$

iii $\frac{1}{3}\text{arsinh}\left(\frac{3x}{4}\right)-\frac{1}{3}\sqrt{16+9x^2}$

8 a $\frac{1}{2}\text{arsinh}(x^2)$ b $\text{artanh}(e^x)$ c $-\text{arsinh}\left(\frac{1}{x}\right)$

9 a $\sinh 2\theta=2x\sqrt{1+x^2}$

10 a $x\sqrt{x^2-1}-\text{arcosh}\,x$ b $\frac{1}{2}x\sqrt{4-x^2}+2\arcsin\left(\frac{x}{2}\right)$

c $\frac{x}{\sqrt{1+4x^2}}$

11 b $k=\ln\sqrt{3}$

12 b $\text{arsinh}\,x-\frac{\sqrt{1+x^2}}{x}$

Exercise 3.4

1 a $\arctan(x+2)$ b $\text{arcosh}\left(\frac{x-6}{5}\right)$

c $\text{arsinh}\left(\frac{x-2}{3}\right)$ d $\text{arcosh}\left(\frac{2x+1}{3}\right)$

e $\frac{1}{\sqrt{2}}\arctan\left(\frac{x-3}{\sqrt{2}}\right)$ f $\text{arcosh}\left(\frac{x-2}{2}\right)$

2 $\arcsin\left(\frac{x-1}{4}\right)$

3 $\ln\left(\frac{5}{2}\right)$, $p=\frac{5}{2}$

4 a $\frac{1}{2}\text{arsinh}(2x-2)$ b $\frac{1}{\sqrt{3}}\text{arcosh}(3x-2)$

c $\frac{2}{3}\text{artanh}\left(\frac{2x-1}{3}\right)$ d $\frac{1}{2}\arcsin\left(\frac{2x-3}{4}\right)$

5 b $\frac{\pi}{6}\sqrt{2}$, $a=2$

6 b 0.36 cubic units (2 decimal places)

7 a $\arctan(x+1)$

8 a $2(9+x^2)^{\frac{1}{2}}+\text{arsinh}\left(\frac{x}{3}\right)$ b $2(x^2-4x-5)^{\frac{1}{2}}+\text{arcosh}\left(\frac{x-2}{3}\right)$

c $(x^2-2x+5)^{\frac{1}{2}}+\text{arsinh}\left(\frac{x-1}{2}\right)$

11 b $\frac{1}{2}\ln\left|\frac{x}{2-x}\right|+c$

Exercise 3.5

1 a $x\,\text{arcosh}\,x-(x^2-1)^{\frac{1}{2}}$ b $x\,\text{artanh}\,3x+\frac{1}{6}\ln|1-9x^2|$

c $x\arcsin\frac{1}{2}x+(4-x^2)^{\frac{1}{2}}$

2 a $2\ln(2\sqrt{2}+3)-\sqrt{2}$ b $\frac{\pi}{4}+\sqrt{2}-1$ c $\frac{1}{2}\ln\left(\frac{27}{16}\right)$

3 b $x^2\arctan x+\arctan x-x$

4 a $2\sqrt{x}\arcsin\sqrt{x}+2(1-x^2)^{\frac{1}{2}}$

5 a $x\,\text{arsinh}\left(\frac{1}{x}\right)+\text{arsinh}\,x$ b $x^2\,\text{artanh}\,x-\text{artanh}\,x+x$

c $2\sqrt{x}\,\text{arcosh}\left(\frac{1}{2}x+1\right)-4\sqrt{x+4}$

7 a $A=1$, $B=-1$

8 b $9\sqrt{3}\ln(\sqrt{3}+2)-4$

9 a $x-\cos x\,\text{artanh}(\sin x)$

b $\sinh x\arcsin(\tanh x)-\ln\cosh x$

c $e^x\,\text{artanh}(e^x)+\frac{1}{2}\ln|1-e^{2x}|$

11 b $\frac{2\pi}{3}-\ln(2+\sqrt{3})$

12 b $\frac{\pi}{24}+\frac{\sqrt{3}}{16}$

13 a $k=\frac{\pi}{4}$

14 a $(1+x^2)^{\frac{1}{2}}\operatorname{arsinh}x-x$

b $x\operatorname{arsinh}^2 x-2\sqrt{1+x^2}\operatorname{arsinh}x+2x$

c $P\left(1,\ln\left(1+\sqrt{2}\right)\right)$

Exercise 3.6

1 b $-e^{-x}(x^2+2x+2)$

2 b $\frac{1}{8}e^{4x}(8x^2-4x+1)$

3 a $x^2(x^2-1)^{n-1}$ c $-\frac{16}{35}$

4 c $(x^4+12x^2+24)\cosh x-(4x^3+24x)\sinh x$, $P(x)=x^4+12x^2+24$

5 b $\frac{1}{2}(e^2-5)$

6 b $\frac{3}{8}\pi$

7 b $22\sqrt{3}+3\ln\left(2+\sqrt{3}\right)$

8 b i $\pi(3-2\pi^2)$ ii $\frac{1}{4}\pi^2(3-\pi^2)$

9 c $\frac{1}{16}\pi$

Exercise 3.7

1 a $\frac{14}{27}$ units b $\frac{3}{2}$ units c $\frac{56}{3}$ units

2 a $a=\frac{1}{2}$, $b=2$

3 a $\frac{1}{4}\sinh 2\theta+\frac{1}{2}\theta$ b $\frac{15}{32}+\frac{1}{2}\ln 2$ units

4 a $a=\sqrt{2}$ b $p=\frac{1}{4}$, $q=1$

5 b $k=\frac{1}{6}\pi$

6 a $\frac{112}{27}$ units b 19 units c $\frac{38}{3}$ units

7 a $t=2$ c 4 units

8 b $\frac{116}{15}$ units

9 b $4\left(\sqrt{2}-1\right)$ units

10 a $a=1$

Exercise 3.8

1 b $\frac{56}{3}\pi$ square units

2 a A: $x=-\ln 2$, B: $x=\ln 2$

3 b $\frac{151}{36}\pi$ square units

4 a $x=3$

5 $\frac{76}{3}\pi$ square units

6 $\frac{61}{108}\pi$ square units

7 b $C(5, 9)$

8 $\frac{38}{3}\pi$ square units

9 $a=\sqrt{2}$, $b=\frac{5}{3}$

Review 3 (+c is assumed in all answers where appropriate)

1 a $\frac{1}{2}\cosh^2\theta-\cosh\theta$ b $k=\ln 2$

2 b $\frac{16}{105}$

3 b $\frac{\pi}{8}\ln 3$ cubic units, $a=3$

4 a $\frac{1}{2}\left(t\sqrt{1+t^2}+\operatorname{arsinh}t\right)$

5 $\frac{28}{3}\sqrt{2}\pi$ square units

6 b $\frac{10}{3}$

7 a $a=2$

8 b $4\pi(6-\pi^2)$, $a=4$, $b=6$

9 $\ln\left(2+\sqrt{3}\right)$

10 b $1+\frac{1}{3}\ln 2$

11 a $a=2$ d $\frac{1}{64}(28-19\ln 3)$

12 a $\frac{1}{3}\sqrt{x^2-1}(x^2+2)$

Revision 1

1 $x=\ln\left(\frac{1}{3}\right)$

2 b $x=\ln(1+\sqrt{2})$, $\ln(2+\sqrt{5})$

3 b $\frac{160}{3}\pi$ square units

4 b $6-2e$

5 b $x=\frac{1}{2}\ln 2$

6 $a=17$

7 b $y=x+\ln\left(3+\sqrt{8}\right)-\sqrt{2}$

9 b $\frac{1}{4}(2+\pi)$ units

10 c $\frac{1}{4}\pi-\frac{1}{\sqrt{2}}\ln(1+\sqrt{2})$

11 $\frac{7}{3}+\frac{1}{2}\ln\left(\frac{3}{2}\right)$, $a=\frac{7}{3}$, $b=\frac{3}{2}$

12 c $\frac{13}{15}-\frac{1}{4}\pi$

13 a $\left(\ln 2,\ln 2-\frac{55}{8}\right)$, $\left(\ln(1+\sqrt{2}),\ln(1+\sqrt{2})-5\sqrt{2}\right)$

b Stationary point at $x=\ln 2$ is a maximum

Stationary point at $x=\ln\left(1+\sqrt{2}\right)$ is a minimum

14 b $2\pi\arctan 3$ cubic units

15 $\sqrt{x^2-1}+\operatorname{arcosh}x+c$, c an arbitrary constant

16 b $x=-\ln 2$

17 a $-\tanh x\operatorname{sech}x$ b $x=\ln 2$

18 b $\frac{2016}{5}$

19 c $x=\pm\ln\left(\frac{3+\sqrt{5}}{2}\right)$

20 a $a=9$, $b=2$ b $\frac{41}{27}\sqrt{41}-1$ units

21 b 6.590 square units.

Chapter 4

Before you start

1 a i $\left(\frac{1}{2},\frac{1}{2}\right)$ ii $(-2,-1)$ b $k=\pm\sqrt{2}$

2 a i $4y=6x+13$ ii $y=\sqrt{2}-\frac{1}{2}x$ iii $4y=3x+\sqrt{3}$

b $y=-x$

3 a $x=-2$ b $ty=x+2t^2$ c $R\left(-2,\frac{2}{t}(t^2-1)\right)$

Exercise 4.1

1 a

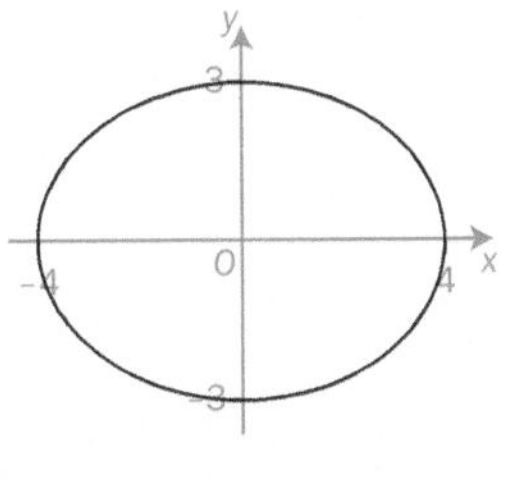

b

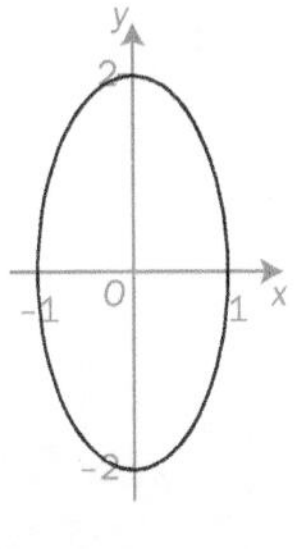

FP3

c

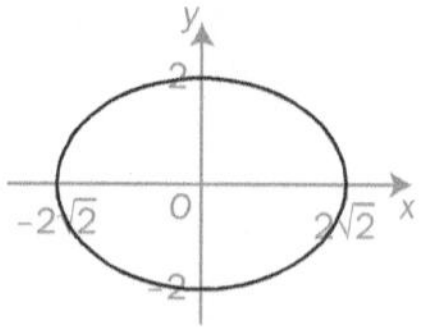

d

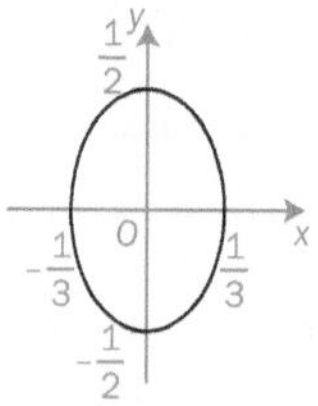

3 **b**

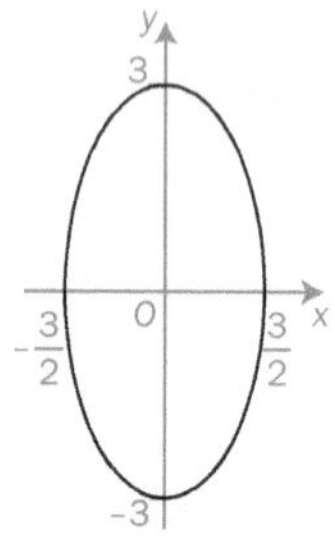

Major axis has length 6 units

4 $(-2,0),\ \left(\frac{10}{13}, \frac{36}{13}\right)$

5 **a**

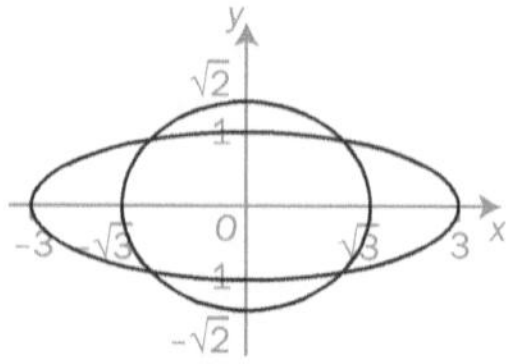

b $\left(\frac{3}{5}\sqrt{5}, \pm\frac{2}{5}\sqrt{5}\right), \left(-\frac{3}{5}\sqrt{5}, \pm\frac{2}{5}\sqrt{5}\right)$

6 **a**

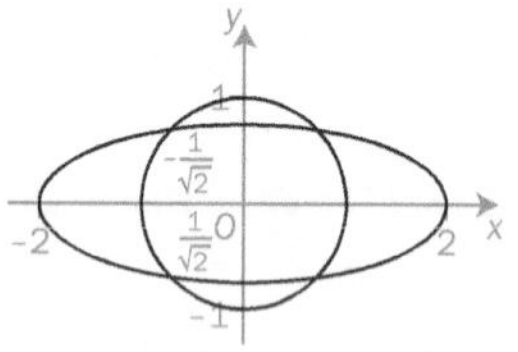

b i $\left(\pm\frac{2}{7}\sqrt{7}, \pm\frac{1}{7}\sqrt{21}\right)$

(all four combinations)

7 **b** $a=\sqrt{6},\ b=\sqrt{3}$ **c** $\frac{x^2}{6}+y^2=1$

8 **a**

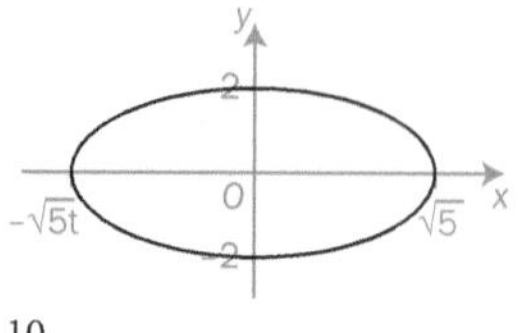

c $\frac{10}{3}$ square units

9 **a** $h=4,\ k=\frac{1}{4}$ **b** $\frac{64}{3}\pi$ cubic units

10 **b** $e=\frac{1}{2}$

Exercise 4.2

1 **a** $e=\frac{1}{3}$ **b** $e=\frac{1}{2}\sqrt{3}$ **c** $e=\frac{1}{2}$

d $e=\frac{1}{3}\sqrt{5}$ **e** $e=\frac{1}{3}\sqrt{3}$

2 **a**

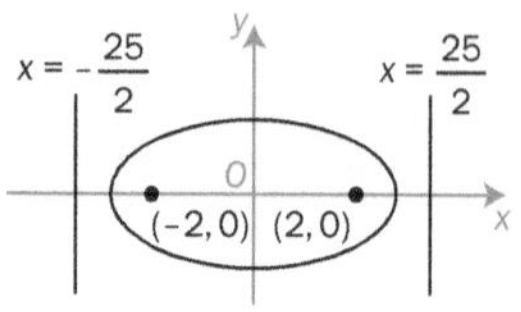

b

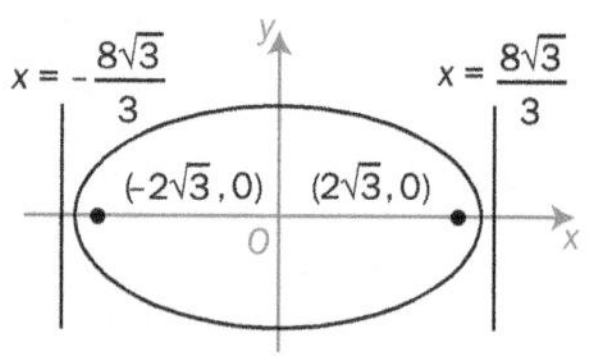

c

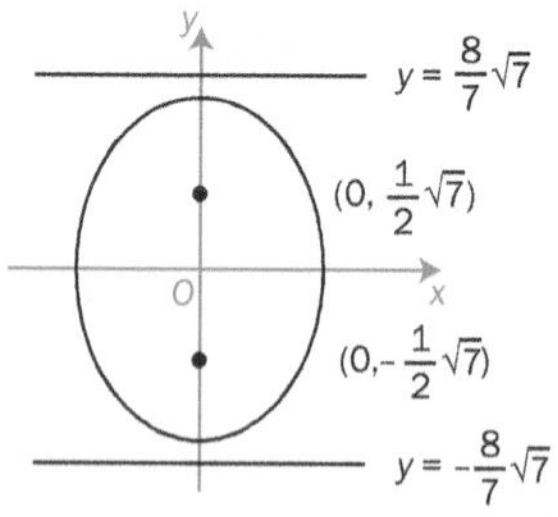

3 **a** $e=\frac{1}{2}\sqrt{3}$ **b** $b=2, 8$

4 **a** $e=\frac{2}{3}$ **b** $S(2,0), S'(-2,0), x=\pm\frac{9}{2}$ **c** $P\left(2, \pm\frac{5}{3}\right)$

5 **a** $e=\frac{1}{3}\sqrt{3}$

b i $P\left(\frac{3}{2}\sqrt{3}, \frac{1}{2}\sqrt{6}\right)$ ii $R\left(\frac{1}{4}\sqrt{3}, \frac{1}{4}\sqrt{94}\right)$ iii $T\left(\sqrt{3}, 2\right)$

6 **a** $e=\frac{1}{2}$

b

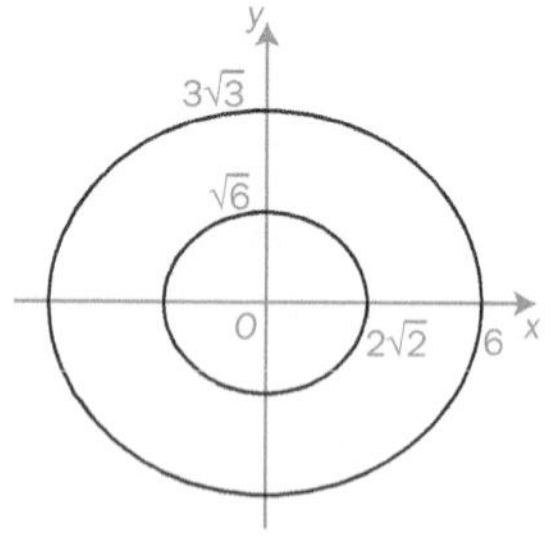

c $k=4\sqrt{2},\ \left(4\sqrt{2}, \pm\sqrt{3}\right)$

8 **b** $2a(1+e)$

Exercise 4.3

1 **a** $e=2$ **b** $e=\sqrt{5}$ **c** $e=\frac{4}{3}$

2 **a** $S(\pm4,0),\ x=\pm1,\ y=\pm\sqrt{3}x$

b $S(\pm4,0),\ x=\pm3,\ y=\pm\frac{1}{3}\sqrt{3}x$

c $S\left(\pm\frac{1}{2}\sqrt{5}, 0\right),\ x=\pm\frac{1}{10}\sqrt{5},\ y=\pm2x$

3 **a** (−1, 0), (2, 3)

b

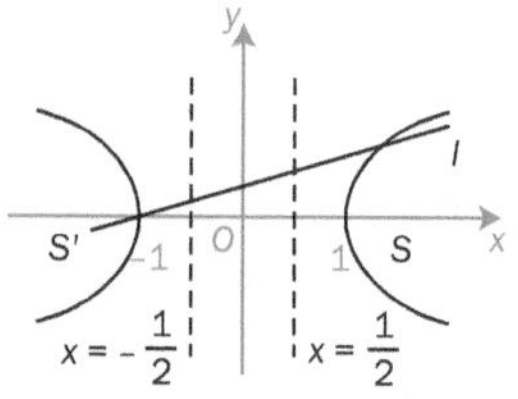

c 1 square unit

4 **a** $e=\frac{3}{4}\sqrt{2}$ **b** $P_1(4, 1), P_2(4, -1)$

5 **a** $(\pm3, 0)$

6 **a** i $P\left(\frac{16}{3}, \frac{35}{9}\right)$ **b** $\frac{140}{9}$ square units

FP3

7 a $S(3\sqrt{2},0)$

b

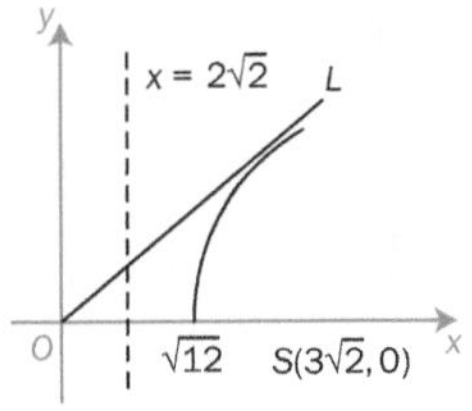

d $2+4\sqrt{2}, -2+4\sqrt{2}$

8 a $ae-a$

Exercise 4.4

1 a $y=x-2$ b $y=3-x$

2 a $3x-6y+22=0$ b $3x+6y-1=0$

3 a $P\left(\sqrt{2},\frac{7}{3}\right)$

4 b $Q(-3,2)$

5 a No b Yes c Yes

6 a $c=\pm5$ b $m=\pm3$

7 b $a=3, b=\sqrt{7}$ c $P\left(-\frac{9}{4},\frac{7}{4}\right)$

9 a $a=4, b=2\sqrt{11}$

Exercise 4.5

1 a $x=4\cos\theta, y=3\sin\theta$ b $x=3\cos\theta,\ y=\sqrt{3}\sin\theta$

c $x=2\cos\theta,\ y=2\sqrt{2}\sin\theta$

2 a $\frac{x^2}{25}+\frac{y^2}{9}=1$ b $\frac{x^2}{5}+\frac{y^2}{2}=1$ c $9x^2+\frac{9}{4}y^2=1$

3 a Second quadrant b Fourth quadrant

c Second quadrant d Third quadrant

4 a $\theta_1=\frac{1}{6}\pi$ c $-\frac{1}{2}\sqrt{3}$

5 b $-\frac{3}{2}\sqrt{3}$ c $Q\left(\frac{4}{5}\sqrt{5},\frac{3}{5}\sqrt{5}\right)$

6 b $3y+2x=9$ d $x=\frac{9}{2}$

8 b $\left(\sqrt{\frac{3}{2}},1\right)$

9 b $y=3x-3$ c $\left(\frac{3}{7},-\frac{12}{7}\right)$

Exercise 4.6

1 a $x=5\sec\theta, y=3\tan\theta$

b $x=\sec\theta, y=2\tan\theta$

c $x=2\sec\theta,\ y=\sqrt{3}\tan\theta$

2 a $\frac{x^2}{9}-\frac{y^2}{16}=1$ b $\frac{x^2}{16}-y^2=1$ c $2x^2-\frac{y^2}{2}=1$

3 a $a=\sqrt{3}, b=\sqrt{6}$ b $P\left(2,\sqrt{2}\right)$

c $y=\sqrt{2}\left(x-1\right),\ p=1, q=-1$

$y=\sqrt{2}\left(3-x\right),\ p=-1,\ q=3$

4 b $15y+18x+130=0$

5 a $e=2$ c $P\left(\frac{5}{2},\frac{3}{2}\sqrt{3}\right)$

6 b $S(5,0)$ c $\frac{4}{5}$

Exercise 4.7

1 c

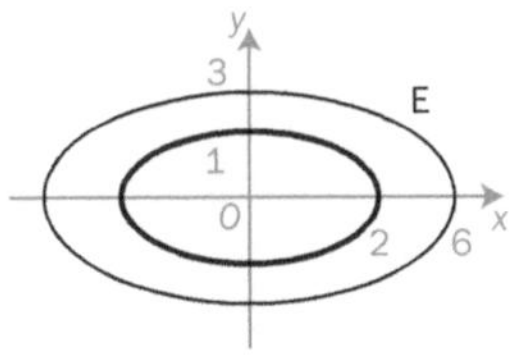

2 b $ST=\sqrt{5}$

3 a $U(3\sec\theta,0), V(0,2\operatorname{cosec}\theta)$

4 c $\frac{1}{t}y-x=\frac{1}{t^2}$

d Part of the line with equation $x=1$ for which $y\geqslant2$

5 b $4t^2y+x=4ct$

6 b $e=\frac{\sqrt{6}}{3}$

7 b $y=\frac{\sqrt{2}}{t}x+\frac{at}{\sqrt{2}}$

d

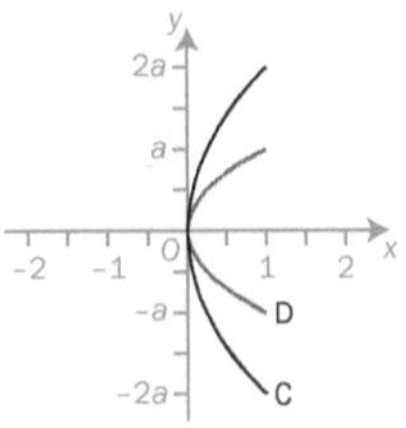

8 a $C\left(0,\frac{a^2+b^2}{b}\tan\theta\right), D\left(\frac{a^2+b^2}{a}\sec\theta,0\right)$

9 a $y_0=\frac{b^2c}{a^2+b^2}$ b $a^2y+b^2x=0$ c $\frac{x^2}{a^4}-\frac{y^2}{b^4}=1$

10 a $m^2a^2-b^2=c^2$ d $(-ae, a(1-e^2))$

Review 4

1 a $e=\frac{1}{2}\sqrt{2}$ b $x=\pm2\sqrt{2}$ c $2\sqrt{2}-2$

3 a $b=\sqrt{6}$ b $\frac{x^2}{8}+\frac{y^2}{6}=1$

c

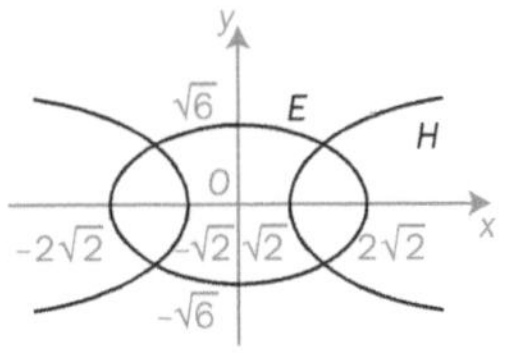

d $\frac{48}{5}\sqrt{2}$ square units

5 b $P\left(-2,\frac{5}{3}\right)$

6 a i $S(3,0), S'(-3,0)$ ii $x=\pm\frac{4}{3}$ c ii $P\left(\frac{2}{3}\sqrt{14},\frac{5}{3}\right)$

7 a $S(0,4), S'(0,-4)$

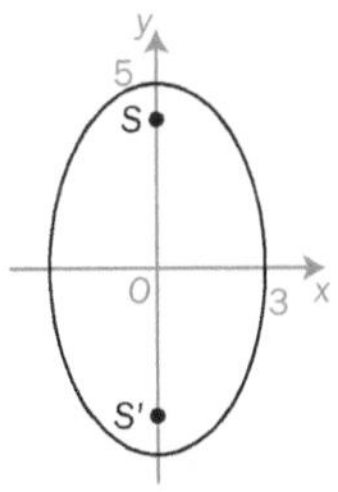

c $OQ\times OR=16$

8 c $y=\pm\left(\frac{\sqrt{e^2-1}}{1+e^2}\right)x$

FP3

Chapter 5

Before you start

1 **a** $\begin{pmatrix} 3 & 2 \\ -1 & 3 \end{pmatrix}$ **b** $\begin{pmatrix} 5 & 3 \\ -2 & 1 \end{pmatrix}$

c $\begin{pmatrix} 11 & 11 \\ -11 & 0 \end{pmatrix}$ **d** $\begin{pmatrix} 9 & 0 \\ 14 & 16 \end{pmatrix}$

2 **a** $\mathbf{M}^{\mathrm{T}} = \begin{pmatrix} 5 & 7 \\ 3 & 6 \end{pmatrix}$, $\det \mathbf{M} = 9$ **b** $k = 2, -3$

c i $-\frac{1}{10}\begin{pmatrix} 1 & -3 \\ -4 & 2 \end{pmatrix}$ ii $\frac{1}{k^2+1}\begin{pmatrix} k & -1 \\ 1 & k \end{pmatrix}$

Exercise 5.1

1 **a** $\mathbf{AB} = \begin{pmatrix} 8 & 4 & 14 \\ 21 & 13 & 27 \\ 18 & 9 & 26 \end{pmatrix}$, $\mathbf{BA} = \begin{pmatrix} 10 & 26 & 8 \\ 10 & 29 & 7 \\ 12 & 25 & 8 \end{pmatrix}$

b $\mathbf{AB} = \begin{pmatrix} 2 & -7 & 13 \\ 3 & 11 & 7 \\ 1 & -14 & 12 \end{pmatrix}$, $\mathbf{BA} = \begin{pmatrix} 10 & -12 & 1 \\ -1 & 12 & 12 \\ 10 & -10 & 3 \end{pmatrix}$

2 **a** $a = 5, b = 1, c = 3$ **b** $\begin{pmatrix} 6 & 15 & 10 \\ 13 & 16 & 12 \\ 4 & 7 & 4 \end{pmatrix}$

3 **a** $\mathbf{A}$ **b** $\mathbf{AB}$ **c** $\mathbf{O}$, the zero matrix

4 **a** $(\mathbf{AA}^{\mathrm{T}})^{\mathrm{T}} = (\mathbf{A}^{\mathrm{T}})^{\mathrm{T}}\mathbf{A}^{\mathrm{T}} = \mathbf{AA}^{\mathrm{T}}$

b $\mathbf{I} = \mathbf{AA}^{-1} = \mathbf{A}^{-1}\mathbf{A} \Rightarrow \mathbf{I}^{\mathrm{T}} = (\mathbf{AA}^{-1})^{\mathrm{T}} = (\mathbf{A}^{-1}\mathbf{A})^{\mathrm{T}}$

$\therefore \mathbf{I} = (\mathbf{A}^{-1})^{\mathrm{T}}\mathbf{A}^{\mathrm{T}} = \mathbf{A}^{\mathrm{T}}(\mathbf{A}^{-1})^{\mathrm{T}} = (\mathbf{A}^{-1})^{\mathrm{T}}\mathbf{A} = \mathbf{A}(\mathbf{A}^{-1})^{\mathrm{T}}$

Inverse unique $\Rightarrow (\mathbf{A}^{-1})^{\mathrm{T}} = \mathbf{A}$

5 True for $n = 1$ (trivially), suppose true for $n = k$

$(\mathbf{A}^{\mathrm{T}})^{k+1} = (\mathbf{A}^{\mathrm{T}})^{k}\mathbf{A}^{\mathrm{T}} = (\mathbf{A}^{k})^{\mathrm{T}}\mathbf{A}^{\mathrm{T}} = (\mathbf{A}\mathbf{A}^{k})^{\mathrm{T}} = (\mathbf{A}^{k+1})^{\mathrm{T}}$

Exercise 5.2

1 **a** $\begin{pmatrix} 17 \\ 10 \\ 7 \end{pmatrix}$ **b** $\begin{pmatrix} -2 \\ 4 \\ -4 \end{pmatrix}$

2 **a** $p = 2, q = 1$ **b** $\begin{pmatrix} 16 \\ 7 \\ 13 \end{pmatrix}$

3 **b** $p = 4, q = 1$ **c** $\begin{pmatrix} 11 \\ 3 \\ 10 \end{pmatrix}$

4 **a** $\frac{1}{2}\begin{pmatrix} 2 & -4 \\ -1 & 3 \end{pmatrix}$ **b** $\begin{pmatrix} 4 \\ 3 \end{pmatrix}$ **c** $\begin{pmatrix} 82 \\ 116 \end{pmatrix}$

5 **a** $y = 4x + 5$ **b** $y = 5 - 6x$ **c** $y = \frac{3}{2}x - \frac{5}{2}$

6 **b** $\begin{pmatrix} -4 & -1 \\ 2 & 1 \end{pmatrix}$

7 **a** i The line with equation $y = \frac{2}{3}x + 2$

ii The single point (-6, -3)

b $m = -\frac{1}{2}$, $c = \frac{1}{2}$

Exercise 5.3

1 **a** -15 **b** -30 **c** 15

d -40 **e** 29 **f** 12

2 **a** $24 - 7x$ **b** $2(x - 8)$ **c** $(x + 2)^2$

d $(x - 2)(x + 2)^2$ **e** $(x - 1)(x^2 + x + 1)$

f $x(x + 1)(2 - x)$

3 **a** $x = -1, 2$

4 **a** $p = 2, 8$ **b** $p = 5 \pm \sqrt{14}$

5 **b** Min value = 1, when $x = 0$

6 **a** -11 **b** $k = 2, \frac{5}{6}$ **c** $k = 1, \frac{23}{5}$

7 $k = \frac{3}{2}$, det = 2

8 **a** $x = 2, -1 \pm \sqrt{5}$ **b** $x = 3, \pm\sqrt{6}$

11 -3

Exercise 5.4

1 **a** $\frac{1}{12}\begin{pmatrix} 2 & 3 & -1 \\ -6 & 3 & 3 \\ 8 & -6 & 2 \end{pmatrix}$ **b** $\frac{1}{6}\begin{pmatrix} -2 & 1 & 1 \\ 8 & 5 & -1 \\ -6 & -3 & 3 \end{pmatrix}$

c $\frac{1}{34}\begin{pmatrix} 8 & -13 & 2 \\ -2 & -1 & 8 \\ -2 & 16 & 8 \end{pmatrix}$

2 **b** $\begin{pmatrix} -5 & -7 & 4 \\ 1 & 2 & -1 \\ 7 & 9 & -5 \end{pmatrix}$

3 **a** $\frac{1}{112}\begin{pmatrix} -3 & -7 & 41 \\ -7 & 21 & 21 \\ 16 & 0 & -32 \end{pmatrix}$ **c** $\frac{1}{8}\begin{pmatrix} 4 & -2 & 16 \\ 0 & 0 & 32 \\ -2 & 3 & -32 \end{pmatrix}$

4 **a** -5 **b** $\mathbf{A}^{-1} = \frac{1}{5}\begin{pmatrix} 0 & 5 & 0 \\ 2 & 2-2k & -1 \\ -1 & k-6 & 3 \end{pmatrix}$

5 **b** $\frac{1}{22}\begin{pmatrix} 4 & -1-2x & 8 \\ -2 & x+6 & -4 \\ 2x-12 & 3-x^2 & 4x-2 \end{pmatrix}$ **c** $x = 1$

6 **a** $\frac{1}{6}\begin{pmatrix} 1 & -1 & 0 \\ -1 & -11 & 6 \\ 2 & 28 & -12 \end{pmatrix}$ **b** $a = -\frac{1}{2}$, $b = \frac{1}{2}$, $c = 0$

7 **a** $\begin{pmatrix} 0 & 2 & -5 \\ 1 & 3 & 0 \\ 0 & 1 & -3 \end{pmatrix}$ **b** $\begin{pmatrix} 0 & -8 & -3 \\ 1 & 3 & 4 \\ 0 & -5 & -2 \end{pmatrix}$

c $\begin{pmatrix} 1 & -2 & 1 \\ 0 & -1 & 1 \\ 0 & 2 & -1 \end{pmatrix}$ **d** $\begin{pmatrix} 17 \\ 7 \\ 10 \end{pmatrix}$

8 **a** $\mathbf{A} = \begin{pmatrix} 1 & 3 & -1 \\ 2 & 1 & 1 \\ 1 & -1 & 2 \end{pmatrix}$, $a = 4, b = 6, c = 3$

b $\mathbf{A}^{-1} = \frac{1}{3}\begin{pmatrix} -3 & 5 & -4 \\ 3 & -3 & 3 \\ 3 & 4 & 5 \end{pmatrix}$ $x = 2, y = 1, z = 1$

9 i $x = 3, y = -1, z = 2$ ii $x = 0, y = 3, z = 2$

Exercise 5.5

Unless stated otherwise, any scalar multiple of the given eigenvectors are acceptable answers.

1 **a** $\lambda_1 = -2$, $\mathbf{v}_1 = \begin{pmatrix} 1 \\ -1 \end{pmatrix}$, $\lambda_2 = 4$, $\mathbf{v}_2 = \begin{pmatrix} 1 \\ 1 \end{pmatrix}$

b $\lambda_1 = -1$, $\mathbf{v}_1 = \begin{pmatrix} 1 \\ -2 \end{pmatrix}$, $\lambda_2 = 5$, $\mathbf{v}_2 = \begin{pmatrix} 1 \\ 1 \end{pmatrix}$

c $\lambda_1 = 1$, $\mathbf{v}_1 = \begin{pmatrix} 1 \\ 1 \end{pmatrix}$, $\lambda_2 = 6$, $\mathbf{v}_2 = \begin{pmatrix} 1 \\ -4 \end{pmatrix}$

2 **a** $\lambda = -3$ **c** $\lambda_2 = 5$, $\mathbf{v}_2 = \begin{pmatrix} 7 \\ 1 \end{pmatrix}$

3 **a** $\lambda_1 = -2, \lambda_2 = 5$

4 a $\lambda_1 = 0, \lambda_2 = 5$ b $\mathbf{v}_1 = \begin{pmatrix} 1 \\ -2 \end{pmatrix}, \mathbf{v}_2 = \begin{pmatrix} 2 \\ 1 \end{pmatrix}$

5 b $\lambda_1 = 3, \mathbf{v}_1 = \begin{pmatrix} 1 \\ 2 \end{pmatrix}$

c i $\lambda_2 = -3,\ \mathbf{v}_2 = \begin{pmatrix} 1 \\ -1 \end{pmatrix}$ ii $y = -x$

6 a $y = -2x, y = -x$ b $y = -\frac{3}{4}x,\ y = \frac{2}{3}x$

7 a $a = 6$ b $\begin{pmatrix} 2 \\ -3 \end{pmatrix}$ c $\lambda = 8$

8 a $\lambda_1 = -4, \lambda_2 = 5$ b $p = 2, q = -3$ c $\lambda'_1 = -\frac{1}{4}, \lambda'_2 = \frac{1}{5}$

Exercise 5.6

1 a $\lambda_1 = 0, \mathbf{v}_1 = \begin{pmatrix} 1 \\ 1 \\ -1 \end{pmatrix}, \lambda_2 = 1, \mathbf{v}_2 = \begin{pmatrix} 1 \\ 0 \\ 0 \end{pmatrix}, \lambda_3 = 3, \mathbf{v}_3 = \begin{pmatrix} 1 \\ 4 \\ 2 \end{pmatrix}$

b $\lambda_1 = -1, \mathbf{v}_1 = \begin{pmatrix} 1 \\ -1 \\ 0 \end{pmatrix}, \lambda_2 = 1, \mathbf{v}_2 = \begin{pmatrix} 1 \\ 3 \\ -2 \end{pmatrix},$

$\lambda_3 = 3, \mathbf{v}_3 = \begin{pmatrix} 1 \\ 1 \\ 0 \end{pmatrix}$

c $\lambda_1 = -1, \mathbf{v}_1 = \begin{pmatrix} -3 \\ 2 \\ 1 \end{pmatrix}, \lambda_2 = 1, \mathbf{v}_2 = \begin{pmatrix} -3 \\ -2 \\ 3 \end{pmatrix}, \lambda_3 = 5, \mathbf{v}_3 = \begin{pmatrix} 3 \\ 2 \\ 1 \end{pmatrix}$

d $\lambda_1 = -2, \mathbf{v}_1 = \begin{pmatrix} 0 \\ 1 \\ -1 \end{pmatrix}, \lambda_2 = 0, \mathbf{v}_2 = \begin{pmatrix} -3 \\ -2 \\ 1 \end{pmatrix}, \lambda_3 = 4, \mathbf{v}_3 = \begin{pmatrix} -3 \\ 2 \\ 1 \end{pmatrix}$

2 a $\lambda_1 = -2, \lambda_2 = 2, \lambda_3 = 4$

b $\mathbf{v}_1 = \begin{pmatrix} 0 \\ 1 \\ -1 \end{pmatrix}, \mathbf{v}_2 = \begin{pmatrix} 1 \\ 0 \\ 0 \end{pmatrix}, \mathbf{v}_3 = \begin{pmatrix} 0 \\ 1 \\ 1 \end{pmatrix}$

3 b $\begin{pmatrix} \frac{2}{3} \\ \frac{1}{3} \\ \frac{2}{3} \end{pmatrix}, \begin{pmatrix} -\frac{2}{3} \\ -\frac{1}{3} \\ -\frac{2}{3} \end{pmatrix}$

4 a $\lambda_1 = 3$ b $\lambda_2 = -1$ c $\begin{pmatrix} 0 \\ 1 \\ 1 \end{pmatrix}$

5 a $\begin{pmatrix} 0 \\ 2 \\ 1 \end{pmatrix}$ b $\begin{pmatrix} \frac{2}{3} \\ -\frac{2}{3} \\ -\frac{1}{3} \end{pmatrix}$

6 b $\begin{pmatrix} 0 \\ 1 \\ 1 \end{pmatrix}, \begin{pmatrix} 1 \\ 2 \\ 1 \end{pmatrix}$ c 30°

7 b $\lambda_1 = -2, \mathbf{v}_1 = \begin{pmatrix} 1 \\ 2 \\ 0 \end{pmatrix}$

8 a $\lambda_1 = -1, \mathbf{v}_1 = \begin{pmatrix} 1 \\ 1 \\ 2 \end{pmatrix}, \lambda_2 = 2, \mathbf{v}_2 = \begin{pmatrix} 1 \\ 1 \\ 1 \end{pmatrix}, \lambda_3 = 3, \mathbf{v}_3 = \begin{pmatrix} 2 \\ 1 \\ 1 \end{pmatrix}$

b $\lambda_1 = -4, \mathbf{v}_1 = \begin{pmatrix} 1 \\ -1 \\ 1 \end{pmatrix}, \lambda_2 = 2, \mathbf{v}_2 = \begin{pmatrix} 1 \\ -1 \\ -1 \end{pmatrix}, \lambda_3 = 4, \mathbf{v}_3 = \begin{pmatrix} -2 \\ 1 \\ 0 \end{pmatrix}$

9 a $\begin{pmatrix} 1 \\ -1 \\ 1 \end{pmatrix}$ b $\lambda = 2$, double root c $\begin{pmatrix} 1 \\ 0 \\ 1 \end{pmatrix}$ and $\begin{pmatrix} 0 \\ 1 \\ 1 \end{pmatrix}$

10 a $-3, 6$

b $\lambda_1 = 3, \mathbf{v}_1 = \begin{pmatrix} 2 \\ 0 \\ 1 \end{pmatrix}, \lambda_2 = -3, \mathbf{v}_2 = \begin{pmatrix} 1 \\ 1 \\ 0 \end{pmatrix}, \lambda_3 = 6, \mathbf{v}_3 = \begin{pmatrix} 0 \\ 1 \\ 1 \end{pmatrix}$

c $p = 1, q = 0$ e $9\sqrt{3}$ square units

11 a $\lambda = 3, \pm 6$ b $a = 0, b = -1$

Exercise 5.7

1 a Diagonal and symmetric
b Symmetric and orthogonal
c Symmetric

2 a $\begin{pmatrix} -\frac{2}{3} \\ \frac{1}{3} \\ \frac{2}{3} \end{pmatrix}$ b $\begin{pmatrix} -\frac{\sqrt{2}}{3} \\ \frac{\sqrt{3}}{3} \\ \frac{2}{3} \end{pmatrix}$ c $\begin{pmatrix} \frac{1}{3} \\ \frac{2\sqrt{2}}{3} \\ 0 \end{pmatrix}$ d $\begin{pmatrix} \frac{\sqrt{6}}{6} \\ \frac{\sqrt{3}}{2} \\ -\frac{\sqrt{3}}{6} \end{pmatrix}$

3 a $b = 15, c = -10$ b $\begin{pmatrix} 25 & 0 & 0 \\ 0 & 25 & 0 \\ 0 & 0 & 25 \end{pmatrix}$ c $\frac{1}{25}\begin{pmatrix} 2 & 1 & 2 \\ 15 & 0 & -10 \\ 3 & -1 & 3 \end{pmatrix}$

5 b $\begin{pmatrix} \frac{\sqrt{3}}{2} & \frac{\sqrt{3}}{6} & \frac{\sqrt{6}}{6} \\ 0 & \frac{\sqrt{6}}{3} & -\frac{\sqrt{3}}{3} \\ \frac{1}{2} & -\frac{1}{2} & -\frac{\sqrt{2}}{2} \end{pmatrix}$

6 b $a = -1, d = 1$
c Rotation 180° about O, enlargement, scale factor 9 centre O.

7 c either $q = \frac{1}{6}\sqrt{6}$, $r = \frac{1}{3}\sqrt{6}$ and $s = -\frac{1}{6}\sqrt{6}$

or $q = -\frac{1}{6}\sqrt{6}$, $r = -\frac{1}{3}\sqrt{6}$ and $s = \frac{1}{6}\sqrt{6}$

8 b Any pair of non-commutative 2×2 matrices e.g $\mathbf{A} = \begin{pmatrix} 2 & 1 \\ 1 & 1 \end{pmatrix}, \mathbf{B} = \begin{pmatrix} 0 & 2 \\ 2 & 1 \end{pmatrix}$

9 b $\det \mathbf{A} = \pm 1$

Exercise 5.8

1 b $\lambda_1 = 1, \lambda_2 = -1, \lambda_3 = 5$

c $\mathbf{P} = \begin{pmatrix} \frac{1}{\sqrt{2}} & -\frac{1}{\sqrt{3}} & \frac{1}{\sqrt{6}} \\ 0 & \frac{1}{\sqrt{3}} & \frac{2}{\sqrt{6}} \\ \frac{1}{\sqrt{2}} & \frac{1}{\sqrt{3}} & -\frac{1}{\sqrt{6}} \end{pmatrix}, \mathbf{D} = \begin{pmatrix} 1 & 0 & 0 \\ 0 & -1 & 0 \\ 0 & 0 & 5 \end{pmatrix}$

2 b $\mathbf{v}_2 = \begin{pmatrix} 2 \\ 1 \\ 1 \end{pmatrix}, \mathbf{v}_3 = \begin{pmatrix} 0 \\ 1 \\ -1 \end{pmatrix}$

c $\mathbf{P} = \begin{pmatrix} -\frac{1}{\sqrt{3}} & \frac{2}{\sqrt{6}} & 0 \\ \frac{1}{\sqrt{3}} & \frac{1}{\sqrt{6}} & \frac{1}{\sqrt{2}} \\ \frac{1}{\sqrt{3}} & \frac{1}{\sqrt{6}} & -\frac{1}{\sqrt{2}} \end{pmatrix}, \mathbf{D} = \begin{pmatrix} -3 & 0 & 0 \\ 0 & 0 & 0 \\ 0 & 0 & 2 \end{pmatrix}$

3 a $\mathbf{P}=\begin{pmatrix}\frac{1}{\sqrt{5}} & \frac{2}{\sqrt{30}} & \frac{2}{\sqrt{6}}\\ 0 & -\frac{5}{\sqrt{30}} & \frac{1}{\sqrt{6}}\\ -\frac{2}{\sqrt{5}} & \frac{1}{\sqrt{30}} & \frac{1}{\sqrt{6}}\end{pmatrix}, \mathbf{D}=\begin{pmatrix}3 & 0 & 0\\ 0 & -2 & 0\\ 0 & 0 & 4\end{pmatrix}$

b $\mathbf{P}=\begin{pmatrix}0 & -\frac{2}{\sqrt{6}} & \frac{1}{\sqrt{3}}\\ \frac{1}{\sqrt{2}} & \frac{1}{\sqrt{6}} & \frac{1}{\sqrt{3}}\\ -\frac{1}{\sqrt{2}} & \frac{1}{\sqrt{6}} & \frac{1}{\sqrt{3}}\end{pmatrix}, \mathbf{D}=\begin{pmatrix}3 & 0 & 0\\ 0 & 1 & 0\\ 0 & 0 & 4\end{pmatrix}$

c $\mathbf{P}=\begin{pmatrix}\frac{1}{\sqrt{3}} & \frac{1}{\sqrt{2}} & \frac{1}{\sqrt{6}}\\ \frac{1}{\sqrt{3}} & -\frac{1}{\sqrt{2}} & \frac{1}{\sqrt{6}}\\ \frac{1}{\sqrt{3}} & 0 & -\frac{2}{\sqrt{6}}\end{pmatrix}, \mathbf{D}=\begin{pmatrix}2 & 0 & 0\\ 0 & 1 & 0\\ 0 & 0 & 5\end{pmatrix}$

4 a $\lambda_1=3$ b $\lambda_2=-2, \lambda_3=2$

c $\mathbf{P}=\begin{pmatrix}0 & \frac{\sqrt{3}}{2} & \frac{1}{2}\\ 1 & 0 & 0\\ 0 & \frac{1}{2} & -\frac{\sqrt{3}}{2}\end{pmatrix}, \mathbf{D}=\begin{pmatrix}3 & 0 & 0\\ 0 & 2 & 0\\ 0 & 0 & -2\end{pmatrix}$

5 a $\mathbf{P}=\begin{pmatrix}\frac{1}{\sqrt{2}} & 0 & \frac{1}{\sqrt{2}}\\ 0 & 1 & 0\\ \frac{1}{\sqrt{2}} & 0 & -\frac{1}{\sqrt{2}}\end{pmatrix}, \mathbf{D}=\begin{pmatrix}0 & 0 & 0\\ 0 & 1 & 0\\ 0 & 0 & 2\end{pmatrix}$ c $\begin{pmatrix}0 & 0 & 0\\ 0 & 1 & 0\\ -2 & 0 & 2\end{pmatrix}$

6 a $\lambda_1=3$

b $\mathbf{P}=\begin{pmatrix}0 & \frac{1}{\sqrt{3}} & -\frac{2}{\sqrt{6}}\\ \frac{1}{\sqrt{2}} & \frac{1}{\sqrt{3}} & \frac{1}{\sqrt{6}}\\ -\frac{1}{\sqrt{2}} & \frac{1}{\sqrt{3}} & \frac{1}{\sqrt{6}}\end{pmatrix}, \mathbf{D}=\begin{pmatrix}-1 & 0 & 0\\ 0 & 3 & 0\\ 0 & 0 & -3\end{pmatrix}$

c $\begin{pmatrix}1\\ 5\\ 0\end{pmatrix}$

7 a $\begin{pmatrix}-\frac{2}{\sqrt{6}} & \frac{1}{\sqrt{3}} & 0\\ \frac{1}{\sqrt{6}} & \frac{1}{\sqrt{3}} & \frac{1}{\sqrt{2}}\\ \frac{1}{\sqrt{6}} & \frac{1}{\sqrt{3}} & -\frac{1}{\sqrt{2}}\end{pmatrix}$ b $\begin{pmatrix}\frac{1}{\sqrt{6}} & \frac{1}{\sqrt{2}} & \frac{1}{\sqrt{3}}\\ \frac{2}{\sqrt{6}} & 0 & -\frac{1}{\sqrt{3}}\\ \frac{1}{\sqrt{6}} & -\frac{1}{\sqrt{2}} & \frac{1}{\sqrt{3}}\end{pmatrix}$

8 a $a=-2$ b $\mathbf{P}=\begin{pmatrix}\frac{1}{\sqrt{3}} & \frac{1}{\sqrt{2}} & \frac{1}{\sqrt{6}}\\ -\frac{1}{\sqrt{3}} & \frac{1}{\sqrt{2}} & -\frac{1}{\sqrt{6}}\\ \frac{1}{\sqrt{3}} & 0 & -\frac{2}{\sqrt{6}}\end{pmatrix}, \mathbf{D}=\begin{pmatrix}3 & 0 & 0\\ 0 & 6 & 0\\ 0 & 0 & 6\end{pmatrix}$

9 a $\lambda=\sqrt{5}$ b $\begin{pmatrix}0 & -\frac{1}{\sqrt{2}} & \frac{1}{\sqrt{2}}\\ \frac{1}{\sqrt{5}} & -\frac{\sqrt{10}}{5} & -\frac{\sqrt{10}}{5}\\ \frac{2}{\sqrt{5}} & \frac{1}{\sqrt{10}} & \frac{1}{\sqrt{10}}\end{pmatrix}$

10 a $\mathbf{B}=\begin{pmatrix}1 & 2 & 0\\ 2 & 4 & 0\\ 0 & 0 & 1\end{pmatrix}=\mathbf{B}^{\mathrm{T}}$

b $\mathbf{P}=\begin{pmatrix}\frac{2}{\sqrt{5}} & 0 & \frac{1}{\sqrt{5}}\\ -\frac{1}{\sqrt{5}} & 0 & \frac{2}{\sqrt{5}}\\ 0 & 1 & 0\end{pmatrix}$ $\mathbf{D}=\begin{pmatrix}0 & 0 & 0\\ 0 & 1 & 0\\ 0 & 0 & 5\end{pmatrix}$

c $\mathbf{X}=\mathbf{AP}=\begin{pmatrix}0 & 0 & 0\\ 0 & 1 & 0\\ 0 & 0 & -\sqrt{5}\end{pmatrix}$

Review 5

1 a $x=3,-5$ b -16

2 a $k=-2$ b $\begin{pmatrix}-6\\ 3\\ -6\end{pmatrix}$

3 a $2y+3x=8, a=2, b=3$ b $y=x$

4 a $\lambda=1,7$ b $\lambda_1=1:\begin{pmatrix}-2\\ 1\end{pmatrix}, \lambda_2=7:\begin{pmatrix}1\\ 1\end{pmatrix}$

c $y=x, y=-\frac{1}{2}x$

5 a $\lambda=-3$ c $\lambda=2,3$

6 a $\lambda=2$ b $\lambda=1,3$ c $\begin{pmatrix}1\\ -1\\ -2\end{pmatrix}, \begin{pmatrix}1\\ 1\\ 0\end{pmatrix}$

7 a $\begin{pmatrix}7 & 4 & 10\\ 7 & 2 & 10\\ 2 & 3 & 2\end{pmatrix}$ b $\begin{pmatrix}7\\ 6\\ 10\end{pmatrix}$

8 b $\begin{pmatrix}1\\ 3\\ 0\end{pmatrix}$ c $a=-1, b=0$ d $\begin{pmatrix}25\\ -25\\ 0\end{pmatrix}$

9 b $\frac{1}{(4-6k)}\begin{pmatrix}2 & -1-2k & -2k\\ -2 & 3-k & 2k\\ -6 & 7 & 4\end{pmatrix}$ c $k=-1$ d z-axis

10 b $\begin{pmatrix}1\\ -6\\ 2\end{pmatrix}$

11 a $\lambda_1=1, \lambda_2=3, \lambda_3=4$ b $\begin{pmatrix}-1\\ 1\\ 1\end{pmatrix}$

c $\mathbf{P}=\begin{pmatrix}\frac{1}{\sqrt{6}} & \frac{1}{\sqrt{2}} & -\frac{1}{\sqrt{3}}\\ -\frac{1}{\sqrt{6}} & \frac{1}{\sqrt{2}} & \frac{1}{\sqrt{3}}\\ \frac{2}{\sqrt{6}} & 0 & \frac{1}{\sqrt{3}}\end{pmatrix}, \mathbf{D}=\begin{pmatrix}1 & 0 & 0\\ 0 & 3 & 0\\ 0 & 0 & 4\end{pmatrix}$

12 a $p=-1$ b $\lambda=2:\begin{pmatrix}1\\ 0\\ 1\end{pmatrix}, \lambda=-3:\begin{pmatrix}-1\\ 1\\ 1\end{pmatrix}$

c $\mathbf{P}=\begin{pmatrix}\frac{1}{\sqrt{6}} & \frac{1}{\sqrt{2}} & -\frac{1}{\sqrt{3}}\\ \frac{2}{\sqrt{6}} & 0 & \frac{1}{\sqrt{3}}\\ -\frac{1}{\sqrt{6}} & \frac{1}{\sqrt{2}} & \frac{1}{\sqrt{3}}\end{pmatrix}, \mathbf{D}=\begin{pmatrix}0 & 0 & 0\\ 0 & 2 & 0\\ 0 & 0 & -3\end{pmatrix}$

13 b $\frac{1}{k(k-2)}\begin{pmatrix} -k & 0 & k \\ k^2-6 & 4-2k & 6-2k \\ 3 & k-2 & -3 \end{pmatrix}$ c $k=-1$

d i $\lambda=3$ ii $\begin{pmatrix}1\\1\\0\end{pmatrix}$

Chapter 6

Before you start

1 a $q=-3$ c $a=-\frac{2}{3},\ b=-\frac{4}{3}$

2 a $5\sqrt{2}$ b $2\sqrt{6}$ c $\sqrt{10}$

3 a $l_1: \mathbf{r}=(\mathbf{i}+\mathbf{j}+2\mathbf{k})+s(3\mathbf{i}-\mathbf{j}+2\mathbf{k}),\ s\in\mathbb{R}$
$l_2: \mathbf{r}=(7\mathbf{i}+5\mathbf{j}-12\mathbf{k})+t(3\mathbf{i}+\mathbf{j}-4\mathbf{k}),\ t\in\mathbb{R}$

b $P(-2,2,0)$ d $3\sqrt{26}$ units

Exercise 6.1

1 a $-3\mathbf{i}+8\mathbf{j}+2\mathbf{k}$ b $-2\mathbf{i}+3\mathbf{j}+16\mathbf{k}$
c $\frac{5}{2}\mathbf{i}-\mathbf{j}-\frac{3}{2}\mathbf{k}$ d $-4\mathbf{i}+6\mathbf{j}-8\mathbf{k}$

2 a $\mathbf{a}\times\mathbf{b}=8\mathbf{i}-3\mathbf{j}-7\mathbf{k},\ \mathbf{a}\times\mathbf{c}=7\mathbf{i}-\mathbf{j}-11\mathbf{k}$
b $15\mathbf{i}-4\mathbf{j}-18\mathbf{k}$

3 b $q=-18$ c $\frac{7}{2}\mathbf{i}+9\mathbf{j}-\mathbf{k}$

4 b $p=5,\ q=-2$

5 a $2\mathbf{c}$ b $7\mathbf{c}$ c $-1\mathbf{c}$

6 a e.g $\mathbf{a}\times(\mathbf{b}+\mathbf{c})$ b e.g $(\mathbf{a}-\mathbf{b})\times\mathbf{c}$
c e.g $(\mathbf{a}-\mathbf{c})\times(\mathbf{b}+\mathbf{c})$

7 a $\mathbf{c}=-4\mathbf{i}+3\mathbf{j}-2\mathbf{k}$ b $-\mathbf{i}+5\mathbf{k}$

8 a $(p-4q)\,\mathbf{j}+2\,(p-4q)\mathbf{k}$ b 0

9 b Any vector of the form $\lambda(\mathbf{a}+\mathbf{b})$ for non-zero $\lambda\in\mathbb{R}$ e.g $\mathbf{c}=5\mathbf{i}+6\mathbf{k}$

12 a $\frac{\sqrt{3}}{2}$ square units b 30° c $\frac{3\sqrt{11}}{2}$ square units

Exercise 6.2

1 a $\mathbf{r}=(2\mathbf{i}+2\mathbf{j}+\mathbf{k})+\lambda\,(\mathbf{i}-\mathbf{j}+6\mathbf{k})+\mu\,(2\mathbf{i}+\mathbf{j}+\mathbf{k}),\ \lambda,\mu\in\mathbb{R}$
b $\mathbf{r}=(7\mathbf{i}-2\mathbf{j}+3\mathbf{k})+\lambda(-2\mathbf{i}+4\mathbf{j}-4\mathbf{k})+\mu(-\mathbf{i}-4\mathbf{j}+\mathbf{k}),\ \lambda,\mu\in\mathbb{R}$
c $\mathbf{r}=(\mathbf{j}+\mathbf{k})+\lambda\,(2\mathbf{i}-\mathbf{j}+3\mathbf{k})+\mu(-\mathbf{i}-3\mathbf{j}),\ \lambda,\mu\in\mathbb{R}$

2 a $P(17,6,-6)$ b $s=18$

3 b $a=6$ c $\mathbf{r}=\lambda(8\mathbf{i}-\mathbf{j}+2\mathbf{k})+\mu(6\mathbf{i}+2\mathbf{j}+6\mathbf{k}),\ \lambda,\mu\in\mathbb{R}$

4 a $\mathbf{r}=(\mathbf{i}+2\mathbf{j}+4\mathbf{k})+\lambda(2\mathbf{i}-\mathbf{j}+\mathbf{k})+\mu(\mathbf{i}-2\mathbf{j}),\ \lambda,\mu\in\mathbb{R}$
b $Q(0,-8,0),\ R\left(0,0,\frac{8}{3}\right)$
c $\mathbf{r}=(-4\mathbf{i})+\lambda(\mathbf{i}-2\mathbf{j})+\mu(3\mathbf{i}+2\mathbf{k}),\ \lambda,\mu\in\mathbb{R}$
No plane can be parallel to all three coordinate axes.

6 a $C(4,7,-1)$
b $\mathbf{r}=(2\mathbf{i}-\mathbf{j}+\mathbf{k})+\lambda(\mathbf{i}+4\mathbf{j}+\mathbf{k})+\mu(\mathbf{i}+4\mathbf{j}-\mathbf{k}),\ \lambda,\mu\in\mathbb{R}$

7 b $\mathbf{r}=(4\mathbf{i}+3\mathbf{j}+2\mathbf{k})+\lambda(2\mathbf{j}+\mathbf{k})+\mu(\mathbf{i}+\mathbf{j}+\mathbf{k}),\ \lambda,\mu\in\mathbb{R}$
c $p=-1,\ q=2$

Exercise 6.3

2 b $\hat{\mathbf{n}}=\frac{4}{5}\mathbf{i}+\frac{3}{5}\mathbf{k}$ (or $\hat{\mathbf{n}}=-\frac{4}{5}\mathbf{i}-\frac{3}{5}\mathbf{k}$)

3 b $D(4,-1,5)$ or $D(0,7,-3)$

4 a $p=2,\ q=-4$ b $\frac{1}{\sqrt{29}}(2\mathbf{i}+3\mathbf{j}-4\mathbf{k}),\ \frac{1}{\sqrt{29}}(-2\mathbf{i}-3\mathbf{j}+4\mathbf{k})$

5 a $\mathbf{n}=\mathbf{k}$ (that is $0\mathbf{i}+0\mathbf{j}+\mathbf{k}$) b $\mathbf{n}=\mathbf{j}$
c $\mathbf{n}=\mathbf{j}+\mathbf{k}$ d $\mathbf{n}=-\mathbf{i}+\mathbf{j}$

6 a $a=1$ c $P'(-3,-1,-7)$

Exercise 6.4

2 a $\frac{7}{2}$ square units b $\frac{3}{2}\sqrt{5}$ square units
c $2\sqrt{6}$ square units

3 a $\overrightarrow{AB}=3\mathbf{i}+3\mathbf{k},\ \overrightarrow{AC}=\mathbf{i}-\mathbf{j}+2\mathbf{k}$

4 a $\overrightarrow{AB}=-5\mathbf{i}+3\mathbf{j}-3\mathbf{k},\ \overrightarrow{AD}=-2\mathbf{i}-2\mathbf{j}-\mathbf{k}$
Area $=13\sqrt{2}$ square units

5 b $\frac{3}{2}\sqrt{2}$ square units
c The points A, B and C are collinear.

6 a $\hat{\mathbf{n}}=-\frac{3}{5}\mathbf{j}-\frac{4}{5}\mathbf{k}$ b $\hat{\mathbf{n}}=\frac{1}{9}\mathbf{i}+\frac{4}{9}\mathbf{j}-\frac{8}{9}\mathbf{k}$
c $\hat{\mathbf{n}}=\frac{2}{3}\mathbf{i}-\frac{2}{3}\mathbf{j}-\frac{1}{3}\mathbf{k}$ d $\hat{\mathbf{n}}=\frac{1}{\sqrt{3}}\mathbf{i}+\frac{1}{\sqrt{3}}\mathbf{j}-\frac{1}{\sqrt{3}}\mathbf{k}$

8 One-quarter

9 a $\overrightarrow{AB}=\mathbf{i}+2\mathbf{j},\ \overrightarrow{AC}=2\mathbf{i}+2\mathbf{j}-\mathbf{k}$
b $\mathbf{r}=3\mathbf{i}+\mathbf{j}-2\mathbf{k}+\lambda(\mathbf{i}+2\mathbf{j})+\mu(2\mathbf{i}+2\mathbf{j}-\mathbf{k})\lambda,\ \mu\in\mathbb{R}$
c $\overrightarrow{AB}\times\overrightarrow{AC}=-2\mathbf{i}+\mathbf{j}-2\mathbf{k}$
$\mathbf{r}=4\mathbf{i}+2\mathbf{j}-\frac{5}{2}\mathbf{k}+t(-2\mathbf{i}+\mathbf{j}-2\mathbf{k})\ t\in\mathbb{R}$
e 6 cubic units

Exercise 6.5

1 a 8 b 23 c 47

2 133

3 b 28

4 a $\sin\theta=\frac{4}{7}\sqrt{3}$ b $16\sqrt{3}$

Exercise 6.6

1 59 cubic units

2 b $\frac{46}{3}$ cubic units

3 a $\overrightarrow{AB}=2\mathbf{i}-3\mathbf{j}+2\mathbf{k}\ \ \overrightarrow{AC}=2\mathbf{i}-6\mathbf{j}\ \ \overrightarrow{AD}=4\mathbf{i}+3\mathbf{j}+4\mathbf{k}$
b 6 cubic units

4 a 24 cubic units b $\frac{52}{3}$ cubic units

5 a $p=7,\ -\frac{1}{5}$
b $p=7$: Area $=\frac{9}{2}\sqrt{6}$ square units
$p=-\frac{1}{5}$: Area $=\frac{3}{2}\sqrt{6}$ square units

6 a No b Yes c Yes d No

Exercise 6.7

1 a $\frac{x-3}{4}=\frac{y-2}{-2}=\frac{z-1}{3}$ b $\frac{x-1}{2}=\frac{y+2}{5},\ z=-1$
c $\frac{x}{4}=\frac{z-2}{-2},\ y=1$

2 a $\mathbf{r}=(5\mathbf{i}+3\mathbf{j}+\mathbf{k})+\lambda\,(2\mathbf{i}+2\mathbf{j}+3\mathbf{k}),\ \lambda\in\mathbb{R}$
b $\mathbf{r}=(-3\mathbf{i}-\mathbf{k})+\lambda(4\mathbf{i}+\mathbf{j}-2\mathbf{k}),\ \lambda\in\mathbb{R}$
c $\mathbf{r}=(2\mathbf{i}-2\mathbf{j}-4\mathbf{k})+\lambda\,(\mathbf{j}+5\mathbf{k}),\ \lambda\in\mathbb{R}$

3 $P(7,4,1)$

4 a $p=6,\ q=5$

5 $\mathbf{r}=\left(\frac{1}{2}\mathbf{i}+3\mathbf{j}+\frac{1}{3}\mathbf{k}\right)+\lambda\left(2\mathbf{i}-2\mathbf{j}-\frac{2}{3}\mathbf{k}\right),\ \lambda\in\mathbb{R}$

Exercise 6.8

1 a $(\mathbf{r}-2\mathbf{i}-3\mathbf{j}-\mathbf{k})\times(3\mathbf{i}-\mathbf{j}+\mathbf{k})=\mathbf{0}$
b $(\mathbf{r}-4\mathbf{i}+2\mathbf{k})\times(2\mathbf{i}-5\mathbf{j}-3\mathbf{k})=\mathbf{0}$
c $(\mathbf{r}-3\mathbf{j}-\mathbf{k})\times(2\mathbf{i}-\mathbf{j})=\mathbf{0}$

2 a $\frac{4}{5}\mathbf{i}-\frac{3}{5}\mathbf{j}$ c $(\mathbf{r}+3\mathbf{i}-5\mathbf{j}-3\mathbf{k})\times(4\mathbf{i}-3\mathbf{j})=\mathbf{0}$

3 $(\mathbf{r}+3\mathbf{i}-2\mathbf{j}-\mathbf{k})\times(2\mathbf{i}+\mathbf{j}+4\mathbf{k})=\mathbf{0}$

4 The locus of R is a straight line, passing through A and which is parallel to $\mathbf{b}$.

Exercise 6.9

1 a $\mathbf{r}.(5\mathbf{i}-3\mathbf{j}+\mathbf{k})=36$ b $\mathbf{r}.(4\mathbf{i}-\mathbf{j}-3\mathbf{k})=-10$

2 a $\frac{4}{5}\mathbf{i}-\frac{3}{5}\mathbf{k}$ b $k=-5$ c $P(10,-5,-14)$ or $P(-14,-5,4)$

3 a $2x+y+z=15$ b $3x-2y-z=11$
c $5x+2y-3z=7$

4 a $\hat{\mathbf{n}}=\frac{2}{7}\mathbf{i}+\frac{3}{7}\mathbf{j}+\frac{6}{7}\mathbf{k}$ b $\hat{\mathbf{n}}=\frac{5}{21}\mathbf{i}-\frac{4}{21}\mathbf{j}-\frac{20}{21}\mathbf{k}$

5 b $2x+y-2z=0$ c $t=2$

6 a $3x+4y-2z=5$ b $4x-7y+2z=11$

7 b $4x-y+8z=10$ c $p=-1, q=-4$

8 a $d=2$ c $C(-7,-3,1)$ d $3x+y-2z=-26$

9 a $m=1, n=-1$ b $2x-y+4z+5=0$

10 a $-3\mathbf{i}-\mathbf{j}+5\mathbf{k}$ c $k=2$
$x=4, z-2=\frac{1+y}{5}$

Exercise 6.10

1 a $P(1,1,-2)$ b $P(2,0,3)$ c $P(4,-3,3)$

2 a $P\left(1,10,\frac{7}{2}\right)$ b $B(2,9,3)$

3 a $\mathbf{r}=(7\mathbf{i}-5\mathbf{j}+6\mathbf{k})+t(2\mathbf{i}-3\mathbf{j}+\mathbf{k}), t\in\mathbb{R}$ b $P(3,1,4)$

4 a $-x+3y+z=28$ b $P(-1,8,3)$

5 a $P(2,1,-1)$ b 3 units
c $T(4,-1,0)$ or $T\left(4,\frac{7}{5},\frac{6}{5}\right)$

6 a $P(3,0,2)$ b $R(1,1,3)$ c $\frac{1}{6}\pi$

7 c $Q\left(-\frac{9}{2},3,\frac{7}{2}\right)$

8 a 36 square units b $2x+2y-z=8$ d 24 square units

9 a $A(2,1,1)$ b i $B(4,-1,-3)$

Exercise 6.11

1 a $\sqrt{14}$ units b $\frac{1}{7}\sqrt{21}$ units c 4 units d $\frac{\sqrt{26}}{2}$ units

2 a $A:\frac{1}{18}\sqrt{6}, B:\frac{1}{18}\sqrt{6}$ b Yes, the line is parallel to the plane.

3 b $\frac{10}{3}$ cubic units

4 a 3 units b $3\sqrt{3}$ units

5 a $4x-3y+5z=10$ b $4x-3y+5z=20$
c $\frac{5}{3}$ cubic units

6 a $P(4,1,-6)$ c $PQ=\sqrt{21}$ units

7 a 2 units b $2\sqrt{3}$ units c $\frac{4}{9}\sqrt{5}$ units

8 Shortest distance = 0

9 b i $p=-14$ ii $p=-4, \Pi: x+2y=2$

10 a $\overrightarrow{AB}\times\overrightarrow{AC}=-2\mathbf{i}-2\mathbf{j}-8\mathbf{k}$
$x+y+4z-9=0$
b $k=4$ c $\frac{2\sqrt{6}}{3}$

Exercise 6.12

1 a $\mathbf{r}=3\mathbf{j}-2\mathbf{k}+t(4\mathbf{i}+2\mathbf{j}+\mathbf{k}), t\in\mathbb{R}$
b $\mathbf{r}=5\mathbf{j}+2\mathbf{k}+t(2\mathbf{i}-3\mathbf{j}+\mathbf{k}), t\in\mathbb{R}$
c $\mathbf{r}=2\mathbf{i}+\mathbf{k}+t(\mathbf{j}+2\mathbf{k}), t\in\mathbb{R}$

2 b $\mathbf{r}=-\mathbf{k}+t(2\mathbf{i}+\mathbf{j}+2\mathbf{k}), t\in\mathbb{R}$
c $B(8,4,7)$ or $B(-4,-2,-5)$

3 a $d=2$ c $p=-5$

4 a $2\mathbf{i}+2\mathbf{j}+\mathbf{k}$ b $-2\mathbf{i}+\mathbf{j}+2\mathbf{k}, \theta=\frac{1}{4}\pi$

Review 6

1 a $-9\mathbf{i}-3\mathbf{j}+3\mathbf{k}$ c $k=\frac{7}{2}, -\frac{15}{2}$

2 a $\mathbf{a}\times\mathbf{b}$ is parallel to $\mathbf{p}$ since both vectors are perpendicular to Π. The vector product of two parallel vectors is the zero vector $\mathbf{0}$.

b $\mathbf{p}.(\mathbf{p}\times\mathbf{b})=0$
By definition, $\mathbf{p}\times\mathbf{b}$ is a vector perpendicular to $\mathbf{p}$ (and $\mathbf{b}$).

3 a $A(8,-10,-3)$ b $a=10, b=-14$ c $P'(6,-6,-17)$

4 a $-6\mathbf{i}+3\mathbf{j}-2\mathbf{k}$ b $\frac{7}{6}$ cubic units
c $p=4, q=-9$ d $\frac{1}{2}\sqrt{2}$ units

5 b $a=1, b=-2$ c $P(6,2,0)$

6 a $d=1$ b $\mathbf{r}=(\mathbf{j}+2\mathbf{k})+t(5\mathbf{i}-6\mathbf{j}+2\mathbf{k}), t\in\mathbb{R}$
c $p=-3, q=6$ d 0.3 units

7 a $\overrightarrow{AB}=-2\mathbf{i}+3\mathbf{j}-\mathbf{k}$ $\overrightarrow{AC}=\mathbf{i}+3\mathbf{j}+2\mathbf{k}$
b $\frac{3}{2}\sqrt{19}$ square units c $\mathbf{r}=(\mathbf{j}-\mathbf{k})+t(\mathbf{i}+\mathbf{k}), t\in\mathbb{R}$
e $D(6,1,5)$ or $D(-6,1,-7)$

8 b $p=-2, q=3$ d $P\left(-\frac{4}{3},\frac{11}{3},-\frac{7}{3}\right)$

9 b $Q(0,3,-2)$
c $\mathbf{r}=(-3\mathbf{i}-5\mathbf{k})+t(5\mathbf{i}+\mathbf{j}+7\mathbf{k}), t\in\mathbb{R}$

10 b $P(-2,-2,-2)$ d $2x-y-3z=4$

11 a $\mathbf{r}=(\mathbf{i}+2\mathbf{j}+\mathbf{k})+\lambda(2\mathbf{i}+\mathbf{j}+\mathbf{k})+\mu(3\mathbf{i}-2\mathbf{j}-\mathbf{k}), \lambda, u\in\mathbb{R}$
c $5\sqrt{3}$ square units

12 a $p=3$ b $p=\frac{4}{11}$

13 b $d=-\frac{12}{17}, e=\frac{21}{17}$ c $Q\left(\frac{2}{3},\frac{1}{3},-\frac{7}{3}\right)$

Revision 2

1 a $y=6x-8$ b $\lambda=1,4$ c $y=-2x, y=x$

2 a $-2\mathbf{i}-2\mathbf{j}+2\mathbf{k}$ b $2\sqrt{3}$ square units

3 b $t=\frac{1}{3}\pi, \frac{5}{3}\pi$

4 a $p=4, q=-9$ c $C(-1,2,-3)$ d $a=3, b=-6$

5 a $a=4$ b 16 square units

6 b $p=-1, q=-4$ c $k(\mathbf{i}-2\mathbf{j}+\mathbf{k}), k\neq 0$

7 a $(-5-4c)\mathbf{i}-(6+5c)\mathbf{j}+\mathbf{k}$
b $c=-2$ c $\mathbf{r}.(3\mathbf{i}+4\mathbf{j}+\mathbf{k})=7$ d $-5\mathbf{i}-3\mathbf{j}+8\mathbf{k}$

8 b $\frac{1}{(20-4k)}\begin{pmatrix}-4 & 8-2k & 4\\ 8-2k & 3k-16 & 2\\ 4 & 2 & -4\end{pmatrix}$
c $\lambda=-1$ d $k(2\mathbf{i}+\mathbf{j}+2\mathbf{k}), k\neq 0$

9 a $k=\pm 9$ b $36x^2+8y^2=49, p=36, q=8$ c $\frac{1}{3}\sqrt{7}$

10 b $\frac{9}{\sqrt{35}}$ c $\mathbf{r}=(\mathbf{i}+2\mathbf{j}+2\mathbf{k})+s(-\mathbf{i}+5\mathbf{j}+3\mathbf{k})+t(2\mathbf{i}-2\mathbf{j}-4\mathbf{k}), s, t\in\mathbb{R}$

11 a $d=1$ c $\sqrt{14}$ d $\sqrt{154}$

12 a $p=3$ b $k=18$
c $a=2\sqrt{2}, b=-\sqrt{2}, c=-2\sqrt{2}$ d $54\sqrt{2}$

13 a $-15\mathbf{i}-10\mathbf{j}-10\mathbf{k}$ b $\mathbf{r}.(3\mathbf{i}+2\mathbf{j}+2\mathbf{k})=7$
c $(\mathbf{r}-3\mathbf{i}+\mathbf{j})\times(2\mathbf{i}-\mathbf{j}-2\mathbf{k})=\mathbf{0}$ d $P\left(\frac{13}{9},-\frac{2}{9},\frac{14}{9}\right)$

14 a $\lambda_1=-1$ c i $\lambda_2=1, \lambda_3=6$
ii $\lambda_2=1:\begin{pmatrix}0\\3\\1\end{pmatrix}, \lambda_3=6:\begin{pmatrix}5\\-1\\3\end{pmatrix}$

d $\mathbf{P}=\begin{pmatrix}\frac{2}{\sqrt{14}} & 0 & \frac{5}{\sqrt{35}}\\ \frac{1}{\sqrt{14}} & \frac{3}{\sqrt{10}} & -\frac{1}{\sqrt{35}}\\ -\frac{3}{\sqrt{14}} & \frac{1}{\sqrt{10}} & \frac{3}{\sqrt{35}}\end{pmatrix}, \mathbf{D}=\begin{pmatrix}-1 & 0 & 0\\ 0 & 1 & 0\\ 0 & 0 & 6\end{pmatrix}$

e $\mathbf{D}^2=\begin{pmatrix}1 & 0 & 0\\ 0 & 1 & 0\\ 0 & 0 & 36\end{pmatrix}$

FP3

Index

FP3

FP3